The Future of Post-Human Etiology

Towards a New Theory
of Cause and Effect

Volume 2

The Future of Post-Human Etiology

Towards a New Theory of Cause and Effect

Volume 2

By

Peter Baofu

Nova Science Publishers, Inc.
New York

The Future of Post-Human Etiology: Towards a New Theory of Cause and Effect, Volume 2, by Peter Baofu

NOTICE TO THE READER
The Publisher has taken reasonable care in the preparation of this book, but makes no expressed or implied warranty of any kind and assumes no responsibility for any errors or omissions. No liability is assumed for incidental or consequential damages in connection with or arising out of information contained in this book. The Publisher shall not be liable for any special, consequential, or exemplary damages resulting, in whole or in part, from the readers' use of, or reliance upon, this material. Any parts of this book based on government reports are so indicated and copyright is claimed for those parts to the extent applicable to compilations of such works.

Independent verification should be sought for any data, advice or recommendations contained in this book. In addition, no responsibility is assumed by the publisher for any injury and/or damage to persons or property arising from any methods, products, instructions, ideas or otherwise contained in this publication.

This publication is designed to provide accurate and authoritative information with regard to the subject matter covered herein. It is sold with the clear understanding that the Publisher is not engaged in rendering legal or any other professional services. If legal or any other expert assistance is required, the services of a competent person should be sought. FROM A DECLARATION OF PARTICIPANTS JOINTLY ADOPTED BY A COMMITTEE OF THE AMERICAN BAR ASSOCIATION AND A COMMITTEE OF PUBLISHERS.

Additional color graphics may be available in the e-book version of this book.

Library of Congress Cataloging-in-Publication Data

ISBN - 978-1-63321-101-8

Published by Nova Science Publishers, Inc. † New York

To Those in the Future World beyond Cause and Effect

BOOKS ALSO BY PETER BAOFU

Category I: Social Sciences and Related Fields

- 65. *The Future of Post-Human Accounting* (2014)
- 64. *The Future of Post-Human Waste* (2012)
- 63. *The Future of Post-Human Migration* (2012)
- 62. *The Future of Post-Human Criminality* (2012)
- 61. *The Future of Post-Human Geography* (2011)
- 60. *The Future of Post-Human Gambling* (2011)
- 59. *The Future of Post-Human Education* (2011)
- 58. *The Future of Post-Human War and Peace* (2010)
- 57. *The Future of Post-Human Law* (2010)
- 56. *The Future of Post-Human Organization* (2009)
- 55. *The Future of Post-Human Mass Media* (2009)
- 54. *The Rise of Authoritarian Liberal Democracy* (2007)
- 53. *Beyond the World of Titans, and the Remaking of World Order* (2007)
- 52. *Beyond Capitalism to Post-Capitalism* (2005)
- 51. Volume 1: *Beyond Democracy to Post-Democracy* (2004)
- 50. Volume 2: *Beyond Democracy to Post-Democracy* (2004)
- 49. *The Future of Capitalism and Democracy* (2002)

Category II: Natural Sciences and Related Fields

Category III: The Humanities and Related Fields

- 29. Volume 1: *The Future of Post-Human Etiology* (2014)
- 28. *The Future of Post-Human Thanatology* (2013)
- 27. *The Future of Post-Human Sports* (2013)
- 26. *The Future of Post-Human Culinary Art* (2012)
- 25. *The Future of Post-Human History* (2012)
- 24. *The Future of Post-Human Performing Arts* (2012)
- 23. *The Future of Post-Human Literature* (2011)
- 22. *The Future of Post-Human Humor* (2011)
- 21. *Beyond Ethics to Post-Ethics* (2011)
- 20. *The Future of Post-Human Religion* (2010)
- 19. *The Future of Post-Human Chess* (2010)
- 18. *The Future of Post-Human Martial Arts* (2009)
- 17. *The Future of Post-Human Creative Thinking* (2009)
- 16. *The Future of Post-Human Knowledge* (2008)
- 15. *The Future of Aesthetic Experience* (2007)
- 14. *Beyond Civilization to Post-Civilization* (2006)
- 13. Volume 1: *The Future of Human Civilization* (2000)
- 12. Volume 2: *The Future of Human Civilization* (2000)

Category IV: Formal Sciences and Related Fields

CONTENTS

Volume 1

Part One: Introduction

Part Two: Cause

Volume 2

Part Three: Effect

Part Four: Conclusion

TABLES

ACKNOWLEDGMENTS

This book, like all other previous ones of mine, is no exception and is written to challenge conventional wisdom or, more precisely, in the current context, the one on etiology—and to replace it with an original way of thinking about its future fate (especially, though not exclusively, in relation to cause and effect).

As a result, this book receives no external funding nor help from any formal organization or institution, because of its political incorrectness—as this is something that I often stressed (and repeated) in all my previous books.

My only reward is the joy of conceiving something original in the intellectual history of etiology.

In any event, I bear the sole responsibility for the ideas presented in this book.

ABBREVIATIONS

ALD = Peter Baofu. 2007. *The Rise of Authoritarian Liberal Democracy: A Preface to a New Theory of Comparative Political Systems.* Cambridge, England: Cambridge Scholars Publishing, Ltd.

BCIV = Peter Baofu. 2006. *Beyond Civilization to Post-Civilization: Conceiving a Better Model of Life Settlement to Supersede Civilization.* NY: Peter Lang Publishing, Inc.

BCPC = Peter Baofu. 2005. *Beyond Capitalism to Post-Capitalism: Conceiving a Better Model of Wealth Acquisition to Supersede Capitalism.* NY: The Edwin Mellen Press.

BCOS = Peter Baofu. 2010. *Beyond Cosmology to Post-Cosmology: A Preface to a New Theory of Different Worlds.* Cambridge, England: Cambridge International Science Publishing, Ltd.

BDPD1 = Peter Baofu. 2004. Volume 1. *Beyond Democracy to Post-Democracy: Conceiving a Better Model of Governance to Supersede Democracy.* NY: The Edwin Mellen Press.

BDPD2 = Peter Baofu. 2004. Volume 2. *Beyond Democracy to Post-Democracy: Conceiving a Better Model of Governance to Supersede Democracy.* NY: The Edwin Mellen Press.

BEPE = Peter Baofu. 2011. *Beyond Ethics to Post-Ethics: A Preface to a New Theory of Morality and Immorality.* Charlotte, NC: Infomration Age Publishing.

BHR = Peter Baofu. 2014. *Beyond Human Resources to Post-Human Resources: Towards a New Theory of Quantity and Quality in Demographics.*

BNN = Peter Baofu. 2006. *Beyond Nature and Nurture: Conceivng a Better Way to Understand Genes and Memes.* Cambridge, England: Cambridge Scholars Publishing, Ltd.

BNR = Peter Baofu. 2013. *Beyond Natural Resources to Post-Human Resources: Towards a New Theory of Diversity and Discontinuity.* Cambridge, England: Cambridge Scholars Publishing, Ltd.

BWT = Peter Baofu. 2007. *Beyond the World of Titans, and the Renaking of World Order: A Preface to a New Logic of Empire-Building.* Cambridge, England: Cambridge Scholars Publishing, Ltd.

FAE = Peter Baofu. 2007. *The Future of Aesthetic Experience: Conceiving a Better Way to Understand Beauty, Ugliness and the Rest.* Cambridge, England: Cambridge Scholars Publishing, Ltd.

FC = Peter Baofu. 2007. *The Future of Complexity: Conceiving a Better Way to Understand Order and Chaos.* London, United Kingdom: World Scientific Publishing Co.

FCD = Peter Baofu. 2002. *The Future of Capitalism and Democracy.* MD: The University Press of America.

FHC1 = Peter Baofu. 2000. Volume 1. *The Future of Human Civilization.* NY: The Edwin Mellen Press.

FHC2 = Peter Baofu. 2000. Volume 2. *The Future of Human Civilization.* NY: The Edwin Mellen Press.

FIA = Peter Baofu. 2008. *The Future of Information Architecture: Conceiving a Better Way to Understand Taxonomy, Network, and Intelligence.* Oxford, England: Chandos Publishing (Oxford) Limited.

FPHA = Peter Baofu. 2011. *The Future of Post-Human Acoustics: A Preface to a New Theory of Sound and Silence.* Cambridge, England: Cambridge International Science Publishing, Ltd.

FPHACCO = Peter Baofu. 2014. *The Future of Post-Human Accounting: Towards a New Theory of Addition and Subtraction in Information Management.* Charlotte, NC: Information Age Publishing.

FPHAERO1 = Peter Baofu. 2014. Volume 1. *The Future of Post-Human Aerology: A Preface to a New Theory of Predictability and Nonpredictability.* Hauppauge, NY: Nova Science Publishers, Inc.

FPHAERO2 = Peter Baofu. 2014. Volume 2. *The Future of Post-Human Aerology: A Preface to a New Theory of Predictability and Nonpredictability.* Hauppauge, NY: Nova Science Publishers, Inc.

FPHARCH = Peter Baofu. 2012. *The Future of Post-Human Architecture: A Preface to a New Theory of Form and Function.* Cambridge, England: Cambridge International Science Publishing, Ltd.

FPHC = Peter Baofu. 2004. *The Future of Post-Human Consciousness.* NY: The Edwin Mellen Press.

FPHCA = Peter Baofu. 2012. *The Future of Post-Human Culinary Art: Towards a New Theory of Ingredients and Techniques.* England: Cambridge Scholars Publishing, Ltd.

FPHCHEM = Peter Baofu. 2011. *The Future of Post-Human Chemistry: A Preface to a New Theory of Substances and their Changes.* England: Cambridge Scholars Publishing, Ltd.

FPHCHESS = Peter Baofu. 2010. *The Future of Post-Human Chess: A Preface to a New Theory of Tactics and Strategy.* Cambridge, England: Cambridge International Science Publishing, Ltd.

FPHCOM = Peter Baofu. 2011. *The Future of Post-Human Computing: A Preface to a New Theory of Hardware and Software.* Cambridge, England: Cambridge International Science Publishing, Ltd.

FPHCRIM = Peter Baofu. 2012. *The Future of Post-Human Criminality: A Preface to a New Theory of Heroes and Villains.* Cambridge, England: Cambridge International Science Publishing, Ltd.

FPHCT = Peter Baofu. 2009. *The Future of Post-Human Creative Thinking: A Preface to a New Theory of Invention and Innovation.* Cambridge, England: Cambridge Scholars Publishing, Ltd.

FPHDA = Peter Baofu. 2011. *The Future of Post-Human Data Analysis: A Preface to a New Theory of Quantitative and Qualitative Research.* Cambridge, England: Cambridge International Science Publishing, Ltd.

FPHE = Peter Baofu. 2009. *The Future of Post-Human Engineering: A Preface to a New Theory of Technology.* Cambridge, England: Cambridge Scholars Publishing, Ltd.

FPHEDU = Peter Baofu. 2011. *The Future of Post-Human Education: A Preface to a New Theory of Teaching and Learning.* Cambridge, England: Cambridge International Science Publishing, Ltd.

FPHETIO1 = Peter Baofu. 2014. Volume 1. *The Future of Post-Human Etiology: Towards a New Theory of Cause and Effect.* Hauppauge, NY: Nova Science Publishers, Inc.

FPHETIO2 = Peter Baofu. 2014. Volume 2. *The Future of Post-Human Etiology: Towards a New Theory of Cause and Effect.* Hauppauge, NY: Nova Science Publishers, Inc.

FPHFS = Peter Baofu. 2010. *The Future of Post-Human Formal Science: A Preface to a New Theory of Abstraction and Application.* Cambridge, England: Cambridge Scholars Publishing, Ltd.

FPHG = Peter Baofu. 2009. *The Future of Post-Human Geometry: A Preface to a New Theory of Infinity, Symmetry, and Dimensionality.* Cambridge, England: Cambridge Scholars Publishing, Ltd.

FPHGAM = Peter Baofu. 2011. *The Future of Post-Human Gambling: A Preface to a New Theory of Risk and Caution.* Cambridge, England:

Cambridge International Science Publishing, Ltd.

FPHGEOG = Peter Baofu. 2011. *The Future of Post-Human Geography: A Preface to a New Theory of Environments and their Interactions.* Cambridge, England: Cambridge International Science Publishing, Ltd.

FPHGEOL = Peter Baofu. 2010. *The Future of Post-Human Geology: A Preface to a New Theory of Statics and Dynamics.* Cambridge, England: Cambridge International Science Publishing, Ltd.

FPHH = Peter Baofu. 2011. *The Future of Post-Human Humor: A Preface to a New Theory of Joking and Laughing.* Cambridge, England: Cambridge International Science Publishing, Ltd.

FPHHC = Peter Baofu. 2013. *The Future of Post-Human Health Care: Towards a New Theory of Mind and Body.* Hauppauge, NY: Nova Science Publishers, Inc.

FPHHIST = Peter Baofu. 2012. *The Future of Post-Human History: A Preface to a New Theory of Universality and Relativity.* Cambridge, England: Cambridge Scholars Publishing, Ltd.

FPHK = Peter Baofu. 2008. *The Future of Post-Human Knowledge: A Preface to a New Theory of Methodology and Ontology.* Oxford, England: Chandos Publishing (Oxford) Limited.

FPHL = Peter Baofu. 2009. *The Future of Post-Human Language: A Preface to a New Theory of Structure, Context, and Learning.* Cambridge, England: Cambridge Scholars Publishing, Ltd.

FPHLAW = Peter Baofu. 2010. *The Future of Post-Human Law: A Preface to a New Theory of Necessity, Contingency, and Justice.* Cambridge, England: Cambridge Scholars Publishing, Ltd.

FPHLIT = Peter Baofu. 2011. *The Future of Post-Human Literature: A Preface to a New Theory of Fiction and Non-Fiction.* Cambridge, England: Cambridge International Science Publishing, Ltd.

FPHMA = Peter Baofu. 2009. *The Future of Post-Human Martial Arts: A Preface to a New Theory of the Body and Spirit of Warriors.* Cambridge, England: Cambridge Scholars Publishing, Ltd.

FPHMIG = Peter Baofu. 2012. *The Future of Post-Human Migration: A Preface to a New Theory of Sameness, Otherness, and Identity.* Cambridge, England: Cambridge Scholars Publishing, Ltd.

FPHML = Peter Baofu. 2008. *The Future of Post-Human Mathematical Logic: A Preface to a New Theory of Rationality.* Cambridge, England: Cambridge Scholars Publishing, Ltd.

FPHMM = Peter Baofu. 2009. *The Future of Post-Human Mass Media: A Preface to a New Theory of Technology.* Cambridge, England: Cambridge Scholars Publishing, Ltd.

FPHMORP = Peter Baofu. 2013. *The Future of Post-Human Morphology: Towards a New Theory of Typologies and Rules.* Hauppauge, NY: Nova Science Publishers, Inc.

FPHO = Peter Baofu. 2009. *The Future of Post-Human Organization: A Preface to a New Theory of Communication, Decision-Making, and Leadership..*Cambridge, England: Cambridge Scholars Publishing, Ltd.

FPHP = Peter Baofu. 2010. *The Future of Post-Human Personality: A Preface to a New Theory of Normality and Abnormality.* Cambridge, England: Cambridge International Science Publishing, Ltd.

FPHPHON = Peter Baofu. 2014. *The Future of Post-Human Phonology: Towards a New Theory of Generality and Specifcity.* Hauppauge, NY: Nova Science Publishers, Inc.

FPHPA = Peter Baofu. 2012. *The Future of Post-Human Performing Arts: A Preface to a New Theory of the Body and its Presence.* Cambridge, England: Cambridge Scholars Publishing, Ltd.

FPHPADM = Peter Baofu. 2014. *The Future of Post-Human Public Administration: Towards a New Theory of Policy and Implementation.*

FPHPROB = Peter Baofu. 2013. *The Future of Post-Human Probability: Towards a New Theory of Objectivity and Subjectivity.* Hauppauge, NY: Nova Science Publishers, Inc.

FPHR = Peter Baofu. 2010. *The Future of Post-Human Religion: A Preface to a New Theory of Spirituality.* Cambridge, England: Cambridge International Science Publishing, Ltd.

FPHS = Peter Baofu. 2010. *The Future of Post-Human Sexuality: A Preface to a New Theory of the Body and Spirit of Love-Makers.* Cambridge, England: Cambridge Scholars Publishing, Ltd.

FPHSEM = Peter Baofu. 2012. *The Future of Post-Human Semantics: A Preface to a New Theory of Internality and Externality.* Cambridge, England: Cambridge Scholars Publishing, Ltd.

FPHSPORT = Peter Baofu. 2013. *The Future of Post-Human Sports: Towards a New Theory of Training and Winning.* Cambridge, England: Cambridge Scholars Publishing, Ltd.

FPHST = Peter Baofu. 2006. *The Future of Post-Human Space-Time: Conceivng a Better Way to Understand Space and Time.* New York:

Peter Lang Publishing, Inc.

FPHTHAN = Peter Baofu. 2013. *The Future of Post-Human Thanatology: Towards a New Theory of Death and After-Death.* Berlin, Germany: Logos Verlag Berlin.

FPHTRAN = Peter Baofu. 2012. *The Future of Post-Human Transportation: A Preface to a New Theory of Networks and Operations.* Cambridge, England: Cambridge Scholars Publishing, Ltd.

FPHU = Peter Baofu. 2008. *The Future of Post-Human Unconsciousness: A Preface to a New Theory of Anomalous Experience.* Cambridge, England: Cambridge Scholars Publishing, Ltd.

FPHUP = Peter Baofu. 2009. *The Future of Post-Human Urban Planning: A Preface to a New Theory of Density, Void, and Sustainability.* Cambridge, England: Cambridge Scholars Publishing, Ltd.

FPHVA = Peter Baofu. 2014. *The Future of Post-Human Visual Arts: Towards a New Theory of Techniques and Spirits.*

FPHW = Peter Baofu. 2012. *The Future of Post-Human Waste: Towards a New Theory of Uselessness and Usefulness.* Cambridge, England: Cambridge Scholars Publishing, Ltd.

FPHWP = Peter Baofu. 2010. *The Future of Post-Human War and Peace: A Preface to a New Theory of Aggression and Pacificity.* Cambridge, England: Cambridge Scholars Publishing, Ltd.

• PART THREE •

Effect

CHAPTER 3
EFFECT AND ITS AMBIVALENCE

From without, no wonderful effect is
wrought within ourselves, unless some
interior, responding wonder meets it.
—Herman Melville (TH 2014a)

The Potency of Effect

As already addressed in *Sec. 1.3*, etiology involves both cause and
effect.

The relationship between cause and effect (in the context of etiology)
is dialectic, since there is no analysis of cause without that of effect, and
vice versa—to be eventually transcended altogether later.

Yet, a scholarly danger here is to reduce the analysis of one to that of
the other; thus, this book is to devote a whole chapter on each, with the
understanding, of course, that the two are related.

This dialectic relationship between cause and effect (in the context of
etiology) can be revealed by showing how and why the analysis of cause
(in Chapter Two) is inadequate without the inclusion of effect, just as the
examination of effect (in Chapter Three) is insufficient without the
consideration of cause.

The issues concerning effect (in the context of etiology) are to be
addressed in this chapter (Chapter Three), whereas the issues concerning
cause (in the context of etiology) were already analyzed in the previous
chapter (Chapter Two).

With this dialectic treatment in mind—a good way to examine effect
and its ambivalence (in the context of etiology) is by way of the evaluation
of the extent to which it is in fact both possible (or impossible) and
desirable (or undesirable).

This can be done by way of a comprehensive analysis of effect (in the
context of etiology) from the four perspectives of the mind, nature,

society, and culture (in accordance to my sophisticated methodological holism, as explained in *Sec. 1.9*).

In other words, this chapter is organized in four main sections, namely, in relation to (3.2) effect and the mind, (3.3) effect and nature, (3.4) effect and society, and (3.5) effect and culture—to be addressed hereafter, in that order (and summarized in *Table 3.1*).

Effect and the Mind

Effect, when examined from the perspective of the mind, can illuminate its possibility (or impossibility) and desirability (or undesirability), and this can be shown by way of two case studies, namely, (3.2.1) effect, medicine, and adverse effect, and (3.2.2) effect, intentionality, and consequences—to be addressed in what follows, respectively.

Effect, Medicine, and Adverse Effect

A good way to evaluate the possibility (or impossibility) and desirability (or undesirability) of effect from the perspective of the mind is to explore effect, medicine, and adverse effect.

An argument in the literature is that "a medication or other intervention such as surgery" can result in "an undesired harmful effect" known as "adverse effect.," which can harm the patient, both psychologically and physiologically. (WK 2014o)

Definitions of Adverse Effects

The term "adverse effect" can be defined in different ways, as described below.

For instance, in pharmacology, "adverse events" are defined as "any untoward medical occurrence in a patient or clinical investigation subject administered a pharmaceutical product and which does not necessarily have to have a causal relationship with this treatment." (WK 2014o)

In medicine, "adverse effect" is defined as "an undesired harmful effect resulting from a medication or other intervention such as surgery. An adverse effect may be termed a 'side effect,' when judged to be secondary to a main or therapeutic effect. If it results from an unsuitable or incorrect dosage or procedure, this is called a medical error and not a complication. Adverse effects are sometimes referred to as 'iatrogenic' because they are generated by a physician/treatment. Some adverse effects only occur only when starting, increasing or discontinuing a treatment." (WK 2014o)

In clinical trials, "adverse effects" are defined to make them different from "serious adverse events [SAE]. Generally, any event which causes death, permanent damage, birth defects, or requires hospitalization is considered an SAE. The results of these trials are often included in the labeling of the medication to provide information both for patients and the prescribing physicians." (WK 2014o)

In general, adverse effects are "harmful," because of the results "such as morbidity, mortality, alteration in body weight, levels of enzymes, loss of function, or as a pathological change detected at the microscopic, macroscopic or physiological level. It may also be indicated by symptoms reported by a patient. Adverse effects may cause a reversible or irreversible change, including an increase or decrease in the susceptibility of the individual to other chemicals, foods, or procedures, such as drug interactions." (WK 2014o)

Reporting Systems of Adverse Effects

To study "adverse effects," they need to be reported, so "in many countries, adverse effects are required by law to be reported, researched in clinical trials and included into the patient information accompanying medical devices and drugs for sale to the public. Investigators in human clinical trials are obligated to report these events in clinical study reports." (WK 2013o)

For illustration, consider different reporting systems below (as summarized in *Table 3.2*).

(a) United Kingdom
The first reporting system of adverse effects to be introduced here is in the United Kingdom.

In the U.K., "the Yellow Card Scheme is a United Kingdom initiative run by the Medicines and Healthcare products Regulatory Agency (MHRA) and the Commission on Human Medicines (CHM) to gather information on adverse effects to medicines. This includes all licensed medicines, from medicines issued on prescription to medicines bought over the counter from a supermarket. The scheme also includes all herbal supplements and unlicensed medicines found in cosmetic treatments. Adverse drug reactions (ADRs) can be reported by a number of health care professionals including physicians, pharmacists and nurses, as well as patients." (WK 2014o)

(b) United States

The second reporting system of adverse effects to be introduced here is in the United States.

In the U.S., "several reporting systems have been built, such as the Vaccine Adverse Event Reporting System (VAERS), the Manufacturer and User Facility Device Experience Database (MAUDE) and the Special Nutritionals Adverse Event Monitoring System. MedWatch is the main reporting center, operated by the Food and Drug Administration." (WK 2014o)

(c) Australia

The third reporting system of adverse effects to be introduced here is in Australia.

In Australia, there is "the Adverse Drug Reactions Advisory Committee (ADRAC), a subcommittee of the Australian Drug Evaluation Committee (ADEC). Reporting is voluntary, and ADRAC requests healthcare professionals to report all adverse reactions to its current drugs of interest, and serious adverse reactions to any drug. ADRAC publishes the Australian Adverse Drug Reactions Bulletin every two months. The Government's Quality Use of Medicines program is tasked with acting on this reporting to reduce and minimize the number of preventable adverse effects each year." (WK 2014o)

(d) New Zealand

The fourth reporting system of adverse effects to be introduced here is in New Zealand.

In New Zealand, "adverse reaction reporting is an important component of New Zealand's pharmacovigilance activities. The Centre for Adverse Reactions Monitoring (CARM) in Dunedin is New Zealand's national monitoring centre for adverse reactions. It collects and evaluates spontaneous reports of adverse reactions to medicines, vaccines, herbal products and dietary supplements from health professionals in New Zealand. Currently the CARM database holds over 80,000 reports and provides New Zealand-specific information on adverse reactions to these products, and serves to support clinical decision making when unusual symptoms are thought to be therapy related." (WK 2014o)

(e) Canada

And the fifth reporting system of adverse effects to be introduced here is in Canada.

In Canada, "adverse reaction reporting is an important component of the surveillance of marketed health products conducted by the Health Products and Food Branch (HPFB) of Health Canada. Within HPFB, the

Marketed Health Products Directorate leads the coordination and implementation of consistent monitoring practices with regards to assessment of signals and safety trends, and risk communications concerning regulated marketed health products. MHPD also works closely with international organizations to facilitate the sharing of information. Adverse reaction reporting is mandatory for the industry and voluntary for consumers and health professionals." (WK 2014o)

Situations of Adverse Effects

Adverse effects can also be analyzed in terms of different situations. For illustration, consider two main situations below (as summarized in *Table 3.2*).

(a) Medical Procedures
The first example of the situations of adverse effects to be described here concerns "medical procedures."

In "medical procedures" like "surgery," there can be "a number of undesirable or harmful effects, such as infection, hemorrhage, inflammation, scarring, loss of function, or changes in local blood flow. They can be reversible or irreversible, and a compromise must be found by the physician and the patient between the beneficial or life-saving consequences of surgery versus its adverse effects. For example, a limb may be lost to amputation in case of untreatable gangrene, but the patient's life is saved. Presently, one of the greatest advantages of minimally invasive surgery, such as laparoscopic surgery, is the reduction of adverse effects."(WK 2014o)

There are also "nonsurgical physical procedures, such as high-intensity radiation therapy," which "may cause burns and alterations in the skin. In general, these therapies try to avoid damage to healthy tissues while maximizing the therapeutic effect. Vaccination may have adverse effects due to the nature of its biological preparation, sometimes using attenuated pathogens and toxins. Common adverse effects may be fever, malaise and local reactions in the vaccination site. Diagnostic procedures may also have adverse effects, depending much on whether they are invasive, minimally invasive or noninvasive. For example, allergic reactions to radiocontrast materials often occur, and a colonoscopy may cause the perforation of the intestinal wall." (WK 2014o)

(b) Drug Reaction
And the second example of the situations of adverse effects to be described here concerns "drug reaction."

In drug reaction, there can be "adverse effects" which "occur as a collateral or side effect of many interventions, but they are particularly important in pharmacology, due to its wider, and sometimes uncontrollable, use by way of self-medication. Thus, responsible drug use becomes an important issue here. Adverse effects, like therapeutic effects of drugs, are a function of dosage or drug levels at the target organs, so they may be avoided or decreased by means of careful and precise pharmacokinetics, the change of drug levels in the organism in function of time after administration." (WK 2014o)

In other cases, "adverse effects may also be caused by drug interaction. This often occurs when patients fail to inform their physician and pharmacist of all the medications they are taking, including herbal and dietary supplements. The new medication may interact agonistically or antagonistically (potentiate or decrease the intended therapeutic effect), causing significant morbidity and mortality around the world. Drug-drug and food-drug interactions may occur, and so-called 'natural drugs' used in alternative medicine can have dangerous adverse effects. For example, extracts of St John's wort (*Hypericum perforatum*), a phytotherapic used for treating mild depression are known to cause an increase in the cytochrome P450 enzymes responsible for the metabolism and elimination of many drugs, so patients taking it are likely to experience a reduction in blood levels of drugs they are taking for other purposes, such as cancer chemotherapeutic drugs, protease inhibitors for HIV and hormonal contraceptives." (WK 2014o)

Problems with the Study on Medicine and Adverse Effect

However, to the critics, the argument on effect, medicine, and adverse effect has some major problems. Consider, for illustration, a few examples below (as summarized in *Table 3.2*).

Firstly, one main criticism of the argument on effect, medicine, and adverse effect is that the claim for "adverse effect" can be controversially false.

For instance, to the critics, "sometimes, putative medical adverse effects are regarded as controversial and generate heated discussions in society and lawsuits against drug manufacturers. One example is the recent controversy as to whether autism was linked to the MMR vaccine (or by thiomersal, a mercury-based preservative used in some vaccines). No link has been found in several large studies, and despite removal of thimerosal from vaccines a decade ago the rate of autism has not decreased as would be expected if it had been the causative agent." (WK 2014o; USFDA 2014; R. Jaslow 2012)

Secondly, another main criticism of the argument on effect, medicine, and adverse effect is that the claim for "adverse effect" can be exaggerated, without putting the cost-benefit analysis in a proper perspective.

For instance, to the critics, "due to the exceedingly high impact on public health of widely used medications, such as hormonal contraception and hormone replacement therapy, which may affect millions of users, even marginal probabilities of adverse effects of a severe nature, such as breast cancer, have led to public outcry and changes in medical therapy, although its benefits largely surpassed the statistical risks." (WK 2014o)

Thirdly, still another main criticism of the study on effect, medicine, and adverse effect is that adverse effects can be psychological.

For instance, "in medicine, "a nocebo…is a harmless substance that creates harmful effects in a patient who takes it. The nocebo effect is the negative reaction experienced by a patient who receives a nocebo… .[N]ocebo…effects are entirely psychogenic" and "result from a subject's expectations about how the substance will affect him or her. Though they originate exclusively from psychological sources, nocebo effects can be either psychological or physiological." (WK 2014mm)

Fourthly, an additional main criticism of the study on effect, medicine, and adverse effect is that adverse effects can be ambiguous.

For instance, to the critics, "part of the difficulty is identifying the source of a complaint. A headache in a patient taking medication for influenza may be caused by the underlying disease or may be an adverse effect of the treatment. In patients with end-stage cancer, death is a very likely outcome and whether the drug is the cause or a bystander is often difficult to discern." (WK 2014o)

Fifthly, another additional main criticism of the study on effect, medicine, and adverse effect is that there can be beneficial side-effects too.

For instance, unlike "adverse effect," there is an opposite case involving "placebo," which is "an inert substance that creates either a positive response or no response in a subject who takes it. The phenomenon in which a placebo creates a positive response in the subject to which it is administered is called the placebo effect." (WK 2014mm)

Sixthly, still another additional main criticism of the study on effect, medicine, and adverse effect is that there is no universal definition of "adverse effect."

For instance, to the critics, there are different definitions of "adverse effects" as described earlier.

And seventhly, one last main criticism of the study on effect, medicine, and adverse effect is that reporting systems of adverse effects are not often effective.

For instance, to the critics, "research suggests that the...[adverse] events are often inadequately reported in publicly available reports." (WK 2014o; J. Ioannidis 2001; R. Chou 2005) There are different reasons for these limitations; for instance, "in practice, it is at the discretion of the professional to determine whether a medical event is at all related to the therapy. For example, a leg fracture in a skiing accident in a patient who years before took antibiotics for pneumonia is not likely to get reported. As a result, routine adverse effects reporting often may not include long-term and subtle effects that may ultimately be attributed to a therapy." (WK 2014o)

Beyond Medicine and Adverse Effect

These criticisms of the analysis of effect, medicine, and adverse effect should not be misunderstood as a total rejection of its validity but serve to show us the two opposing sides of the debate, such that the possibility (or impossibility) and desirability (or undesirability) of effect (from the perspective of the mind with effect, medicine, and adverse effect as a case study here) are not to the extent that the respective defenders would like us to believe.

In fact, the analysis of effect, medicine, and adverse effect can teach us a valuable lesson on the ontological principles in existential dialectics, and good examples include the formalness-informalness principle, the absoluteness-relativeness principle, the partiality-totality principle, the predictability-unpredictability principle, the explicability-inexplicability principle, the fiction-reality principle, the cognitiveness-noncognitiveness principle, the finiteness-transfiniteness principle, the preciseness-vagueness principle, the simpleness-complicatedness principle, the openness-hiddenness principle, the denseness-emptiness principle, the rule-exception principle, the indispensability-dispensability principle, the prototypicality-variation principle, the change-constancy principle, the order-chaos principle, the slowness-quickness principle, the expansion-contraction principle, the optimality-nonoptimality principle, the simultaneity-nonsimultaneity principle, the isolation-interaction principle, the theory-praxis principle, the convention-novelty principle, the evolution-transformation principle, the symmetry-asymmetry principle, the softness-hardness principle, the seriousness-playfulness principle, the activeness-inactivess principle, the selfness-otherness principle, the regression-progression principle, the same-difference principle, the stability-reaction principle, the functionality-nonfunctionality principle, the intentionality-nonintentionality principle. the survivability-non-survivability principle, and the materiality-nonmateriality principle.

For instance, in relation to the formalness-informalness principle, if there is formalness (e.g., the formal logical requirement of soundness, completeness, and consistency in a system of ideas, as in the argument on adverse effects), there is informalness (e.g., the non-formal existence of unsoundness, incompleteness, and inconsistency in the argument on adverse effects, as shown in the criticisms that the claim for "adverse effect" can be controversially false, that the claim for "adverse effect" can be exaggerated without putting the cost-benefit analysis in a proper perspective, that adverse effects can be psychological, that adverse effects can be ambiguous, that there can be beneficial side-effects too, that there is no universal definition of "adverse effect," and that reporting systems of adverse effects are not often effective). And the reverse direction also holds true.

In relation to the absoluteness-relativeness principle, if there is absoluteness (e.g., the absolute view against drug manufacturers in regard to the controversy about autism linked to the MMR vaccine), there is relativeness (e.g., what is right for those against drug manufacturers in regard to the controversy about autism linked to the MMR vaccine is not necessarily so for the critics, who pointed out that "no link has been found in several large studies"). And the reverse direction also holds true.

In relation to the partiality-totality principle, if there is partiality (e.g., the partial view on the controversy about autism linked to the MMR vaccine by the advocates), there is totality (e.g., the more holistic view on the controversy about autism linked to the MMR vaccine, such that the whole is not the sum of its parts, that is, it cannot be reduced to the sum of opposing views by the advocates, the skeptics, the critics, etc., since there will emerge new views in the future not yet known today, just as there are already alternative views nowadays which do not side exclusively with any of them, as is the analysis here). And the reverse direction also holds true.

In relation to the predictability-unpredictability principle, if there is predictability (e.g., the predictable tendency that "public outcry" can exaggerate the adverse effects of "hormonal contraception and hormone replacement therapy," like "breast cancer"), there is unpredictability (e.g., the more difficult task to predict exactly the extent to which a particular case of "hormonal contraception and hormone replacement therapy" will actually lead to "breast cancer" on a particular occasion, since its probabilities are very marginal). And the reverse direction also holds true.

In relation to the explicability-inexplicability principle, if there is explicability (e.g., the explanation, by those who carried out "lawsuits against drug manufacturers," on the basis that "autism was linked to the MMR vaccine"), there is inexplicability (e.g., the lack of sufficient explanation, by those who carried out "lawsuits against drug manufacturers," of why the claim that "autism was linked to the MMR vaccine" is necessarily true, since, to the critics, "no link has been found in several large studies, and despite removal of thimerosal from vaccines a decade ago the rate of autism has not decreased as would be expected if it had been the causative"). And the reverse direction also holds true.

In relation to the fiction-reality principle, if there is fiction (e.g., the fictional aspect of "hormonal contraception and hormone replacement therapy," insofar as "even marginal probabilities of adverse effects of a severe nature, such as breast cancer, have led to public outcry and changes in medical therapy, although its benefits largely surpassed the statistical risks"), there is reality (e.g., the realistic aspect of "hormonal contraception and hormone replacement therapy," insofar as there are "probabilities of adverse effects of a severe nature, such as breast cancer," although they are marginal). And the reverse direction also holds true.

In relation to the cognitiveness-noncognitiveness principle, if there is cognitiveness (e.g., a view of things on the basis of reason and evidences, as shown in the empirical finding about the possible adverse effects of "the MMR vaccine"), there is noncognitiveness (e.g., a view of things on the basis of non-cognitive factors like envy, jealousy, power, nationality, race, gender, age, class, greed, lust, status, faith, anger, sadness, joy, fear, wish, etc.—as shown in emotions surrounding the "public outcry" and "lawsuits against drug manufacturers" in regard to the claim about "autism...linked to the MMR vaccine," even though "no link has been found in several large studies, and despite removal of thimerosal from vaccines a decade ago the rate of autism has not decreased as would be expected if it had been the causative agent"). And the reverse direction also holds true.

In relation to the finiteness-transfiniteness principle, if there is finiteness (e.g., the finite number of the types of situations in regard to adverse effects, as shown in the two types as discussed earlier), there is transfiniteness (e.g., the transfinite number of all the individual instances of adverse effects that have ever occurred in history, regardless of which types of situations they belong to). And the reverse direction also holds true.

In relation to the preciseness-vagueness principle, if there is preciseness (e.g., the precise identification of 5 reporting systems of adverse effects in the article aforecited), there is vagueness (e.g., the vagueness in the identification of the 5 reporting systems of adverse effects in the article aforecited, since it is not clear why there must be only these 5, not 6, 7, 8, 9, and so on). And the reverse direction also holds true.

In relation to the simpleness-complicatedness principle, if there is simpleness (e.g., the relatively simple analysis of "adverse effects" by the advocates), there is complicatedness (e.g., the relatively more complicated analysis of "adverse effects," by challenging the claims and assumptions, as shown in the problems pointed out by the critics as cited). And the reverse direction also holds true.

In relation to the openness-hiddenness principle, if there is openness (e.g., the open exploration of the adverse effects of "the MMR vaccine"), there is hiddenness (e.g., the hidden bias in the "public outcry" and "lawsuits against drug manufacturers" in regard to the claim about "autism...linked to the MMR vaccine," because "no link has been found in several large studies, and despite removal of thimerosal from vaccines a decade ago the rate of autism has not decreased as would be expected if it had been the causative agent"). And the reverse direction also holds true.

In relation to the denseness-emptiness principle, if there is denseness (e.g., the relatively denser concentration of concerns with harmful side-effects by those in the "public outcry" and "lawsuits against drug manufacturers" in regard to the claim about "autism...linked to the MMR vaccine"), there is emptiness (e.g., the relatively less dense, or more empty, concentration of concerns with beneficial side-effects by those in the "public outcry" and "lawsuits against drug manufacturers" in regard to the claim about "autism...linked to the MMR vaccine"). And the reverse direction also holds true.

In relation to the rule-exception principle, if there are rules (e.g., the usual generalization, procedure, habit, or tendency that "the harmful outcome" of adverse effects is not death but "is usually indicated by some result such as morbidity, mortality, alteration in body weight, levels of enzymes, loss of function, or as a pathological change detected at the microscopic, macroscopic or physiological level"), there are exceptions (e.g., a case to which a rule does not apply, such as the exceptional case involving "serious adverse events" or SAE, which can "cause...death"). (WK 2014o) And the reverse direction also holds true.

In relation to the indispensability-dispensability principle, if there is indispensability (e.g., the need for something or someone, like the requirement of reporting systems "in many countries," where "adverse effects are required by law to be reported, researched in clinical trials and included into the patient information accompanying medical devices and drugs for sale to the public," in the article aforecited), there is dispensability (e.g., the superfluity of something or someone, like the dispensable suggestion of reporting adverse effects in Australia, where "reporting is voluntary," not required). And the reverse direction also holds true.

In relation to the prototypicality-variation principle, if there is prototypicality (e.g., the prototype, like the example about the original act known as "National Childhood Vaccine Injury Act [NCVIA]" in 1986, requiring reporting systems of adverse effects in the U.S.), there is variation (e.g., different variants of the prototptye, as shown in many studies since the original act known as "National Childhood Vaccine Injury Act [NCVIA]" in 1986, requiring reporting systems of adverse effects in the U.S.—like the later one known as "the Vaccine Adverse Event Reporting System" in 1990, though with its own variation, contribution, and disagreement). (WK 2014nn) And the reverse direction also holds true.

In relation to the change-constancy principle, if there is change (e.g., the ever new ways to study causation, as shown in the work on "adverse effects"), there is constancy (e.g., the ever constant existence of different problems with the ever new ways to study causation, as shown in the problems with the work on "adverse effects" pointed out by the critics). And the reverse direction also holds true.

In relation to the order-chaos principle, if there is order (e.g., the more or less orderly view on "adverse effects," if looked from the sole vantage point of those in the "public outcry" against "hormonal contraception and hormone replacement therapy" in regard to the "adverse effects of a severe nature, such as breast cancer"), there is chaos (e.g., the more or less chaotic view on "hormonal contraception and hormone replacement therapy" in regard to the "adverse effects of a severe nature, such as breast cancer," if looked from the multiple, conflicting vantage points of both the advocates and the critics, especially in regard to the problems aforecited, such that they do not add up to much of anything coherent). And the reverse direction also holds true.

In relation to the slowness-quickness principle, if there is slowness (e.g., the relatively slower speed of a drug to be effective, if there are "adverse effects"), there is quickness (e.g., the relatively quicker speed of a drug to be effective, if there is no adverse effect of any kind). And the reverse direction also holds true.

In relation to the expansion-contraction principle, if there is expansion (e.g., the relative spread of required "reporting systems" of adverse effects nowadays, since "in many countries, adverse effects are required by law to be reported"), there is contraction (e.g., the relative decline of voluntary "reporting systems" of adverse effects nowadays, since, only in a few countries, reporting is voluntary by law). And the reverse direction also holds true.

In relation to the optimality-nonoptimality principle, if there is optimality (e.g., the search for highly favorable options, like the quest for the most "systematic reviews and meta-analyses of therapeutic interventions" so as to provide "more complete reporting of harm from clinical trials"), there is nonoptimality (e.g., the existence of non-optimal alternatives to optimality, like the argument for more realistic studies by the critics, who pointed out different problems with reporting systems aforecited). (WK 2014o) And the reverse direction also holds true.

In relation to the simultaneity-nonsimultaneity principle, if there is simultaneity (e.g., the occurrence of different things more or less at the same time, such as the simultaneous co-existence of "harmful" and beneficial" effects of drugs, in general), there is nonsimultaneity (e.g., the occurrence of something after something else, as shown in the finding that beneficial effects of drugs are often known beforehand, but any "medical error" in drug dosage is often discovered afterward). And the reverse direction also holds true.

In relation to the isolation-interaction principle, if there is isolation (e.g., the state of a situation that is separate from others, such as the isolation of adverse effects from public knowledge, if they are not reported), there is interaction (e.g., the influence of entities on one another, such as the interaction between the law and the reporting of adverse effects, like MHRA which requires reporting adverse effects in the U.K.). And the reverse direction also holds true.

In relation to the theory-praxis principle, if there is theory (e.g., the theoretical construction of "probabilities" in the field of statistics), there is praxis (e.g., the practical application of probabilities" in the field of statistics to the field of medicine, like the calculation of "marginal probabilities of adverse effects of a severe nature, such as breast cancer" in "hormonal contraception and hormone replacement therapy"). And the reverse direction also holds true.

In relation to the convention-novelty principle, if there is convention (e.g., the conventional wisdom about the importance of "reporting systems" for the understanding of "adverse effects"), there is novelty (e.g., the alternative novel challenge to the conventional wisdom about the importance of "reporting systems" for the understanding of "adverse effects"—by the new idea about the inherent limitations of "reporting systems" as discussed earlier). And the reverse direction also holds true.

In relation to the evolution-transformation principle, if there is evolution (e.g., the natural evolution of humans to experience diseases or injuries in the state of nature), there is transformation (e.g., the technical transformation of human ability to cope with diseases or injuries by the invention of "drugs" and "surgery," with both harmful and beneficial effects). And the reverse direction also holds true.

In relation to the symmetry-asymmetry principle, if there is symmetry (e.g., the co-existence of different reporting systems in many countries nowadays), there is asymmetry (e.g., reporting adverse effects is voluntary in Australia—but it is required in the U.S. nowadays). And the reverse direction also holds true.

In relation to the softness-hardness principle, if there is softness (e.g., the defense of "the MMR vaccine" by its drug manufacturers), there is hardness (e.g., the critique of "the MMR vaccine," as shown in the problems pointed out by those in lawsuits against the drug manufacturers). And the reverse direction also holds true.

In relation to the seriousness-playfulness principle, if there is seriousness (e.g., the serious business of those who try to come up with effective ways of reporting adverse effects), there is playfulness (e.g., the playful part of those who try to come up with effective ways of reporting adverse effects, when they play around with different reporting systems over the decades, as shown in the 5 examples as discussed earlier). And the reverse direction also holds true.

In relation to the activeness-inactivess principle, if there is activeness (e.g., the relative activeness of those who take drugs with effective, not harmful, effects, so they can engage in nornal life activities), there is inactiveness (e.g., the relative inactiveness of those who take drugs with serious harmful effects, so they get very sick and cannot engage in nornal life activities). And the reverse direction also holds true.

In relation to the selfness-otherness principle, if there is selfness (e.g., the tendency to be mostly centered on one's self or group, as shown in those with "lawsuits against drug manufacturers" in regard to the claim about "autism...linked to the MMR vaccine," even though "no link has been found in several large studies, and despite removal of thimerosal from vaccines a decade ago the rate of autism has not decreased as would be expected if it had been the causative agent"), there is otherness (e.g., the tendency to be mostly centered on others, as shown in the academic analysis of both sides of the debate on the claim about "autism...linked to the MMR vaccine," as an advancement in the knowledge of medicine for humanity). And the reverse direction also holds true.

In relation to the regression-progression principle, if there is regression (e.g., the regression made by the use of drugs, as shown in the problems of "adverse effects" pointed out by the critics), there is progression (e.g., the progress made by the use of drugs, as shown in the contribution to the beneficial uses of drugs aforecited). And the reverse direction also holds true.

In relation to the same-difference principle, if there is similarity in outcome (e.g., the contribution to the molding and control of beliefs, values, and behaviors, regardless of whether this be done by way of the required reporting system of adverse effects in the U.K., or by way of the voluntary reporting system of adverse effects in Australia), there is difference in outcome (e.g., the contribution to the molding and control of beliefs, values, and behaviors by way of the required reporting system of adverse effects in the U.K. for a relatively more state-regulated lifeworld—but the contribution to the molding and control of beliefs, values, and behaviors by way of the voluntary reporting system of adverse effects in Australia for a relatively more market-oriented lifeworld). And the reverse direction also holds true.

In relation to the stability-reaction principle, if there is stability (e.g., the situation in the earlier days, when, "because of the lack of these data and uncertainty about methods for synthesising them, individuals conducting systematic reviews and meta-analyses of therapeutic interventions often unknowingly overemphasise health benefit"), there is reaction (e.g., the situation in the earlier days [when, "because of the lack of these data and uncertainty about methods for synthesising them, individuals conducting systematic reviews and meta-analyses of therapeutic interventions often unknowingly overemphasise health benefit] then led to further changes later on, when nowadays, "to balance the overemphasis on benefit, scholars have called for more complete reporting of harm from clinical trials"). (WK 2014o) And the reverse direction also holds true.

In relation to the functionality-nonfunctionality principle, if there is functionality (e.g., the presence of action for which something or someone is fitted, as shown in the creation of "reporting systems," which serves the function of legally requiring the reporting of adverse effects for better understanding), there is nonfunctionality (e.g., the relative lack of action for which something or someone is fitted, as shown in the problems with "reporting systems," such that they are not as functional as the advocates would like us to believe). And the reverse direction also holds true.

In relation to the intentionality-nonintentionality principle, if there is intentionality (e.g., the planning or design of something for a certain outcome, as shown in the intended consequences in regard to reporting adverse effects now required in many countries, as these different laws were intended to do, as discussed earlier), there is nonintentionality (e.g., the relative absence of planning or design of something for a certain outcome, such that the outcome can even be counter-intentional in being the opposite of what was originally planned, as shown in the limitations of reporting systems aforecited—contrary to the original intention of those to construct effective reporting systems). And the reverse direction also holds true.

In relation to the survivability-nonsurvivability principle, if there is survivability (e.g., the relative survival, nowadays, of required "reporting" of adverse effects in many countries), there is non-survivability (e.g., the relative non-survival, nowadays, of voluntary "reporting" of adverse effects in many countries, that is, with the exception of a few countries like Australia). And the reverse direction also holds true.

And in relation to the materiality-nonmateriality principle, if there is materiality (e.g., the material outcome in relation to space-time, matter-energy, Having, etc., like the adverse effect of "hormonal contraception and hormone replacement therapy," such as "breast cancer"), there is non-materiality (e.g., the nonmaterial outcome in relation to the quest for Being, Belonging, etc., like the spiritual search among humans, as shown in the use of "evil eyes" to protect oneself from evil spirits in some religious cultures, even though they do not always produce the effective results). And the reverse direction also holds true.

Effect, Intentionality, and Consequences

Another way to evaluate the possibility (or impossibility) and desirability (or undesirability) of effect from the perspective of the mind is to explore effect, intentionality, and consequences.

An argument in the literature is that, in the social sciences, there are "unintended consequences (sometimes unanticipated consequences or unforeseen consequences)," such that they "are not the ones intended by a purposeful action." (WK 2014j)

History of Unintended Consequences

The history of the idea of "unintended consequences" can be dated back "at least to Adam Smith [2009], the Scottish Enlightenment, and consequentialism (judging by results). However, it was the sociologist Robert K. Merton [1936] who popularized this concept in the twentieth century." (WK 2014j; M. Kaufman 2003; J. Hollander 2003)

In 1936, Merton wrote the paper, "The Unanticipated Consequences of Purposive Social Action," in which he "tried to apply a systematic analysis to the problem of unintended consequences of deliberate acts intended to cause social change. He emphasized that his term 'purposive action...[is exclusively] concerned with 'conduct' as distinct from 'behavior.' That is, with action that involves motives and consequently a choice between various alternatives.' Merton also stated that 'no blanket statement categorically affirming or denying the practical feasibility of all social planning is warranted.'" (WK 2014j)

In our time, "the law of unintended consequences has come to be used as an adage or idiomatic warning that an intervention in a complex system tends to create unanticipated and often undesirable outcomes. Akin to Murphy's law, it is commonly used as a wry or humorous warning against the hubristic belief that humans can fully control the world around them." (WK 2014j; R. Norton 2008)

Causes of Unintended Consequences

There can be different causes of "unintended consequences," of course; but "Robert K. Merton listed five possible causes of unanticipated consequences in 1936," as shown below (and summarized in *Table 3.3*): (WK 2014j; R. Merton 1996)

- "Ignorance"—"It is impossible to anticipate everything, thereby leading to incomplete analysis."
- "Error"—"Incorrect analysis of the problem or following habits that worked in the past but may not apply to the current situation."
- "Immediate Interest"—"which may override long-term interests."
- "Basic Values"—"may require or prohibit certain actions even if the long-term result might be unfavorable" and "these long-term consequences may eventually cause changes in basic values."
- "Self-Defeating Prophecy"—"Fear of some consequence drives people to find solutions before the problem occurs, thus the non-occurrence of the problem is not anticipated."

Unfortunately, "in this paper, Merton announced that he would write a book on the history and analysis of unintended consequences—but this remained unfinished when he died in 2003." (WK 2014j)

Types of Unintended Consequences

In general, there are three main types of unintended consequences to be analyzed, as shown below (and summarized in *Table 3.3*).

(a) Unexpected Benefits

The first type of unintended consequences to be illustrated here concerns "unexpected benefits" (which are "usually referred to as luck, serendipity or a windfall)." (WK 2014j)

For illustration, hereafter are three examples of this type:

- "The medieval policy of setting up large hunting reserves for the nobility has preserved green space, often as parks, throughout England and other places in Europe. Likewise the creation of 'no-man's lands' during the Cold War, in places such as the border between Eastern and Western Europe, and the Korean Demilitarized Zone, has led to large natural habitats." (WK 2014j; IND 2009; K. Connolly 2009)
- "The sinking of ships in shallow waters during wartime has created many artificial coral reefs, which can be scientifically valuable and have become an attraction for recreational divers." (WK 2014j; NBC 2009; NAT 2009)
- "In medicine, most drugs have unintended consequences ('side effects') associated with their use. However, some are beneficial. For instance, aspirin, a pain reliever, is also an anticoagulant that can help prevent heart attacks and reduce the severity and damage from thrombotic strokes. The existence of beneficial side effects also leads to off-label use—prescription or use of a drug for an unlicensed purpose." (WK 2014j; BBC 2001)

But if there are unexpected benefits, there can be unexpected drawbacks, as shown below.

(b) Unexpected Drawbacks

The second type of unintended consequences to be illustrated here concerns "unexpected drawbacks." (WK 2014j)

For illustration, hereafter are four examples of this type:

- "In 1990, the Australian state of Victoria made safety helmets mandatory for all bicycle riders. While there was a reduction in the number of head injuries, there was also an unintended reduction in the number of juvenile cyclists—fewer cyclists obviously leads to fewer injuries, assuming all else being equal. The risk of death and serious injury per cyclist seems to have increased, possibly due to risk compensation. Research by Vulcan et al. found that the reduction in juvenile cyclists was because the youths considered wearing a bicycle helmet unfashionable. A health benefit model developed at Macquarie University in Sydney suggests that, while helmet use reduces 'the risk of head or brain injury by approximately two-thirds or more,' the decrease in exercise caused by reduced cycling as a result of helmets laws is counterproductive in terms of net health." (WK 2014j; D. Robinson 2012; M. Cameron 1994; P. De Jong 2009)

- "Prohibition in the 1920s United States, originally enacted to suppress the alcohol trade, drove many small-time alcohol suppliers out of business and consolidated the hold of large-scale organized crime over the illegal alcohol industry. Since alcohol was still popular, criminal organizations producing alcohol were well-funded and hence also increased their other activities. Similarly, the War on Drugs, intended to suppress the illegal drug trade, instead consolidates the profitability of drug cartels." (WK 2014j; J. Forero 2006; D. Podesta 1993)

- "Most modern technologies have negative consequences that are both unavoidable and unpredictable. For example, almost all environmental problems, from chemical pollution to global warming, are the unexpected consequences of the application of modern technologies. Traffic congestion, deaths and injuries from car accidents, air pollution, and even global warming are unintended consequences of the invention and large scale adoption of the automobile. Hospital infections are the unexpected side-effect of antibiotic resistance, and even human overpopulation is the side-effect of various technological (i.e., agricultural and industrial) revolutions." (WK 2014j)

- "In CIA jargon, 'blowback' describes the unintended, undesirable consequences of covert operations, for example: covert funding of the Afghan Mujahideen, which contributed to the rise of Al-Qaeda." (WK 2014j; M. Weaver 1996; P. Beaumont 2012)

And there is also another type, known as 'perverse effects," as shown below.

(c) Perverse Effects

And the third type of unintended consequences to be illustrated here concerns "perverse effects." (WK 2014j)

For illustration, hereafter are four examples of this type:

- "The term *Streisand Effect* is applied to the internet phenomenon that occurs when an attempt to censor or remove a certain piece of information (such as a photograph, document, etc.) instead causes the information to become widely known and distributed. The fact that a piece of information is being restricted assigns to it a previously nonexistent value in the eyes of the public." (WK 2014j)
- "Theobald Mathew's temperance campaign in 19th-century Ireland (in which thousands of people vowed never to drink alcohol again) led to the consumption of diethyl ether, an intoxicant much more dangerous due to its high flammability, by those seeking to become intoxicated without breaking the letter of their pledge." (WK 2014j; WOR 2006)
- "It was thought that adding south-facing conservatories to British houses would reduce energy consumption by providing extra insulation and warmth from the sun. However, people tended to use the conservatories as living areas, installing heating and ultimately increasing overall energy consumption." (WK 2014j)
- "A reward for ghost nets found along the Normandy coast, offered by the French government between 1980 and 1981, resulted in people vandalizing nets to collect the reward." (WK 2014j; A. Brandt 1972)

Of course, there can be other examples, so the ones above are illustrative, not exhaustive.

Problems with the Study on Intentionality and Consequences

However, to the critics, this study on effect, intentionality, and consequences has some major problems. Consider, for illustration, a few examples below (and summarized in *Table 3.3*).

Firstly, one main criticism of the study on effect, intentionality, and consequences is that Merton did not focus enough on what exactly is meant by "intentionality," since "unintentional" in "unintended consequences" is a term relative to "intentionality" (as its opposite).

For example, precisely here, there has been a heated debate in philosophy on what exactly "intentionality" is, before one is to understand what "unintentionality" is. Daniel Dennett, for one, "offers a taxonomy of the current theories about intentionality," in that some consider it to be too "problematic for science" to handle, whereas others consider it not to be so problematic for science at all. (WK 2014pp)

Secondly, another main criticism of the study on effect, intentionality, and consequences is that it does not distinguish between something ("non-intentional") and something ('unintentional"), so what is "not intentional" does not necessarily mean "unintentional."

For instance, some philosophers argued for some "mental states without intentionality" which are "non-intentional"; Robert K. C. Forman, for one, "argues that some of the unusual states of consciousness typical of mystical experience are Pure Consciousness Events in which awareness exists, but has no object, is not awareness 'of' anything." (WK 2014pp)

Thirdly, still another main criticism of the study on effect, intentionality, and consequences is that Merton's conception of social action is narrow.

For instance, to the critics, "Merton tried to apply a systematic analysis to the problem of unintended consequences of deliberate acts," which, however, is not concerned with "behavior" as "non-purposive action" (but only "conduct" as "deliberate act"). (WK 2014j)

Fourthly, an additional main criticism of the study on effect, intentionality, and consequences is that the world is too complex to have only 5 causes of unintended consequences as suggested by Merton.

For instance, to the critics, there are numerous "possible causes of unintended consequences," which, just to cite some examples, "include the world's inherent complexity (parts of a system responding to changes in the environment), perverse incentives, human stupidity, self-deception, failure to account for human nature or other cognitive or emotional biases,...the chaotic nature of the universe," and so on. (WK 2014j)

And fifthly, another additional main criticism of the study on effect, intentionality, and consequences is that it is not clear if the third type, "perverse results," is redundant.

For instance, "perverse results" can be part of "unexpected benefits" and/or part of "unexpected drawbacks"; thus in either case it is redundant, because it can be classified as a sub-set of the first type, of the second type, or of both types.

Beyond Intentionality and Consequences

These criticisms of the analysis of effect, intentionality, and consequences do not entail a total rejection of its usefulness but serve to show us the two opposing sides of the debate, such that the possibility (or impossibility) and desirability (or undesirability) of effect (from the perspective of the mind with effect, intentionality, and consequences as a case study here) are not to the extent that the respective defenders would like us to believe.

Moreover, the analysis of effect, intentionality, and consequences can cast a bright light on the ontological principles in existential dialectics, and good examples include the formalness-informalness principle, the absoluteness-relativeness principle, the partiality-totality principle, the predictability-unpredictability principle, the explicability-inexplicability principle, the fiction-reality principle, the cognitiveness-noncognitiveness principle, the finiteness-transfiniteness principle, the preciseness-vagueness principle, the simpleness-complicatedness principle, the openness-hiddenness principle, the denseness-emptiness principle, the rule-exception principle, the indispensability-dispensability principle, the prototypicality-variation principle, the change-constancy principle, the order-chaos principle, the slowness-quickness principle, the expansion-contraction principle, the optimality-nonoptimality principle, the simultaneity-nonsimultaneity principle, the isolation-interaction principle, the theory-praxis principle, the convention-novelty principle, the evolution-transformation principle, the symmetry-asymmetry principle, the softness-hardness principle, the seriousness-playfulness principle, the activeness-inactivess principle, the selfness-otherness principle, the regression-progression principle, the same-difference principle, the stability-reaction principle, the functionality-nonfunctionality principle, the intentionality-nonintentionality principle. the survivability-non-survivability principle, and the materiality-nonmateriality principle.

For instance, in relation to the formalness-informalness principle, if there is formalness (e.g., the formal logical requirement of soundness and completeness in a system of ideas, as in the argument on "unintended consequences"), there is informalness (e.g., the non-formal existence of unsoundness and incompleteness in the argument on "unintended consequences," as shown in the criticisms that Merton did not focus enough on what exactly is meant by "intentionality" since "unintentional" in "unintended consequences" is a term relative to "intentionality" [as its opposite], that it does not distinguish between something ["non-intentional"] and something ['unintentional'] so what is "not intentional" does not necessarily mean "unintentional," that Merton's conception of social action is narrow, that the world is too complex to have only 5 causes of unintended consequences as suggested by Merton, and that it is not clear if the third type ["perverse results"] is redundant). And the reverse direction also holds true.

In relation to the absoluteness-relativeness principle, if there is absoluteness (e.g., the absolute view on "covert operations" by the CIA, like "covert funding of the Afghan Mujahideen"), there is relativeness (e.g., what is right for the CIA in regard to "covert funding of the Afghan Mujahideen" is not necessarily so for the critics, who pointed out the problem of "blowback," in that "covert funding of the Afghan

Mujahideen...contributed to the rise of Al-Qaeda."). And the reverse direction also holds true.

In relation to the partiality-totality principle, if there is partiality (e.g., the partial view on the Soviet war in Afghanistan by the CIA), there is totality (e.g., the more holistic view on the Soviet war in Afghanistan, such that the whole is not the sum of its parts, that is, it cannot be reduced to the sum of opposing views by the CIA, the Soviet Union, the critics about "blowback," etc., since there will emerge new views in the future not yet known today, just as there are already alternative views nowadays which do not side exclusively with any of them, as is the analysis here). And the reverse direction also holds true.

In relation to the predictability-unpredictability principle, if there is predictability (e.g., the predictable tendency that people can act "purposively"), there is unpredictability (e.g., the more difficult task to predict exactly the extent to which a particular "purposive action" will yield consequences as intended on a particular future occasion, because of the problems with "unintended consequences" aforediscussed). And the reverse direction also holds true.

In relation to the explicability-inexplicability principle, if there is explicability (e.g., the explanation, by Merton, of unintended consquences on the basis of 5 causes), there is inexplicability (e.g., the lack of sufficient explanation, by Merton, of why his list of 5 causes is necessarily complete, since, to the critics, the world is too complex to have only 5 causes of unintended consequences as suggested by Merton). And the reverse direction also holds true.

In relation to the fiction-reality principle, if there is fiction (e.g., the fictional aspect of the benefits of "safety helmets" required by the Australian state of Victoria in 1990, insofar as "the decrease in exercise caused by reduced cycling as a result of helmets laws is counterproductive in terms of net health"), there is reality (e.g., the realistic aspect of the benefits of "safety helmets" required by the Australian state of Victoria in 1990, insofar as "helmet use reduces 'the risk of head or brain injury by approximately two-thirds or more'"). And the reverse direction also holds true.

In relation to the cognitiveness-noncognitiveness principle, if there is cognitiveness (e.g., a view of things on the basis of reason and evidences, as shown in the empirical finding that there are unintended consequences, even if people act purposively), there is noncognitiveness (e.g., a view of things on the basis of non-cognitive factors like envy, jealousy, power, nationality, race, gender, age, class, greed, lust, status, faith, anger, sadness, joy, fear, wish, etc.—as shown in the persistence of "cognitive or emotional biases" among some people, such that unintended consequences continue to occur, in spite of their being informed about their biases as causes of these consequences). And the reverse direction also holds true.

In relation to the finiteness-transfiniteness principle, if there is finiteness (e.g., the finite number of types of unintended consequences, like the 3 types aforecited), there is transfiniteness (e.g., the transfinite number of all the individual instances of unintended consequences that have ever occurred in history, regardless of which types they belong to). And the reverse direction also holds true.

In relation to the preciseness-vagueness principle, if there is preciseness (e.g., the precise identification of 5 causes of unintended consequences by Merton), there is vagueness (e.g., the vagueness in the identification of the 5 causes of unintended consequences by Merton, since it is not clear why there must be only 5, not 6, 7, 8, 9, and so on). And the reverse direction also holds true.

In relation to the simpleness-complicatedness principle, if there is simpleness (e.g., the relatively simple analysis of unintended consequences by Merton), there is complicatedness (e.g., the relatively more complicated analysis of unintended consequences, by challenging the claims and assumptions, as shown in the problems pointed out by the critics as cited). And the reverse direction also holds true.

In relation to the openness-hiddenness principle, if there is openness (e.g., the open exploration of the need to make "the War on Drugs" so as to "suppress the illegal drug trade"), there is hiddenness (e.g., the hidden bias in the exploration of the need to make "the War on Drugs," because "the War on Drugs, intended to suppress the illegal drug trade, instead consolidates the profitability of drug cartels"). And the reverse direction also holds true.

In relation to the denseness-emptiness principle, if there is denseness (e.g., the relatively denser concentration of concerns with "unintentionality" by Merton in the context of "unintended consequences"), there is emptiness (e.g., the relatively less dense, or more empty, concentration of concerns with "intentionality" and "nonintentionality" by Merton in the context of "unintended consequences"). And the reverse direction also holds true.

In relation to the rule-exception principle, if there are rules (e.g., the usual generalization, procedure, habit, or tendency that Merton's work is to focus more on "unintended consequences" as those which are "not intentional"), there are exceptions (e.g., a case to which a rule does not apply, such as the exceptional case that what is "not intentional" does not necessarily mean "unintentional," because Merton does not distinguish

between something ["non-intentional"] and something ['unintentional"]).
And the reverse direction also holds true.

In relation to the indispensability-dispensability principle, if there is
indispensability (e.g., the need for something or someone, like the
necessary inclusion of "unexpected benefits" and "unexpected drawbacks"
as types of "unintended consequences" by Merton), there is dispensability
(e.g., the superfluity of something or someone, like the dispensable
inclusion of "perverse results," since "perverse results" can be part of
"unexpected benefits" and/or part of "unexpected drawbacks," so in either
case it is redundant, because it can be classified as a sub-set of the first
type, of the second type, or of both types, contrary to Merton's
classification). And the reverse direction also holds true.

In relation to the prototypicality-variation principle, if there is
prototypicality (e.g., the prototype, like the example about the original
work on unintended consequences by Adam Smith in the 18th century),
there is variation (e.g., different variants of the protoptye, as shown in
many studies since the original work on unintended consequences by
Adam Smith in the 18th century —like the later ones by Merton in 1936,
though with its own variation, contribution, and disagreement). And the
reverse direction also holds true.

In relation to the change-constancy principle, if there is change (e.g.,
the ever new ways to study causation, as shown in the work on
"unintended consequences"), there is constancy (e.g., the ever constant
existence of different problems with the ever new ways to study causation,
as shown in the problems with the work on "unintended consequences"
pointed out by the critics). And the reverse direction also holds true.

In relation to the order-chaos principle, if there is order (e.g., the more
or less orderly view on causation, if looked from the sole vantage point of
"purposive acts" for "intended consequences," with "the hubristic belief
that humans can fully control the world around them"), there is chaos
(e.g., the more or less chaotic view on causation, if looked from the
multiple, conflicting vantage points of both the advocates and the critics in
regard to "intended" and "unintended consequences," especially in relation
to different problems aforecited). And the reverse direction also holds true.

In relation to the slowness-quickness principle, if there is slowness
(e.g., the relatively slower speed of rabbits to spread in Australia and New
Zealand, if the introduction of more rabbits in the late 19th century and the
subsequent fur trade did not occur), there is quickness (e.g., the relatively
quicker speed of rabbits to spread in Australia and New Zealand, after "the
introduction of rabbits in Australia and New Zealand for food was

followed by an explosive growth in the rabbit population"). (WK 2014j) And the reverse direction also holds true.

In relation to the expansion-contraction principle, if there is expansion (e.g., the relative expasion of rabbits in New Zealand in the late 19th century), there is contraction (e.g., the relative decline of sheep in New Zealand in the late 19th century, because "many farmers who had overstocked their land lost many of their sheep to starvation as the rabbits spread"). (CHR 2014) And the reverse direction also holds true.

In relation to the optimality-nonoptimality principle, if there is optimality (e.g., the search for highly favorable options, like the quest for the complete mastery of the world, by those who have "the hubristic belief that humans can fully control the world around them"), there is nonoptimality (e.g., the existence of non-optimal alternatives to optimality, like the argument for more realistic studies by the critics, who pointed out different problems with the naïve belief in controlling the world, because, "akin to Murphy's law, [Merton's work] is commonly used as a wry or humorous warning against the hubristic belief that humans can fully control the world around them"). (WK 2014j) And the reverse direction also holds true.

In relation to the simultaneity-nonsimultaneity principle, if there is simultaneity (e.g., the occurrence of different things more or less at the same time, such as the simultaneous co-existence of "sheep" and "rabbits" in New Zealand in the later part of the 19th century), there is nonsimultaneity (e.g., the occurrence of something after something else, such as the "loss" of "many...sheep" due to "starvation" after "the rabbits spread" in New Zealand in the late 19th century). (CHR). And the reverse direction also holds true.

In relation to the isolation-interaction principle, if there is isolation (e.g., the state of a situation that is separate from others, such as the isolation of Australia and New Zealand from any rabbits prior to the 19th century), there is interaction (e.g., the influence of entities on one another, such as "the introduction of rabbits in Australia and New Zealand for food was followed by an explosive growth in the rabbit population," to the extent that "rabbits have become a major feral pest in these countries"). (WK2014j) And the reverse direction also holds true.

In relation to the theory-praxis principle, if there is theory (e.g., the theoretical construction of "unintended consequences" by Merton in the field of sociology), there is praxis (e.g., the practical application of "unintended consequences" by Merton in the field of sociology to the field of ecology, such as the study on "the introduction of rabbits to Australia by Europeans, which became economically and environmentally damaging"). (WK 2014j) And the reverse direction also holds true.

In relation to the convention-novelty principle, if there is convention (e.g., the conventional wisdom against "the hubristic belief that humans can fully control the world around them" in the older days), there is novelty (e.g., the alternative novel challenge to the conventional wisdom against "the hubristic belief that humans can fully control the world around them" in the older days—by the new idea of Merton about "unintended consequences"). And the reverse direction also holds true.

In relation to the evolution-transformation principle, if there is evolution (e.g., the natural evolution of humans to anticipate things in the state of nature, albeit in a primitive way), there is transformation (e.g., the technical transformation of human ability to understand the nature of anticipating things by the invention of the research on "unintended consequences" and their causes). And the reverse direction also holds true.

In relation to the symmetry-asymmetry principle, if there is symmetry (e.g., the co-existence of different entities like animals and humans), there is asymmetry (e.g., humans have "self-defeating prophecy," on average—but animals do not have "self-defeating prophecy," on average). And the reverse direction also holds true.

In relation to the softness-hardness principle, if there is softness (e.g., the defense of the idea of "unintended consequences" by the advocates like Merton), there is hardness (e.g., the critique of the idea of "unintended consequences" by the critics, as shown in the problems aforecited). And the reverse direction also holds true.

In relation to the seriousness-playfulness principle, if there is seriousness (e.g., the serious business of those who try to understand the causes of "unintended consequences"), there is playfulness (e.g., the playful part of those who try to understand the causes of "unintended consequences," when they play around with different possible causes over the decades, like the ones by Merton and the alternative ones by others aforecited). And the reverse direction also holds true.

In relation to the activeness-inactivess principle, if there is activeness (e.g., the relative activeness of rabbits in New Zealand when they were introduced and rapidly spread in the late 19th century), there is inactiveness (e.g., the relative inactiveness of many sheep in New Zealand when they were almost wiped out by the rabbits when the latter rapidly spread in the late 19th century). (CHR 2014) And the reverse direction also holds true.

In relation to the selfness-otherness principle, if there is selfness (e.g., the tendency to be mostly centered on one's self or group, as shown in the opposition by many juvenile cyclists to the introduction of a law to require the use of safety helmets, because "the youths considered wearing a bicycle helmet unfashionable"), there is otherness (e.g., the tendency to be mostly centered on others, as shown in the introduction of a law to require the use of safety helmets so as to increase "public health" like the reduction of head injuries, in Australia in 1990). And the reverse direction also holds true.

In relation to the regression-progression principle, if there is regression (e.g., the regression made by the introduction of a law to require the use of safety helmets in Australia in 1990, as shown in the problem that "the decrease in exercise caused by reduced cycling as a result of helmets laws is counterproductive in terms of net health"), there is progression (e.g., the progress made by the introduction of a law to require the use of safety helmets in Australia in 1990, as shown in the contribution to the reduction of "head or brain injury by approximately two-thirds or more"). And the reverse direction also holds true.

In relation to the same-difference principle, if there is similarity in outcome (e.g., the contribution to the molding and control of beliefs, values, and behaviors, regardless of whether this be done by way of the "mandatory" use of safety helmets, or by way of voluntary the "use of safety helmets"), there is difference in outcome (e.g., the contribution to the molding and control of beliefs, values, and behaviors by way of the "mandatory" use of safety helmets for a relatively more state-regulated lifeworld, in spite of its unintended consequences—but the contribution to the molding and control of beliefs, values, and behaviors by way of the voluntary "use of safety helmets" for a relatively more market-oriented lifeworld, in spite of its contribution to head injuries). And the reverse direction also holds true.

In relation to the stability-reaction principle, if there is stability (e.g., the relatively more stable condition of not wearing safety helmets in Australia prior to 1990), there is reaction (e.g., not wearing safety helmets in Australia prior to 1990 then led to further changes later on, when in 1990 there was a law introduced to require the use of safety helmets, in spite of its unintended consequences). And the reverse direction also holds true.

In relation to the functionality-nonfunctionality principle, if there is functionality (e.g., the presence of action for which something or someone is fitted, as shown in the introduction of a law to require the use of safety helmets in Australia in 1990, which serves the function to enhance public health, like the reduciton of head injuries), there is nonfunctionality (e.g., the relative lack of action for which something or someone is fitted, as shown in the problem that "the decrease in exercise caused by reduced cycling as a result of helmets laws is counterproductive in terms of net health," such that it is not as functional as the advocates would like us to believe). And the reverse direction also holds true.

In relation to the intentionality-nonintentionality principle, if there is intentionality (e.g., the planning or design of something for a certain outcome, as shown in the intended consequences in regard to the reduction of head injuries, as those who supported a law to require the use of safety helmets in Australia in 1990 intended to have for public health), there is nonintentionality (e.g., the relative absence of planning or design of something for a certain outcome, such that the outcome can even be counter-intentional in being the opposite of what was originally planned, as shown in "the decrease in exercise caused by reduced cycling as a result of helmets laws" which "is counterproductive in terms of net health"—contrary to the original intention of those who supported the law to require the use of safety helmets in Australia in 1990, as a way to enhance public health). And the reverse direction also holds true.

In relation to the survivability-nonsurvivability principle, if there is survivability (e.g., the relative survival of rabbits in New Zealand in the late 19th century, as they rapidly spread after introduction), there is non-survivability (e.g., the relative non-survival of sheep in New Zealand in the late 19th century, because "many farmers who had overstocked their land lost many of their sheep to starvation as the rabbits spread"). And the reverse direction also holds true.

And in relation to the materiality-nonmateriality principle, if there is materiality (e.g., the material outcome in relation to space-time, matter-energy, Having, etc., like the use of the idea of "unintended consequences" to understand the "unintended consequences of environmental intervention" in the examples aforecited), there is non-materiality (e.g., the nonmaterial outcome in relation to the quest for Being, Belonging, etc., like the spiritual search among humans to be God-men for the mastering of the world, which, however, is countered by the idea of "unintended consequences" as "a wry or humorous warning against the hubristic belief that humans can fully control the world around them"). And the reverse direction also holds true.

Effect and Nature

Effect, when examined from the perspective of nature, can show us in a controversial way its possibility (or impossibility) and desirability (or undesirability), and this can be shown by way of two case studies, namely,

(3.3.1) effect, nature, and chaos theory, and (3.3.2) effect, quantum physics, and Zeno Effect—to be addressed in what follows, respectively.

Effect, Nature, and Chaos Theory

A good way to evaluate the possibility (or impossibility) and desirability (or undesirability) of effects from the perspective of nature is to explore effect, nature, and chaos theory.

An argument in the literature is that, "in chaos theory, the butterfly effect is the sensitive dependency on initial conditions in which a small change at one place in a deterministic nonlinear system can result in large differences in a later state." (WK 2014q)

History of Two Classics of Chaos Theory

The term "chaos theory" refers to "a field of study in mathematics, with applications in several disciplines including meteorology, physics, engineering, economics, biology, and philosophy. Chaos theory studies the behavior of dynamical systems that are highly sensitive to initial conditions—an effect which is popularly referred to as the butterfly effect. Small differences in initial conditions (such as those due to rounding errors in numerical computation) yield widely diverging outcomes for such dynamical systems, rendering long-term prediction impossible in general. This happens even though these systems are deterministic, meaning that their future behavior is fully determined by their initial conditions, with no random elements involved. In other words, the deterministic nature of these systems does not make them predictable." (WK 2014qq; S. Kellert 1993; C. Werndl 2009)

Although there were some beginning works on "chaos" in the first half of the twentieth century, "chaos theory became formalized as such only after mid-century, when it first became evident for some scientists that linear theory, the prevailing system theory at that time, simply could not explain the observed behavior of certain experiments like that of the logistic map. What had been beforehand excluded as measure imprecision and simple 'noise' was considered by chaos theories as a full component of the studied systems. The main catalyst for the development of chaos theory was the electronic computer. Much of the mathematics of chaos theory involves the repeated iteration of simple mathematical formulas, which would be impractical to do by hand. Electronic computers made these repeated calculations practical, while figures and images made it possible to visualize these systems." (WK 2014qq)

(a) Edward Lorenz

Early chaos theory owed much to the pioneering research by Edward Lorenz at M.I.T., "whose interest in chaos came about accidentally through his work on weather prediction in 1961. Lorenz was using a simple digital computer, a Royal McBee LGP-30, to run his weather simulation. He wanted to see a sequence of data again and to save time he started the simulation in the middle of its course. He was able to do this by entering a printout of the data corresponding to conditions in the middle of his simulation which he had calculated last time." (WK 2014qq)

However, "the weather that the machine began to predict was completely different from the weather calculated before. Lorenz tracked this down to the computer printout. The computer worked with 6-digit precision, but the printout rounded variables off to a 3-digit number, so a value like 0.506127 was printed as 0.506. This difference is tiny and the consensus at the time would have been that it should have had practically no effect. However Lorenz had discovered that small changes in initial conditions produced large changes in the long-term outcome. Lorenz's discovery, which gave its name to Lorenz attractors, showed that even detailed atmospheric modeling cannot in general make long-term weather predictions. Weather is usually predictable only about a week ahead." (WK 2014qq; J. Gleick 1987; R. Watts 2007)

(b) Benoit Mandelbrot

Then, "in 1963, Benoît Mandelbrot found recurring patterns at every scale in data on cotton prices. Beforehand, he had studied information theory and concluded noise was patterned like a Cantor set: on any scale the proportion of noise-containing periods to error-free periods was a constant—thus errors were inevitable and must be planned for by incorporating redundancy. Mandelbrot described both the 'Noah effect' (in which sudden discontinuous changes can occur) and the 'Joseph effect' (in which persistence of a value can occur for a while, yet suddenly change afterwards). This challenged the idea that changes in price were normally distributed. In 1967, he published 'How long is the coast of Britain? Statistical self-similarity and fractional dimension,' showing that a coastline's length varies with the scale of the measuring instrument, resembles itself at all scales, and is infinite in length for an infinitesimally small measuring device. Arguing that a ball of twine appears to be a point when viewed from far away (0-dimensional), a ball when viewed from fairly near (3-dimensional), or a curved strand (1-dimensional), he argued that the dimensions of an object are relative to the observer and may be fractional. An object whose irregularity is constant over different scales ('self-similarity') is a fractal (for example, the Menger sponge, the

Sierpiński gasket and the Koch curve or 'snowflake,' which is infinitely long yet encloses a finite space and has a fractal dimension of circa 1.2619). In 1975 Mandelbrot published *The Fractal Geometry of Nature*, which became a classic of chaos theory. Biological systems such as the branching of the circulatory and bronchial systems proved to fit a fractal model." (WK 2014qq; J. Berger 1963; B. Mandelbrot 1963 & 1967)

Nowadays, "the availability of cheaper, more powerful computers broadens the applicability of chaos theory. Currently, chaos theory continues to be a very active area of research, involving many different disciplines (mathematics, topology, physics, social systems, population biology, biology, meteorology, astrophysics, information theory, computational neuroscience, etc.)." (WK 2014qq; A. Motter 2013)

Properties of Chaotic Dynamics

To understand "chaos" further, it is important to study its dynamics, and "a commonly used definition says that, for a dynamical system to be classified as chaotic, it must have the following properties": (WK 2014qq)

- "It must be sensitive to initial conditions."
- "It must be topologically mixing."
- "Its periodic orbits must be dense."

Let's consider this definition more closely in terms of its breakdown into five main properties, in what follows (as summarized in *Table 3.4*).

(a) Sensitivity to Initial Conditions
The first main property of chaotic dynamics has to do with "sensitivity to initial conditions."

This property means that "an arbitrarily small perturbation of the current trajectory may lead to significantly different future behavior.... Sensitivity to initial conditions is popularly known as the 'butterfly effect,' so called because of the title of a paper given by Edward Lorenz in 1972 to the American Association for the Advancement of Science in Washington, D.C. entitled *Predictability: Does the Flap of a Butterfly's Wings in Brazil set off a Tornado in Texas?* The flapping wing represents a small change in the initial condition of the system, which causes a chain of events leading to large-scale phenomena. Had the butterfly not flapped its wings, the trajectory of the system might have been vastly different." (WK 2014qq)

Therefore, "a consequence of sensitivity to initial conditions is that if we start with only a finite amount of information about the system (as is usually the case in practice), then beyond a certain time the system will no longer be predictable. This is most familiar in the case of weather, which is generally predictable only about a week ahead." (WK 2014qq; R. Watts 2007)

(b) Topological Mixing

The second main property of chaotic dynamics has to do with "topological mixing."

This second property is also known as "topological transitivity" and means that "the system will evolve over time so that any given region or open set of its phase space will eventually overlap with any other given region. This mathematical concept of 'mixing' corresponds to the standard intuition, and the mixing of colored dyes or fluids is an example of a chaotic system." (WK 2014qq)

This second property is important, because "sensitive dependence on initial conditions alone does not give chaos. For example, consider the simple dynamical system produced by repeatedly doubling an initial value. This system has sensitive dependence on initial conditions everywhere, since any pair of nearby points will eventually become widely separated. However, this example has no topological mixing, and therefore has no chaos. Indeed, it has extremely simple behavior: all points except 0 will tend to positive or negative infinity." (WK 2014qq)

(c) Density of Periodic Orbits

The third main property of chaotic dynamics has to do with "density of periodic orbits."

This third property means that "every point in the space is approached arbitrarily closely by periodic orbits. The one-dimensional logistic map defined by $x \rightarrow 4 \, x \, (1 - x)$ is one of the simplest systems with density of periodic orbits. For example, $\frac{5-\sqrt{5}}{8} \rightarrow \frac{5+\sqrt{5}}{8} \rightarrow \frac{5-\sqrt{5}}{8}$ (or approximately $0.3454915 \rightarrow 0.9045085 \rightarrow 0.3454915$) is an (unstable) orbit of period 2, and similar orbits exist for periods 4, 8, 16, etc. (indeed, for all the periods specified by Sharkovskii's theorem)." (WK 2014qq)

(d) Strange Attractors

The fourth main property of chaotic dynamics has to do with "strange attractors."

This fourth property means that "some dynamical systems, like the one-dimensional logistic map defined by $x \rightarrow 4 \, x \, (1 - x)$, are chaotic everywhere, but in many cases chaotic behavior is found only in a subset of phase space. The cases of most interest arise when the chaotic behavior takes place on an attractor, since then a large set of initial conditions will lead to orbits that converge to this chaotic region." (WK 2014qq)

Indeed, "an easy way to visualize a chaotic attractor is to start with a point in the basin of attraction of the attractor, and then simply plot its subsequent orbit. Because of the topological transitivity condition, this is likely to produce a picture of the entire final attractor, and indeed...a picture of the general shape of the Lorenz attractor. This attractor results from a simple three-dimensional model of the Lorenz weather system. The Lorenz attractor is perhaps one of the best-known chaotic system diagrams, probably because it was not only one of the first, but it is also one of the most complex and as such gives rise to a very interesting pattern which looks like the wings of a butterfly." (WK 2014qq)

(e) Minimum Complexity of a Chaotic System

And the fifth main property of chaotic dynamics has to do with "minimum complexity of a chaotic system."

This fifth property suggests that "discrete chaotic systems, such as the logistic map, can exhibit strange attractors whatever their dimensionality. In contrast, for continuous dynamical systems, the Poincaré–Bendixson theorem shows that a strange attractor can only arise in three or more dimensions. Finite dimensional linear systems are never chaotic; for a dynamical system to display chaotic behaviour it has to be either nonlinear, or infinite-dimensional." (WK2014qq)

Case Study: The Butterfly Effect

The case study of "the butterfly effect" (as cited earlier) is interesting enough.

The term "butterfly effect" refers to the idea that "a butterfly's wings might create tiny changes in the atmosphere that may ultimately alter the path of a tornado or delay, accelerate or even prevent the occurrence of a tornado in another location. Note that the butterfly does not power or directly create the tornado. The flap of the wings is a part of the initial conditions; one set of conditions leads to a tornado while the other set of conditions doesn't. The flapping wing represents a small change in the initial condition of the system, which causes a chain of events leading to large-scale alterations of events (compare: domino effect). Had the butterfly not flapped its wings, the trajectory of the system might have been vastly different—it's possible that the set of conditions without the butterfly flapping its wings is the set that leads to a tornado." (WK 2014q)

Not surprisingly, "the butterfly effect presents an obvious challenge to prediction, since initial conditions for a system such as the weather can never be known to complete accuracy." (WK 2014q)

Thus, the idea of "the butterfly effect" has been applied to study other natural phenomona; for instance, in physics, "the potential for sensitive dependence on initial conditions (the butterfly effect) has been studied in a number of cases in semiclassical and quantum physics including atoms in strong fields and the anisotropic Kepler problem," and "the sensitive dependence on initial conditions demonstrated in classical motion is included in the semiclassical treatments developed by Martin Gutzwiller and Delos and co-workers." (WK 2014q; E. Heller 1993; M. Gutzwiller 1990 & 1971; J. Gao 1992)

And "other authors suggest that the butterfly effect can be observed in quantum systems. Karkuszewski et al. [2002] consider the time evolution of quantum systems which have slightly different Hamiltonians. They investigate the level of sensitivity of quantum systems to small changes in their given Hamiltonians. Poulin et al. [2004] presented a quantum algorithm to measure fidelity decay, which 'measures the rate at which identical initial states diverge when subjected to slightly different dynamics.' They consider fidelity decay to be 'the closest quantum analog to the (purely classical) butterfly effect.' Whereas the classical butterfly effect considers the effect of a small change in the position and/or velocity of an object in a given Hamiltonian system, the quantum butterfly effect considers the effect of a small change in the Hamiltonian system with a given initial position and velocity. This quantum butterfly effect has been demonstrated experimentally. Quantum and semiclassical treatments of system sensitivity to initial conditions are known as quantum chaos." (WK 2014q; A. Peres 1995; J. Lee 2004)

Problems with the Study on Nature and Chaos theory

However, to the critics, this argument on effect, nature, and chaos theory has some major problems. Consider, for illustration, a few examples below (as summarized in *Table 3.4*).

Firstly, one main criticism of the argument on effect, nature, and chaos theory is that the so-called "butterfly effect" is much exaggerated.

For instance, to the critics, "some scientists have since argued that the weather system is not as sensitive to initial condition as previously believed. David Orrell [2001, 2002, & 2012] argues that the major contributor to weather forecast error is model error, with sensitivity to initial conditions playing a relatively small role." (WK 2014q)

Secondly, another main criticism of the argument on effect, nature, and chaos theory is that the so-called "butterfly effect" misleadingly exclude some other effects in its analysis.

For instance, to the critics, "Stephen Wolfram [2002]...notes that the Lorenz equations are highly simplified and do not contain terms that represent viscous effects; he believes that these terms would tend to damp out small perturbations." (WK 2014q)

Thirdly, still another main criticism of the study on effect, nature, and chaos theory is that the property of "sensitivity to initial conditions" can be redundant.

For instance, "it has been shown that the last two properties in the list [of three properties] above actually imply sensitivity to initial conditions and if attention is restricted to intervals, the second property implies the other two (an alternative, and in general weaker, definition of chaos uses only the first two properties in the above list). It is interesting that the most practically significant condition, that of sensitivity to initial conditions, is actually redundant in the definition, being implied by two (or for intervals, one) purely topological conditions, which are therefore of greater interest to mathematicians." (WK 2014qq; S. Elaydi 1999; W. Basener 2006; M. Vellekoop 1994; A. Medio 2001)

Fourthly, an additional main criticism of the study on effect, nature, and chaos theory is that the butterfly effect can be countered by more complicated forecasting systems.

For instance, although "the butterfly effect presents an obvious challenge to prediction, since initial conditions for a system such as the weather can never be known to complete accuracy," yet "this problem motivated the development of ensemble forecasting, in which a number of forecasts are made from perturbed initial conditions." (WK 2014q; A. Woods 2005)

Fifthly, another additional main criticism of the study on effect, nature, and chaos theory is that the butterfly effect does not apply in some situations.

For instance, "some authors have argued that extreme (exponential) dependence on initial conditions is not expected in pure quantum treatments." (WK 2014q; Z. Rudnick 2008; M. Berry 1989)

And sixthly, still another additional main criticism of the study on effect, nature, and chaos theory is that there is no universal definition of "chaos" in chaos theory.

For instance, as the critics are quick to point out, "there is no universally accepted mathematical definition of chaos," and this remains true, even though some scholars offer some working definitions like the one as discussed earlier.

Beyond Chaos Theory

These criticisms of the study on effect, nature, and chaos theory should not be misconstrued as a total rejection of its usefulness but serve to show us the two opposing sides of the debate, such that the possibility (or impossibility) and desirability (or undesirability) of effect (from the perspective of nature with effect, nature, and chaos theory as a case study here) are not to the extent that the respective defenders would like us to believe.

Furthermore, the analysis of effect, nature, and chaos theory is to shed light on the ontological principles in existential dialectics, and good examples include the formalness-informalness principle, the absoluteness-relativeness principle, the partiality-totality principle, the predictability-unpredictability principle, the explicability-inexplicability principle, the fiction-reality principle, the cognitiveness-noncognitiveness principle, the finiteness-transfiniteness principle, the preciseness-vagueness principle, the simpleness-complicatedness principle, the openness-hiddenness principle, the denseness-emptiness principle, the rule-exception principle, the indispensability-dispensability principle, the prototypicality-variation principle, the change-constancy principle, the order-chaos principle, the slowness-quickness principle, the expansion-contraction principle, the optimality-nonoptimality principle, the simultaneity-nonsimultaneity principle, the isolation-interaction principle, the theory-praxis principle, the convention-novelty principle, the evolution-transformation principle, the symmetry-asymmetry principle, the softness-hardness principle, the seriousness-playfulness principle, the activeness-inactivess principle, the selfness-otherness principle, the regression-progression principle, the same-difference principle, the stability-reaction principle, the functionality-nonfunctionality principle, the intentionality-nonintentionality principle. the survivability-non-survivability principle, and the materiality-nonmateriality principle.

For instance, in relation to the formalness-informalness principle, if there is formalness (e.g., the formal logical requirement of soundness and completeness in a system of ideas, as in the argument on the butterfly effect), there is informalness (e.g., the non-formal existence of unsoundness and incompleteness in the argument on the butterfly effect, as shown in the criticisms that the so-called "butterfly effect" is much exaggerated, that the so-called "butterfly effect" misleadingly exclude some other effects in its analysis, that the property of "sensitivity to initial conditions" can be redundant, that the butterfly effect can be countered by more complicated forecasting systems, that the butterfly effect does not apply in some situations, and that there is no universal definition of "chaos" in chaos theory). And the reverse direction also holds true.

In relation to the absoluteness-relativeness principle, if there is absoluteness (e.g., the absolute view on the "butterfly effect" by the advocates), there is relativeness (e.g., what is right for the advocates in regard to the "butterfly effect" is not necessarily so for the critics, who pointed out that the so-called "butterfly effect" is much exaggerated, that the so-called "butterfly effect" misleadingly exclude some other effects in its analysis, that the butterfly effect can be countered by more complicated forecasting systems, that the butterfly effect does not apply in some situations, etc.). And the reverse direction also holds true.

In relation to the partiality-totality principle, if there is partiality (e.g., the partial view on the "butterfly effect" by the advocates), there is totality (e.g., the more holistic view on the "butterfly effect," such that the whole is not the sum of its parts, that is, it cannot be reduced to the sum of opposing views by by the advocates, the skeptics, the critics, etc., since there will emerge new views in the future not yet known today, just as there are already alternative views nowadays which do not side exclusively with any of them, as is the analysis here). And the reverse direction also holds true.

In relation to the predictability-unpredictability principle, if there is predictability (e.g., the predictable tendency that "a small change at one place in a deterministic nonlinear system can result in large differences in a later state"), there is unpredictability (e.g., "dynamical systems that are highly sensitive to initial conditions...yield widely diverging outcomes..., rendering long-term prediction impossible in general"). (WK 2014qq) And the reverse direction also holds true.

In relation to the explicability-inexplicability principle, if there is explicability (e.g., the explanation, by those advocates of the "butterfly effect," on the basis that "a small change at one place in a deterministic nonlinear system can result in large differences in a later state"), there is inexplicability (e.g., the lack of sufficient explanation, by those advocates of the "butterfly effect," of why it is necessarily valid, since the critics pointed out different problems, in that the so-called "butterfly effect" is much exaggerated, that the so-called "butterfly effect" misleadingly exclude some other effects in its analysis, that the property of "sensitivity to initial conditions" can be redundant, that the butterfly effect can be countered by more complicated forecasting systems, that the butterfly effect does not apply in some situations, etc.). And the reverse direction also holds true.

In relation to the fiction-reality principle, if there is fiction (e.g., the fictional aspect of the "butterfly effect," insofar as that the so-called "butterfly effect" is much exaggerated, that the so-called "butterfly effect" misleadingly exclude some other effects in its analysis, that the property of "sensitivity to initial conditions" can be redundant, that the butterfly effect can be countered by more complicated forecasting systems, that the butterfly effect does not apply in some situations, etc.), there is reality (e.g., the realistic aspect of the "butterfly effect," insofar as, under certain limited conditions, a small change at one place in a deterministic nonlinear system can result in large differences in a later state"). And the reverse direction also holds true.

In relation to the cognitiveness-noncognitiveness principle, if there is cognitiveness (e.g., a view of things on the basis of reason and evidences, as shown in the empirical finding that there were early studies on chaos theory, like those by Henri Poincaré, G. D. Birkhoff, A. N. Kolmogorov, M.L. Cartwright, J.E. Littlewood, Stephen Smale, and so on), there is noncognitiveness (e.g., a view of things on the basis of non-cognitive factors like envy, jealousy, power, nationality, race, gender, age, class, greed, lust, status, faith, anger, sadness, joy, fear, wish, etc.—as shown in the personal prejudice of the advisor of a graduate student in Chihiro Hayashi's laboratory at Kyoto University, Yoshisuke Ueda, because, when his student "was experimenting with analog computers and noticed, on Nov. 27, 1961, what he called 'randomly transitional phenomena,'" the "advisor...did not allow him to report his findings until 1970," even though it was correct). (WK 2014qq) And the reverse direction also holds true.

In relation to the finiteness-transfiniteness principle, if there is finiteness (e.g., the finite number of the properties of chaotic dynamics, like the 5 aforediscussed), there is transfiniteness (e.g., the transfinite number of all the individual instances of chaotic behavior that have ever occurred in history, regardless of which main properties they have or whether some properties are "redundant" or not, as discussed earlier). And the reverse direction also holds true.

In relation to the preciseness-vagueness principle, if there is preciseness (e.g., the precise identification of 5 main properties of chaotic dynamics in the article aforecited), there is vagueness (e.g., the vagueness in the identification of the 5 main properties of chaotic dynamics in the article aforecited, since it is not clear why there must be only 5, not 2, 3, 4, 6, 7, and so on, since some critics pointed out that the property of "sensitivity to initial conditions" in the list can be redundant). And the reverse direction also holds true.

In relation to the simpleness-complicatedness principle, if there is simpleness (e.g., the relatively simple analysis of the butterfly effect by the advocates), there is complicatedness (e.g., the relatively more complicated analysis of the butterfly effect, by challenging the claims and assumptions, as shown in the problems pointed out by the critics as cited). And the reverse direction also holds true.

In relation to the openness-hiddenness principle, if there is openness (e.g., the open exploration of the existence of the "butterfly effect"), there is hiddenness (e.g., the hidden bias in the open exploration of the existence of the "butterfly effect," since the critics pointed out that the so-called "butterfly effect" is much exaggerated, that the so-called "butterfly effect" misleadingly exclude some other effects in its analysis, that the butterfly effect can be countered by more complicated forecasting systems, that the butterfly effect does not apply in some situations, etc.). And the reverse direction also holds true.

In relation to the denseness-emptiness principle, if there is denseness (e.g., the relatively denser concentration of concerns with the property of "sensitivity to initial conditions" by the advocates of the butterfly effect), there is emptiness (e.g., the relatively less dense, or more empty, concentration of concerns with the property of "sensitivity to initial conditions" by the critics of the butterfly effect, who argued instead that "sensitivity to initial conditions...is actually redundant in the definition, being implied by two [or for intervals, one] purely topological conditions"). And the reverse direction also holds true.

In relation to the rule-exception principle, if there are rules (e.g., the usual generalization, procedure, habit, or tendency that the "butterfly effect" exists in nature), there are exceptions (e.g., a case to which a rule does not apply, such as the exceptional case in regard to the "butterfly effect," in that "extreme [exponential] dependence on initial conditions is not expected in pure quantum treatments"). And the reverse direction also holds true.

In relation to the indispensability-dispensability principle, if there is indispensability (e.g., the need for something or someone, like the necessary inclusion of the second property in the definition of "chaos" as discussed earlier), there is dispensability (e.g., the superfluity of something or someone, like the dispensable inclusion of the property of "sensitivity to initial conditions," since to the critics, "sensitivity to initial conditions...is actually redundant in the definition, being implied by two [or for intervals, one] purely topological conditions"). And the reverse direction also holds true.

In relation to the prototypicality-variation principle, if there is prototypicality (e.g., the prototype, like the example about the original work on chaos theory by Henri Poincaré in the 1880s), there is variation (e.g., different variants of the protoptye, as shown in many studies since the original work on chaos theory by Henri Poincaré in the 1880s—like the later ones by G. D. Birkhoff, A. N. Kolmogorov, M.L. Cartwright, J.E. Littlewood, Stephen Smale, and so on in the 20th century, though each with its own variation, contribution, and disagreement). And the reverse direction also holds true.

In relation to the change-constancy principle, if there is change (e.g., the ever new ways to study effect, as shown in the work on "the butterfly effect"), there is constancy (e.g., the ever constant existence of different problems with the ever new ways to study effect, as shown in the problems with the work on "the butterfly effect" pointed out by the critics). And the reverse direction also holds true.

In relation to the order-chaos principle, if there is order (e.g., "finite dimensional linear systems are never chaotic"), there is chaos (e.g., "for a dynamical system to display chaotic behaviour it has to be either nonlinear, or infinite-dimensional"). (WK 2014qq) And the reverse direction also holds true.

In relation to the slowness-quickness principle, if there is slowness (e.g., the relatively slower speed of chaos theory to be accepted in the 19th century), there is quickness (e.g., the relatively quicker speed of chaos theory to be accepted in the late 20th century). And the reverse direction also holds true.

In relation to the expansion-contraction principle, if there is expansion (e.g., the relative expansion of the use of "electronic computer" to do "the mathematics of chaos theory" nowadays), there is contraction (e.g., the relative decline of the work on "the mathematics of chaos theory" by "hand" nowadays). And the reverse direction also holds true.

In relation to the optimality-nonoptimality principle, if there is optimality (e.g., the search for highly favorable options, like the quest for best ways to do "the mathematics of chaos theory" nowadays by the use of "electronic computer," when "the availability of cheaper, more powerful computers broadens the applicability of chaos theory" in our time), there is nonoptimality (e.g., the existence of non-optimal alternatives to optimality, like the argument for more realistic studies by the critics, who pointed out different problems with "chaos theory," as discussed earlier, regardless of the progress in the development of computers). (WK 2014qq) And the reverse direction also holds true.

In relation to the simultaneity-nonsimultaneity principle, if there is simultaneity (e.g., the occurrence of different things more or less at the same time, such as the simultaneous existence of "computers" and "the mathematics of chaos theory" nowadays), there is nonsimultaneity (e.g., the occurrence of something after something else, such as the practice of doing "the mathematics of chaos theory" by hand in the older days before that of doing "the mathematics of chaos theory" by the use of computers nowadays). And the reverse direction also holds true.

In relation to the isolation-interaction principle, if there is isolation (e.g., the state of a situation that is separate from others, such as the isolation of the work on "the mathematics of chaos theory" from any use of computers in the older days, when it was done by hand), there is interaction (e.g., the influence of entities on one another, such as the interaction between computers and the mathematics of chaos theory" nowadays). And the reverse direction also holds true.

In relation to the theory-praxis principle, if there is theory (e.g., the theoretical construction of "the butterfly effect" in the field of chaos theory), there is praxis (e.g., the practical application of "the butterfly effect" in the field of chaos theory to the field of "quantum physics," since "the potential for sensitive dependence on initial conditions [the butterfly effect] has been studied in a number of cases in semiclassical and quantum physics including atoms in strong fields and the anisotropic Kepler problem"). And the reverse direction also holds true.

In relation to the convention-novelty principle, if there is convention (e.g., the conventional wisdom about the butterfly effect in modern times), there is novelty (e.g., the alternative novel challenge to the conventional wisdom about the butterfly effect in modern times—by the new ideas that the so-called "butterfly effect" is much exaggerated, that the so-called "butterfly effect" misleadingly exclude some other effects in its analysis, that the property of "sensitivity to initial conditions" can be redundant, that the butterfly effect can be countered by more complicated forecasting systems, that the butterfly effect does not apply in some situations, etc.). And the reverse direction also holds true.

In relation to the evolution-transformation principle, if there is evolution (e.g., the natural evolution of humans to encounter unpredictable outcomes in the state of nature), there is transformation (e.g., the technical transformation of human ability to deal with unpredictable outcomes by the invention of chaos theory like "the butterfly effect"). And the reverse direction also holds true.

In relation to the symmetry-asymmetry principle, if there is symmetry (e.g., the co-existence of different "systems" in nature), there is asymmetry (e.g., "finite dimensional linear systems are never chaotic"—but "for a dynamical system to display chaotic behaviour it has to be either nonlinear, or infinite-dimensional"). And the reverse direction also holds true.

In relation to the softness-hardness principle, if there is softness (e.g., the defense of the idea of "the butterfly effect" by the advocates like Lorenz), there is hardness (e.g., the critique of the idea of "the butterfly effect" by the critics like David Orrell and Stephen Wolfram aforecited). And the reverse direction also holds true.

In relation to the seriousness-playfulness principle, if there is seriousness (e.g., the serious business of those who try to understand the nature of "chaos"), there is playfulness (e.g., the playful part of those who try to understand the nature of "chaos," when they play around with different "properties" over the decades, with different views by different researchers aforecited). And the reverse direction also holds true.

In relation to the activeness-inactivess principle, if there is activeness (e.g., the relative activeness of those working on chaos theory nowadays, as there is so much going on in the field), there is inactiveness (e.g., the relative inactiveness of those working on chaos theory in the 19th century, as there was not much going on in the field at that time, which was not yet developed). And the reverse direction also holds true.

In relation to the selfness-otherness principle, if there is selfness (e.g., the tendency to be mostly centered on one's self or group, as shown in the personal prejudice of the advisor of a graduate student in Chihiro Hayashi's laboratory at Kyoto University, Yoshisuke Ueda, because, when his student "was experimenting with analog computers and noticed, on Nov. 27, 1961, what he called 'randomly transitional phenomena,'" the "advisor...did not allow him to report his findings until 1970," even though the idea was correct), there is otherness (e.g., the tendency to be mostly centered on others, as shown in the academic analysis of both sides of the debate on the butterfly effect, as an advancement in the knowledge of physics for humanity). And the reverse direction also holds true.

In relation to the regression-progression principle, if there is regression (e.g., the regression made by the butterfly effect, as shown in the problems pointed out by the critics), there is progression (e.g., the progress made by the butterfly effect, as shown in the contribution to the understanding of "sensitivity to initial conditions" aforecited). And the reverse direction also holds true.

In relation to the same-difference principle, if there is similarity in outcome (e.g., the contribution to the molding and control of beliefs, values, and behaviors, regardless of whether this be done by way of the acceptance of "chaos theory," or by way of the acceptance of "physical determinsm"), there is difference in outcome (e.g., the contribution to the molding and control of beliefs, values, and behaviors by way of the acceptance of "chaos theory" for a relatively more unpredictable view of nature—but the contribution to the molding and control of beliefs, values, and behaviors by way of the acceptance of "physical determinsm" for a relatively more predictable view of nature). And the reverse direction also holds true.

In relation to the stability-reaction principle, if there is stability (e.g., the relatively more stable condition of the popularity of the butterfly effect in modern time), there is reaction (e.g., the popularity of the butterfly effect in modern time then led to further changes later on, when nowadays, there are the criticisms that the so-called "butterfly effect" is much exaggerated, that the so-called "butterfly effect" misleadingly exclude some other effects in its analysis, that the butterfly effect can be countered by more complicated forecasting systems, that the butterfly effect does not apply in some situations, etc.). And the reverse direction also holds true.

In relation to the functionality-nonfunctionality principle, if there is functionality (e.g., the presence of action for which something or someone is fitted, as shown in the proposal of "the butterfly effect," which serves the function of providing an understanding of chaotic dynamics), there is nonfunctionality (e.g., the relative lack of action for which something or someone is fitted, as shown in the different problems with the idea of "the butterfly effect" as discussed earlier, such that it is not as functional as the advocates would like us to believe). And the reverse direction also holds true.

In relation to the intentionality-nonintentionality principle, if there is intentionality (e.g., the planning or design of something for a certain outcome, as shown in the intended consequences in regard to "the butterfly effect," as those who used it intended to explain the nature of chaotic dynamics aforediscussed), there is nonintentionality (e.g., the relative absence of planning or design of something for a certain outcome, such that the outcome can even be counter-intentional in being the opposite of what was originally planned, as shown in the different new criticisms against the idea of "the butterfly effect," as discussed earlier—contrary to the original intention of those who used it to explain the nature of chaotic dynamics). And the reverse direction also holds true.

In relation to the survivability-nonsurvivability principle, if there is survivability (e.g., the relative survival, nowadays, of the practice to do the mathematics of chaos theory by computers), there is non-survivability (e.g., the relative non-survival, nowadays, of the practice to do the mathematics of chaos theory by hand). And the reverse direction also holds true.

And in relation to the materiality-nonmateriality principle, if there is materiality (e.g., the material outcome in relation to space-time, matter-energy, Having, etc., like the use of chaotic theory for the study of chaotic dynamics), there is non-materiality (e.g., the nonmaterial outcome in relation to the quest for Being, Belonging, etc., like the spiritual search among humans for "time travel" with the use of "chaos theory," so as to change "history" for the better, in popular culture). (WK 2014q) And the reverse direction also holds true.

Effect, Quantum Physics, and Zeno Effect

Another good way to evaluate the possibility (or impossibility) and desirability (or undesirability) of effect from the perspective of nature is to explore effect, quantum physics, and Zeno effect.

An argument in the literature is that there is "a situation in which an unstable [excited] particle, if observed continuously, will never decay," and this is known as "the quantum Zeno effect." (WK 2014rr)

Concept of the Quantum Zeno Effect

The term "quantum Zeno effect" derives from a well-known ancient paradox known as "Zeno's arrow paradox," which "states that, since an arrow in flight is not seen to move during any single instant, it cannot possibly be moving at all"—and the reasoning here "depends on the instant of time, a kind of freeze-motion idea that the arrow is 'strobed' at each instant and is seemingly stationary, so how can it move in a succession of stationary events?" (WK 2014rr)

So "quantum Zeno effect," like Zeno's arrow paradox, refers to "a situation in which an unstable [excited] particle, if observed continuously [by an observer casting light or photon on it], will never decay. The term was coined by George Sudarshan [1977] and Baidyanath Misra of the University of Texas in 1977. One can 'freeze' the evolution of the system by measuring it frequently enough in its (known) initial state. The meaning of the term has since expanded, leading to a more technical definition in which time evolution can be suppressed not only by measurement: the quantum Zeno effect is the suppression of unitary time evolution caused by quantum decoherence in quantum systems provided by a variety of sources: measurement, interactions with the environment, stochastic fields, and so on." (WK 2014rr; T. Nakanishi 2001)

The term "quantum decoherence" (above) refers to "the loss of coherence or ordering," or simply the "collapse" of a wave function from its simultaneous multiple "physical possibilities" at the quantym level at the beginning "into a single possibility [the superposition] as seen by an observer" (when using light or photon to measure it), so this "wave function collapse...justifies the framework and intuition of classical physics as an acceptable approximation," meaning that "decoherence is the mechanism by which the classical limit emerges from a quantum starting point and it determines the location of the quantum-classical boundary," from quantum indeterminancy to classcial determinacy. (WK 2014ss)

In other words, this "wave function collapse is the phenomenon in which a wave function—initially in a superposition of several eigenstates [its simultaneous multiple "physical possibilities"]—appears to reduce to a single eigenstate after interaction with a measuring apparatus [by an observer]. It is the essence of measurement in quantum mechanics, and connects the wave function with classical observables like position and momentum," both of which are what the observer looks for, although he cannot know them both (position and momentum) at the same time. (WK 2014tt; D. Griffiths 2005)

Historically, "the first rigorous and general derivation of this effect was presented in 1974 by Degasperis et al. However it has to be mentioned that Alan Turing described it in 1954: 'It is easy to show using standard theory that if a system starts in an eigenstate of some observable, and measurements are made of that observable N times a second, then, even if the state is not a stationary one, the probability that the system will be in the same state after, say, one second, tends to one as N tends to infinity; that is, that continual observations will prevent motion....'" (WK 2014rr; A. Degasperis 1974; C. Teuscher 2004)

In addition, "the idea is contained in the early work by John von Neumann, sometimes called the reduction postulate....According to the reduction postulate, each measurement causes the wavefunction to 'collapse' to a pure eigenstate of the measurement basis. In the context of this effect, an 'observation' can simply be the absorption of a particle, without an observer in any conventional sense." (WK 2014rr)

In any event, the quantum Zeno effect states that "unstable [excited] quantum systems are predicted to exhibit a short time deviation from the exponential decay law. This universal phenomenon has led to the prediction that frequent measurements during this nonexponential period

could inhibit decay of the system, one form of the quantum Zeno effect."
(WK 2014rr; L. Khalfin 1958; M. Raizen 1997)

And "the interaction mentioned is called 'measurement' [in quantum mechanics] because its result can be interpreted in terms of classical mechanics. Frequent measurement prohibits the transition. It can be a transition of a particle from one half-space to another (which could be used for atomic mirror in an atomic nanoscope) as in the time of arrival problem, a transition of a photon in a waveguide from one mode to another, and it can be a transition of an atom from one quantum state to another. It can be a transition from the subspace without decoherent loss of a q-bit to a state with a q-bit lost in a quantum computer. In this sense, for the q-bit correction, it is sufficient to determine whether the decoherence has already occurred or not. All these can be considered as applications of the Zeno effect. By its nature, the effect appears only in systems with distinguishable quantum states, and hence is inapplicable to classical phenomena and macroscopic bodies." (WK 2014rr; D. Kouznetsov 2006; J. Allcock 1969; J. Echanobe 2008; J. Stolze 2008; J. Franson 2006)

Periodic Measurement and the Quantum Zeno Effect

For an illustration of the measurement of the quantum Zeno effect, consider "a system in a state A, which is the eigenstate of some measurement operator. Say the system under free time evolution will decay with a certain probability into state B. If measurements are made periodically, with some finite interval between each one, at each measurement, the wave function collapses to an eigenstate of the measurement operator. Between the measurements, the system evolves away from this eigenstate into a superposition state of the states A and B. When the superposition state is measured, it will again collapse, either back into state A as in the first measurement, or away into state B. However, its probability of collapsing into state B, after a very short amount of time t, is proportional to t^2, since probabilities are proportional to squared amplitudes, and amplitudes behave linearly. Thus, in the limit of a large number of short intervals, with a measurement at the end of every interval, the probability of making the transition to B goes to zero." (WK 2014rr)

Decoherence theory suggests that "the collapse of the wave function is not a discrete, instantaneous event. A 'measurement' is equivalent to strongly coupling the quantum system to the noisy thermal environment for a brief period of time, and continuous strong coupling is equivalent to frequent 'measurement.' The time it takes for the wave function to 'collapse' is related to the decoherence time of the system when coupled [linked] to the environment. The stronger the coupling is, and the shorter the decoherence time, the faster it will collapse. So in the decoherence picture, a perfect implementation of the quantum Zeno effect corresponds to the limit where a quantum system is continuously coupled to the environment, and where that coupling is infinitely strong, and where the 'environment' is an infinitely large source of thermal randomness." (WK 2014rr)

Experiments for the Quantum Zeno Effect

The quantum Zeno effect has been tested experimentally over the years. For illustration, consider two experiments below.

Firstly, "in 1989, David J. Wineland and his group at NIST observed the quantum Zeno effect for a two-level atomic system that was interrogated during its evolution. Approximately 5000 $^9Be^+$ ions were stored in a cylindrical Penning trap and laser cooled to below 250 mK. A resonant RF pulse was applied which, if applied alone, would cause the entire ground state population to migrate into an excited state. After the pulse was applied, the ions were monitored for photons emitted due to relaxation. The ion trap was then regularly 'measured' by applying a sequence of ultraviolet pulses, during the RF pulse. As expected, the ultraviolet pulses suppressed the evolution of the system into the excited state. The results were in good agreement with theoretical models. A recent review describes subsequent work in this area." (WK 2014rr; W. Itano; D. 1990; D. Leibfried 2003)

And secondly, "in 2001, Mark G. Raizen and his group at the University of Texas at Austin, observed the quantum Zeno effect for an unstable quantum system, as originally proposed by Sudarshan and Misra....Ultracold sodium atoms were trapped in an accelerating optical lattice and the loss due to tunneling was measured. The evolution was interrupted by reducing the acceleration, thereby stopping quantum tunneling. The group observed suppression or enhancement of the decay rate, depending on the regime of measurement." (WK 2014rr; M. Fischer 2001)

Applications of the Quantum Zeno Effect

The quantum Zeno effect has been used by different scholars for their own purposes.

For instance, it has been used "in the exploration of controversial theories of quantum mind consciousness within the discipline of cognitive science. In his book *Mindful Universe* (2007), Henry Stapp claims that the mind holds the brain in a superposition of states using the quantum Zeno effect. He advances that this phenomenon is the principal method by which the conscious can effect change, a possible solution to the mind-body dichotomy. Stapp and co-workers do not claim finality of their theory," but they suggest that "the new framework, unlike its classic-physics-based predecessor, is erected directly upon, and is compatible with, the prevailing principles of physics." (WK 2014rr; H. Stapp 2005)

Problems with the Research on the Quantum Zeno Effect

However, to the critics, this study on effect, quantum physics, and Zeno effect has some major problems. Consider, for illustration, a few examples below.

Firstly, one main criticism of the study on effect, quantum physics, and Zeno effect is that there is a controversy over the interpretation of the quantum Zeno effect.

For example, to the critics, "there is controversy over the interpretation of the [quantum Zeno] effect, sometimes referred to as the 'measurement problem' in traversing the interface between microscopic and macroscopic," which is really not very clear. (WK 2014rr Greenstein, G.; & A. Zajonc. 2005; P. Facchi 2002)

Secondly, another main criticism of the study on effect, quantum physics, and Zeno effect is that there is "the time-energy indeterminacy relation" in measuring the quantum Zeno effect, such that it can be much harder to violate the exponential decay law than previously thought.

For instance, to the critics, "one should...mention another crucial problem related to the effect. It has been thoroughly discussed in a paper by Ghirardi [1979] et al..The problem is strictly connected to the time-energy indeterminacy relation. If one wants to make the measurement process more and more frequent, one has to correspondingly decrease the time duration of the measurement itself. But the request that the measurement last only a very short time implies that the energy spread of the state on which reduction occurs becomes more and more large. However, the deviations from the exponential decay law for small times, is crucially related to the inverse of the energy spread so that the region in which the deviations [from the exponential decay law] are appreciable shrinks when one makes the measurement process duration shorter and shorter [so it is harder to violate the law]. An explicit evaluation of these two competing requests shows that it is inappropriate to deal, without taking into account this basic fact, with the actual occurrence and emergence of Zeno's effect." (WK 2014rr)

Thirdly, still another main criticism of the study on effect, quantum physics, and Zeno effect is that, contrary to the quantum Zeno effect, there can be an increase of decay instead under some circumstances.

For instance, to the critics, "an *enhancement* of decay due to frequent measurements could be observed under somewhat more general conditions, leading to the so-called anti-Zeno effect." (WK 2014rr; M. Raizen 1997)

Fourthly, an additional main criticism of the study on effect, quantum physics, and Zeno effect is that the limit of "periodic measurements" is still not clear.

For instance, to the critics, "it is still an open question how closely one can approach the limit of an infinite number of interrogations due to the Heisenberg uncertainty involved in shorter measurement times," and the quantum Zeno effect is no exception (WK 2014rr)

Fifthly, another additional main criticism of the study on effect, quantum physics, and Zeno effect is that the quantum Zeno effect does not apply to all interpretations of quantum theory.

For instance, to the critics, because "the Quantum Zeno effect is dependent upon the reductionist postulate for reconciling the measurement problem," therefore "the Quantum Zeno effect does not apply to all interpretations of quantum theory, in particular, the many-worlds interpretation (a.k.a. the Multiverse Interpretation) and the Quantum Logic Interpretation." (WK 2014rr)

And sixthly, still another additional main criticism of the study on effect, quantum physics, and Zeno effect is that it has been used by some scholars for their questionable purposes.

For instance, in response to Stapp's application of the quantum Zeno effect for his claim about "quantum mind" in the field of "quantum biology," some recent work "criticizes Stapp's model in two aspects: (1) The mind in Stapp's model does not have its own wavefunction or density matrix, but nevertheless can act upon the brain using projection operators. Such usage is not compatible with standard quantum mechanics because one can attach any number of ghostly minds to any point in space that act upon physical quantum systems with any projection operators. Therefore Stapp's model does not build upon 'the prevailing principles of physics,' but negates them. (2) Stapp's claim that quantum Zeno effect is robust against environmental decoherence directly contradicts a basic theorem in quantum information theory according to which acting with projection operators upon the density matrix of a quantum system can never decrease the Von Neumann entropy of the system, but can only increase it." (WK 2014rr; K. Koshino 2005)

Beyond Quantum Zeno Effect

These criticisms of the study on effect, quantum physics, and Zeno effect do not advocate a total rejection of its usefulness but serve to show us the two opposing sides of the debate, such that the possibility (or impossibility) and desirability (or undesirability) of effect (from the perspective of nature with effect, quantum physics, and Zeno effect as a case study here) are not to the extent that the respective defenders would like us to believe.

In addition, the analysis of effect, quantum physics, and Zeno effect can show us something refreshing about the ontological principles in existential dialectics, and good examples include the formalness-informalness principle, the absoluteness-relativeness principle, the partiality-totality principle, the predictability-unpredictability principle, the explicability-inexplicability principle, the fiction-reality principle, the cognitiveness-noncognitiveness principle, the finiteness-transfiniteness principle, the preciseness-vagueness principle, the simpleness-complicatedness principle, the openness-hiddenness principle, the denseness-emptiness principle, the rule-exception principle, the indispensability-dispensability principle, the prototypicality-variation principle, the change-constancy principle, the order-chaos principle, the slowness-quickness principle, the expansion-contraction principle, the optimality-nonoptimality principle, the simultaneity-nonsimultaneity principle, the isolation-interaction principle, the theory-praxis principle, the convention-novelty principle, the evolution-transformation principle, the symmetry-asymmetry principle, the softness-hardness principle, the seriousness-playfulness principle, the activeness-inactivess principle, the selfness-otherness principle, the regression-progression principle, the same-difference principle, the stability-reaction principle, the functionality-nonfunctionality principle, the intentionality-nonintentionality principle the survivability-non-survivability principle, and the materiality-nonmateriality principle.

For instance, in relation to the formalness-informalness principle, if there is formalness (e.g., the formal logical requirement of soundness, completeness, and consistency in a system of ideas, as in the argument on the quantum Zeno effect), there is informalness (e.g., the non-formal existence of unsoundness, incompleteness, and inconsistency in the argument on the quantum Zeno effect, as shown in the criticisms that there is a controversy over the interpretation of the quantum Zeno effect, that there is "the time-energy indeterminacy relation" in measuring the quantum Zeno effect such that it can be much harder to violate the exponential decay law than previously thought, that there can be an increase of decay instead under some circumstances, that the limit of "periodic measurements" is still not clear, that the quantum Zeno effect does not apply to all interpretations of quantum theory, and that it has been used by some scholars for their questionable purposes). And the reverse direction also holds true.

In relation to the absoluteness-relativeness principle, if there is absoluteness (e.g., the absolute view on "the Quantum Zeno effect" by the advocates on the basis of "the reductionist postulate for reconciling the measurement problem"), there is relativeness (e.g., what is right for the advocates of "the Quantum Zeno effect" on the basis of "the reductionist postulate for reconciling the measurement problem" is not necessarily so for the critics, because "the Quantum Zeno effect does not apply to all interpretations of quantum theory, in particular, the many-worlds interpretation...and the Quantum Logic Interpretation"). And the reverse direction also holds true.

In relation to the partiality-totality principle, if there is partiality (e.g., the partial view on "the Quantum Zeno effect" by the advocates of "the reductionist postulate"), there is totality (e.g., the more holistic view on "the Quantum Zeno effect," such that the whole is not the sum of its parts, that is, it cannot be reduced to the sum of opposing views by the advocates of "the reductionist postulate," the advocates of "the many-worlds interpretation," the advocates of "the Quantum Logic Interpretation," etc., since there will emerge new views in the future not yet known today, just as there are already alternative views nowadays which do not side exclusively with any of them, as is the analysis here). And the reverse direction also holds true.

In relation to the predictability-unpredictability principle, if there is predictability (e.g., the predictable tendency that "the Quantum Zeno effect" is dependent on "the reductionist postulate"), there is unpredictability (e.g., the more difficult task to predict exactly "the limit of "periodic measurements" on a particular future occasion, since, to the critics, "it is still an open question how closely one can approach the limit of an infinite number of interrogations due to the Heisenberg uncertainty involved in shorter measurement times"). And the reverse direction also holds true.

In relation to the explicability-inexplicability principle, if there is explicability (e.g., the explanation, by those advocates of "the quantum Zeno effect," of its possibility on the basis of "the reductionist postulate for reconciling the measurement problem"), there is inexplicability (e.g., the lack of sufficient explanation, by those advocates of "the quantum Zeno effect," of why it is necessarily possible, since, to the critics, "the quantum Zeno effect does not apply to all interpretations of quantum theory, in particular, the many-worlds interpretation...and the Quantum Logic Interpretation"). And the reverse direction also holds true.

In relation to the fiction-reality principle, if there is fiction (e.g., the fictional aspect of "the quantum Zeno effect," insofar as Stapp's application of the quantum Zeno effect for his claim about "quantum mind" is rejected by the critics as false, in that "'Stapp's model does not build upon 'the prevailing principles of physics,' but negates them"), there is reality (e.g., the realistic aspect of"the Quantum Zeno effect," insofar as it was tested experimentally over the years, like ones by David J. Wineland and his group at NIST in 1989 and by Mark G. Raizen and his group at the University of Texas at Austin in 2001). And the reverse direction also holds true.

In relation to the cognitiveness-noncognitiveness principle, if there is cognitiveness (e.g., a view of things on the basis of reason and evidences, as shown in the empirical finding that the quantum Zeno effect was tested experimentally by David J. Wineland and his group at NIST in 1989 and by Mark G. Raizen and his group at the University of Texas at Austin in 2001), there is noncognitiveness (e.g., a view of things on the basis of non-cognitive factors like envy, jealousy, power, nationality, race, gender, age, class, greed, lust, status, faith, anger, sadness, joy, fear, wish, etc.—as shown in personal faith by Stapp in the application of the quantum Zeno effect for his claim about "quantum mind," in spite of the rejection by the critics as false, in that "'Stapp's model does not build upon 'the prevailing principles of physics,' but negates them"). And the reverse direction also holds true.

In relation to the finiteness-transfiniteness principle, if there is finiteness (e.g., the finite number of the experiments with the quantum Zeno effect, like the two by David J. Wineland and his group at NIST in 1989 and by Mark G. Raizen and his group at the University of Texas at Austin in 2001 aforecited), there is transfiniteness (e.g., the transfinite number of all the individual subatomic particles that have ever existed in history, regardless of whether they can be used for experiments with the quantum Zeno effect or not). And the reverse direction also holds true.

In relation to the preciseness-vagueness principle, if there is preciseness (e.g., the precise identification of two experiments with the quantum Zeno effect, that is, by David J. Wineland and his group at NIST in 1989 and by Mark G. Raizen and his group at the University of Texas at Austin in 2001, in the article aforecited), there is vagueness (e.g., the vagueness in the identification of the two experiments with the quantum Zeno effect, that is, by David J. Wineland and his group at NIST in 1989 and by Mark G. Raizen and his group at the University of Texas at Austin in 2001, in the article aforecited, since it is not clear why there must be only 2, not 3, 4, 5, 6, and so on). And the reverse direction also holds true.

In relation to the simpleness-complicatedness principle, if there is simpleness (e.g., the relatively simple analysis of the quantum Zeno effect by the advocates), there is complicatedness (e.g., the relatively more complicated analysis of the quantum Zeno effect, by challenging the claims and assumptions, as shown in the problems pointed out by the critics as cited). And the reverse direction also holds true.

In relation to the openness-hiddenness principle, if there is openness (e.g., the open exploration of "the quantum Zeno effect" on the basis of "the reductionist postulate for reconciling the measurement problem"), there is hiddenness (e.g., the hidden bias in the open exploration of "the quantum Zeno effect" on the basis of "the reductionist postulate for reconciling the measurement problem," since the critics point out that "the quantum Zeno effect does not apply to all interpretations of quantum theory, in particular, the many-worlds interpretation…and the Quantum Logic Interpretation"). And the reverse direction also holds true.

In relation to the denseness-emptiness principle, if there is denseness (e.g., the relatively denser concentration of concerns with "the reductionist postulate" by those advocates of "the quantum Zeno effect"), there is emptiness (e.g., the relatively less dense, or more empty, concentration of concerns with "the many-worlds interpretation…and the Quantum Logic Interpretation" by those advocates of "the quantum Zeno effect"). And the reverse direction also holds true.

In relation to the rule-exception principle, if there are rules (e.g., the usual generalization, procedure, habit, or tendency that "an unstable [excited] particle, if observed continuously, will never decay," also known as "the quantum Zeno effect"), there are exceptions (e.g., a case to which a rule does not apply, such as the exceptional case that "an *enhancement* of decay due to frequent measurements could be observed under somewhat more general conditions, leading to the so-called anti-Zeno effect"). And the reverse direction also holds true.

In relation to the indispensability-dispensability principle, if there is indispensability (e.g., the need for something or someone, like the necessary inclusion of "the reductionist postulate" by the advocates of "the quantum Zeno effect"), there is dispensability (e.g., the superfluity of something or someone, like the dispensable inclusion of "the many-worlds interpretation…and the Quantum Logic Interpretation" by those advocates of "the quantum Zeno effect," because "quantum Zeno effect does not apply to all interpretations of quantum theory"). And the reverse direction also holds true.

In relation to the prototypicality-variation principle, if there is prototypicality (e.g., the prototype, like the example about the original description of the quantum Zeno effect by Alan Turing in 1954), there is variation (e.g., different variants of the protoptye, as shown in many studies since the original description of the quantum Zeno effect by Alan Turing in 1954—like the later ones by Degasperis et al. in 1974, George Sudarshan and Baidyanath Misra in 1977, etc., though each with its own variation, contribution, and disagreement). And the reverse direction also holds true.

In relation to the change-constancy principle, if there is change (e.g., the ever new ways to study effect, as shown in the work on the quantum Zeno effect), there is constancy (e.g., the ever constant existence of different problems with the ever new ways to study effect, as shown in the different problems with the work on quantum Zeno effect pointed out by the critics). And the reverse direction also holds true.

In relation to the order-chaos principle, if there is order (e.g., the more or less orderly view on the quantum Zeno effect, if looked from the sole vantage point of the advocates), there is chaos (e.g., the more or less chaotic view on the quantum Zeno effect, if looked from the multiple, conflicting vantage points of both the advocates and the critics, especially in regard to the different problems aforecited, such that they do not add up to much of anything coherent). And the reverse direction also holds true.

In relation to the slowness-quickness principle, if there is slowness (e.g., the weaker the coupling is, and the longer the decoherence time, the slower it will collapse, according to the quantum Zeno effect), there is quickness (e.g., "the stronger the coupling is, and the shorter the decoherence time, the faster it will collapse," according to the quantum Zeno effect). (WK 2014rr) And the reverse direction also holds true.

In relation to the expansion-contraction principle, if there is expansion (e.g., according to "the time-energy indeterminacy relation" in measuring the quantum Zeno effect, "the region in which the deviations [from the exponential decay law] are appreciable" increases "when one makes the measurement process duration" longer and longer), there is contraction (e.g., according to "the time-energy indeterminacy relation" in measuring the quantum Zeno effect, "the region in which the deviations [from the exponential decay law] are appreciable shrinks when one makes the measurement process duration shorter and shorter"). And the reverse direction also holds true.

In relation to the optimality-nonoptimality principle, if there is optimality (e.g., the search for highly favorable options, like the quest for the possibility of the "idealized measurement" of the quantum Zeno effect in the article aforecited), there is nonoptimality (e.g., the existence of non-optimal alternatives to optimality, like the argument for more realistic studies by the critics, who pointed out different problems with the work on the quantum Zeno effect aforecited). And the reverse direction also holds true.

In relation to the simultaneity-nonsimultaneity principle, if there is simultaneity (e.g., the occurrence of different things more or less at the same time, such as the simultaneous existence of multiple "physical possibilities" of a wave function at the quantym level prior to its collapse "into a single possibility [the superposition] as seen by an observer"), there is nonsimultaneity (e.g., the occurrence of something after something else, such as the existence of a wave function with its simultaneous multiple "physical possibilities" at the quantym level first, before its collapse "into a single possibility [the superposition] as seen by an observer" thereafter). And the reverse direction also holds true.

In relation to the isolation-interaction principle, if there is isolation (e.g., the state of a situation that is separate from others, such as the isolation of a subatomic particle with its simultaneous existence of multiple "physical possibilities" of a wave function at the quantym level prior to any quantum decoherence), there is interaction (e.g., the influence of entities on one another, such as the interaction between an unstable or excited particle with a measuring apparatus [by an observer] in a "wave function collapse"). And the reverse direction also holds true.

In relation to the theory-praxis principle, if there is theory (e.g., the theoretical construction of the quantum Zeno effect in the field of quantum physics), there is praxis (e.g., the practical application of the quantum Zeno effect in the field of quantum physics to the field of psychology, like Stapp's application of the quantum Zeno effect for his claim about "quantum mind"). And the reverse direction also holds true.

In relation to the convention-novelty principle, if there is convention (e.g., the conventional wisdom about the quantum Zeno effect), there is novelty (e.g., the alternative novel challenge to the conventional wisdom about the quantum Zeno effect—by the new idea of Stapp in regard to his application of the quantum Zeno effect for his claim about "quantum mind"). And the reverse direction also holds true.

In relation to the evolution-transformation principle, if there is evolution (e.g., the natural evolution of humans to encounter decay of things in the state of nature), there is transformation (e.g., the technical transformation of human ability to understand the decay of things by the invention of quantum physics, like the study of the quantum Zeno effect). And the reverse direction also holds true.

In relation to the symmetry-asymmetry principle, if there is symmetry (e.g., the co-existence of different interpretations of quantum theory), there is asymmetry (e.g., "the quantum Zeno effect" can be applied to the interpretation of quantum theory based on "the reductionist postulate for reconciling the measurement problem"—but "the quantum Zeno effect" cannot be applied to other interpretations of quantum theory like "the many-worlds interpretation…and the Quantum Logic Interpretation," because "the quantum Zeno effect does not apply to all interpretations of quantum theory"). And the reverse direction also holds true.

In relation to the softness-hardness principle, if there is softness (e.g., the defense of the quantum Zeno effect by the advocates aforecited), there is hardness (e.g., the critique of the quantum Zeno effect, as shown in the problems pointed out by the critics aforecited). And the reverse direction also holds true.

In relation to the seriousness-playfulness principle, if there is seriousness (e.g., the serious business of those who try to understand the nature of the quantum Zeno effect), there is playfulness (e.g., the playful part of those who try to understand the nature of the quantum Zeno effect, when they play around with different interpretations over the decades, like its use by Stapp for his claim about "quantum mind"). And the reverse direction also holds true.

In relation to the activeness-inactivess principle, if there is activeness (e.g., the relative activeness of an unstable particle when its time evolution is not suppressed, in the absence of any quantum Zeno effect), there is inactiveness (e.g., the relative inactiveness of an unstable particle when its time evolution is suppressed in the quantum Zeno effect).

In relation to the selfness-otherness principle, if there is selfness (e.g., the tendency to be mostly centered on one's self or group, as shown in the ego of Stapp in his application of the quantum Zeno effect for his claim about "quantum mind," in spite of the rejection by the critics as false), there is otherness (e.g., the tendency to be mostly centered on others, as shown in the academic analysis of both sides of the debate on the quantum Zeno effect, as an advancement in the knowledge of physics for humanity). And the reverse direction also holds true.

In relation to the regression-progression principle, if there is regression (e.g., the regression made by the research on quantum Zeno effect, as shown in the problems pointed out by the critics), there is progression (e.g., the progress made by the research on quantum Zeno effect, as shown in the contribution to the understanding of the exponential decay law aforecited). And the reverse direction also holds true.

In relation to the same-difference principle, if there is similarity in outcome (e.g., the contribution to the molding and control of beliefs, values, and behaviors, regardless of whether this be done by way of the belief in "quantum physics," or by way of the belief in "quantum biology"), there is difference in outcome (e.g., the contribution to the molding and control of beliefs, values, and behaviors by way of the belief in "quantum physics" for a relatively more material worldview—but the contribution to the molding and control of beliefs, values, and behaviors by way of the belief in "quantum biology" for a relatively more spiritual worldview). And the reverse direction also holds true.

In relation to the stability-reaction principle, if there is stability (e.g., the relatively more stable condition of the work on the quantum Zeno effect in the later half of the 20th century), there is reaction (e.g., the work on the quantum Zeno effect in the later half of the 20th century then led to further changes later on, when nowadays, there is the proposal for "quantum mind" in quantum biology). And the reverse direction also holds true.

In relation to the functionality-nonfunctionality principle, if there is functionality (e.g., the presence of action for which something or someone is fitted, as shown in the proposal of the quantum Zeno effect, which serves the function of explaining the nature of "decay" in quantum physics), there is nonfunctionality (e.g., the relative lack of action for which something or someone is fitted, as shown in the different problems with the quantum Zeno effect, such that it is not as functional as the advocates would like us to believe). And the reverse direction also holds true.

In relation to the intentionality-nonintentionality principle, if there is intentionality (e.g., the planning or design of something for a certain outcome, as shown in the intended consequences in regard to the quantum Zeno effect, as those who used it intended to explain the nature of "decay" in quantum physics), there is nonintentionality (e.g., the relative absence of planning or design of something for a certain outcome, such that the outcome can even be counter-intentional in being the opposite of what was originally planned, as shown by Stapp's application of the quantum Zeno effect for his claim about "quantum mind" in quantum biology—contrary to the original intention of those who used it to explain the nature of "decay" in quantum physics). And the reverse direction also holds true.

In relation to the survivability-nonsurvivability principle, if there is survivability (e.g., the relative survival, nowadays, of the interpretation of quantum theory which copes with "the quantum Zeno effect" on the basis of "the reductionist postulate for reconciling the measurement problem"), there is non-survivability (e.g., the relative non-survival, nowadays, of the attempt to apply "the quantum Zeno effect" to other interpretations of quantum theory, because "the quantum Zeno effect does not apply to all interpretations of quantum theory" like "the many-worlds interpretation…and the Quantum Logic Interpretation"). And the reverse direction also holds true.

And in relation to the materiality-nonmateriality principle, if there is materiality (e.g., the material outcome in relation to space-time, matter-energy, Having, etc., like the use of "the quantum Zeno effect" to understand quantum physics in regard to the exponential decay law), there is non-materiality (e.g., the nonmaterial outcome in relation to the quest for Being, Belonging, etc., like the spiritual search among humans for the mind over matter, as shown by Stapp's application of the quantum Zeno effect for his claim about "quantum mind" in quantum biology). And the reverse direction also holds true.

Effect and Society

Effect, when examined from the perspective of society, can reveal to us some powerful features in relation to its possibility (or impossibility) and desirability (or undesirability), and this can be shown by way of two case studies, namely, (3.4.1) effect, politics, and domino theory, and (3.4.2) effect, business, and effectuation—to be addressed hereafter.

Effect, Politics, and Domino Theory

A good way to evaluate the possibility (or impossibility) and desirability (or undesirability) of effect from the perspective of society is to explore effect, politics, and domino theory.

An argument in the literature is that, in accordance to "the domino theory,…if one state in a region came under the influence of communism, then the surrounding countries would follow in a domino effect. The domino theory was used by successive United States administrations during the Cold War to justify the need for American intervention around the world" against the spread of "world communism." (WK 2014s)

History of Domino Theory

Historically, "the domino theory existed from the 1950s to the 1980s....Referring to communism in Indochina, U.S. President Dwight D. Eisenhower put the theory into words during an April 7, 1954 news conference," in which he said: "Finally, you have broader considerations that might follow what you would call the 'falling domino' principle. You have a row of dominoes set up, you knock over the first one, and what will happen to the last one is the certainty that it will go over very quickly. So you could have a beginning of a disintegration that would have the most profound influences." (WK 2014s; NPS 2013)

It all started after the end of WWII, when "in 1945, the Soviet Union brought most of the countries of Eastern Europe and Central Europe under its influence as part of the post-World War II new settlement, while prompting Winston Churchill to declare in a speech in 1946 at Westminster College in Fulton, Missouri" that "from Stettin in the Baltic to Trieste in the Adriatic an 'iron curtain' has descended across the Continent. Behind that line lie all the capitals of the ancient states of Central and Eastern Europe. Warsaw, Prague, Budapest, Belgrade, Bucharest and Sofia; all these famous cities and the populations around them lie in what I must call the Soviet sphere, and all are subject, in one form or another, not only to Soviet influence but to a very high and in some cases increasing measure of control from Moscow." (WK 2014s; M. Kramer 2010)

Then, "in 1949, a Communist backed government, lead by Mao Zedong, was instated in China (officially becoming the People's Republic of China). The installation of the new government was established after the People's Liberation Army defeated the Nationalist Republican Government of China in the aftermath of the Chinese Civil War (1927-1949). Two Chinas were formed—mainland 'Communist China' (People's Republic of China) and 'Nationalist China' Taiwan (Republic of China). The takeover by Communists of the world's most populous nation was seen in the West as a great strategic loss, prompting the popular question at the time, 'Who lost China?' The United States subsequently ended diplomatic relations with China in response to the communist takeover in 1949." (WK 2014s; HIST 2013; R. Tanter 1999)

In the Korean peninsula, "Korea had also partially fallen under Soviet domination at the end of World War II, and in 1950 fighting broke out between Communists and Republicans that soon involved troops from China (on the Communists' side), and the United States and 15 allied countries (on the Republicans' side). The war has not officially ended to this day but the fighting ended in 1953 with an armistice that left Korea divided into two nations, North Korea and South Korea." (WK 2014s)

In Indochina, "in May 1954, the Viet Minh, a Communist and nationalist army, defeated French troops in the Battle of Dien Bien Phu and took control of what became North Vietnam. This caused the French to fully withdraw from the region then known as French Indochina, a process they had begun earlier. The regions were then divided into four independent countries (North Vietnam, South Vietnam, Cambodia and Laos) after a deal was brokered at the 1954 Geneva Conference to end the First Indochina War." (WK 2014s; UNIV 2014; BBC 1954)

It was in this context that "President Eisenhower was the first to refer to countries in danger of Communist takeover as dominoes, in response to a journalist's question about Indochina in an April 7, 1954 news conference, though he did not use the term 'domino theory.' If Communists succeeded in taking over the rest of Indochina, Eisenhower argued, local groups would then have the encouragement, material support and momentum to take over Burma, Thailand, Malaya and Indonesia; all of these countries had large popular Communist movements and insurgencies within their borders at the time."(WK 2014s)

For Eisenhower, the domino effect "would give them a geographical and economic strategic advantage, and it would make Japan, Taiwan, the Philippines, Australia, and New Zealand the front-line defensive states. The loss of regions traditionally within the vital regional trading area of countries like Japan would encourage the front-line countries to compromise politically with communism." (WK 2014s)

However, "Eisenhower's domino theory of 1954 was a specific description of the situation and conditions within Southeast Asia at the time, and he did not suggest a generalized domino theory as others did afterward. The John F. Kennedy administration intervened in Vietnam in the early 1960s to, among other reasons, keep the South Vietnamese 'domino' from falling. When Kennedy came to power there was concern that the communist-led Pathet Lao in Laos would provide the Viet Cong with bases, and that eventually they could take over Laos." (WK 2014s)

Justification of Domino Theory

The empirical justification of domino theory was based on "the spread of communist rule in three Southeast Asian countries in 1975, following the communist takeover of Vietnam: South Vietnam (by the Viet Cong), Laos (by the Pathet Lao), and Cambodia (by the Khmer Rouge). It can further be argued that before they finished taking Vietnam prior to the 1950s, the communist campaigns did not succeed in Southeast Asia. Note the Malayan Emergency, the Huk Rebellion in the Philippines, and the increasing involvement with Communists by Sukarno of Indonesia from the late 1950s until he was deposed in 1965. All of these were unsuccessful Communist attempts to take over Southeast Asian countries which stalled when communist forces were still focused in Vietnam." (WK 2014s)

Some prominent individuals like Walt Rostow and Lee Kuan Yew "have argued that the U.S. intervention in Indochina, by giving the nations of ASEAN time to consolidate and engage in economic growth, prevented a wider domino effect. McGeorge Bundy argues that the prospects for a domino effect, though high in the 1950s and early 1960s, were weakened in 1965 when the Indonesian communist party was destroyed. However, proponents ultimately believe that the efforts during the containment (i.e. Domino Theory) period, ultimately led the demise of the Soviet Union and the end of the Cold War." (WK 2014s)

Other "supporters of the domino theory note the history of communist governments supplying aid to communist revolutionaries in neighboring countries. For instance, China supplied the Vietminh, the North Vietnamese army, with troops and supplies, and the Soviet Union supplied them with tanks and heavy weapons. The fact that the Pathet Lao and Khmer Rouge were both originally part of the Vietminh, not to mention Hanoi's support for both in conjunction with the Viet Cong, also give credence to the theory. The Soviet Union also heavily supplied Sukarno with military supplies and advisors from the time of the Guided Democracy in Indonesia, especially during and after the 1958 civil war in Sumatra." (WK 2014s)

Even the well-known critic of U.S. foreign policy Noam Chomsky (1992) "writes that he believes the Domino theory is roughly accurate, although he put a more positive spin on the threat, writing on the basis that economic improvements to a poor country will always bring better life for its people. If a people in a poor country see another poor country dictate its economy and improve it, the former will of course want to emulate the latter. This is why, he claims, the US put so much effort into suppressing so-called 'people's movements' in Chile, Vietnam, Nicaragua, Laos, Grenada, El Salvador, Guatemala, etc. 'The weaker and poorer a country is, the more dangerous it is as an example. If a tiny, poor country like Grenada can succeed in bringing about a better life for its people, some other place that has more resources will ask, "Why not us?"' Chomsky refers to this as the 'threat of a good example.' Chomsky claims there are two domino effects, one internally discussed between US policy makers, which is that of the 'Good Example', and another for public consumption, that of the spread of Communism." (WK 2014s)

Application of Domino Theory

Domino theory has also been applied to situations outside Southeast Asia.

For instance, "Michael Lind has argued that though the domino theory failed regionally, there was a global wave, as communist or Marxist-Leninist regimes came to power in Benin, Ethiopia, Guinea-Bissau, Madagascar, Cape Verde, Mozambique, Angola, Afghanistan, Grenada, and Nicaragua during the 1970s. The global interpretation of the domino effect relies heavily upon the 'prestige' interpretation of the theory, meaning that the success of Communist revolutions in some countries, though it did not provide material support to revolutionary forces in other countries, did contribute morale and rhetorical support."(WK 2014s)

Interestingly, "Argentine revolutionary Che Guevara wrote an essay, the 'Message to the Tricontinental,' in 1967, calling for 'two, three ... many Vietnams' across the world. Historian Max Boot wrote, 'In the late 1970s, America's enemies seized power in countries from Mozambique to Iran to Nicaragua. American hostages were seized aboard the SS Mayaguez (off Cambodia) and in Tehran. The Red Army invaded Afghanistan. There is no obvious connection with the Vietnam War, but there is little doubt that the defeat of a superpower encouraged our enemies to undertake acts of aggression that they might otherwise have shied away from.'" (WK 2014s; R. Gott 2005; M. Boot 2007)

In fact, "this theory can be further bolstered by the rise in terrorist incidents by left-wing terrorist groups in Western Europe, funded in part by Communist governments, between the 1960s and 1980s. In Italy, this includes the kidnapping and assassination of former Italian Prime Minister Aldo Moro, and the kidnapping of former US Brigadier General James L. Dozier, by the Red Brigades. In West Germany, this includes the terrorist actions of the Red Army Faction. In the far east the Japanese Red Army carried out similar acts. All four, as well as others worked with various Arab and Palestinian terrorists, which like the red brigades were backed by the Soviet Bloc." (WK 2014s; FED 1997, 1998 & 1998a)

Even Richard Nixon, "in the 1977 Frost/Nixon interviews,...defended America's destabilization of the Salvador Allende regime in Chile on domino theory grounds. Borrowing a metaphor he had heard, he stated that a Communist Chile and Cuba would create a 'red sandwich' that could entrap Latin America between them. In the 1980s, the domino theory was used again to justify the Reagan administration's interventions in Central America and the Caribbean region." (WK 2014s; G. Smith 1995)

And, "in his memoirs, former Rhodesian Prime Minister Ian Smith [2008] described the successive rise of authoritarian left-wing governments in Sub-Saharan Africa during decolonization as 'the communists' domino tactic.' The establishment of pro-communist governments in Tanzania (1961–64) and Zambia (1964) and explicitly Marxist-Leninist governments in Angola (1975), Mozambique (1975), and eventually Rhodesia itself (in 1980) are cited by Smith as evidence of 'the insidious encroachment of Soviet imperialism down the continent.'" (WK 2014s)

Problems with the Study on Politics and Domino Theory

However, to the critics, this argument on effect, politics, and domino theory has some major problems. Consider, for illustration, a few examples below.

Firstly, one main criticism of this argument on effect, politics, and domino theory is that the domino theory rests on some false assumptions.

For instance, "critics of the [domino] theory charged that...no such monolithic force as 'world communism' existed. There was already fracturing of communist states at the time, the most serious of which was the rivalry between the Soviet Union and China, known as the Sino-Soviet split, which began in the 1950s." (WK 2014s)

Secondly, another main criticism of this argument on effect, politics, and domino theory is that the domino theory neglects "nationalist" causes.

For instance, "critics of the theory charged that the Indochinese wars were largely...nationalist in nature"; in fact, "Vietnam and Cambodia were at odds from the very beginning. Rivalry between China and the USSR may have exacerbated tensions between them, since Vietnam had affiliated itself with the USSR and Cambodia with China, but nationalism and territorial disputes were obviously more significant factors. Border conflicts, mostly in the form of massacres of Vietnamese peasants carried out by the Khmer Rouge, occurred frequently for the duration of their nearly four years in power, eventually leading to the Cambodian-Vietnamese War of 1978-1979, when Vietnam overthrew the Khmer Rouge and took control of Cambodia. This in turn led China to attack Vietnam in 1979 in the brief Sino-Vietnamese War, and to U.S. and Thai support for the Khmer Rouge, who renounced communism and continued to fight as a guerrilla force against the Vietnamese-backed government until the mid-1990s." (WK 2014s)

Thirdly, still another main criticism of the study on effect, politics, and domino theory is that domino theory also ignores the cancerous problem of domesic corruption.

For instance, to the critics, "the domino theory misrepresented the real nature of the widespread and growing civil opposition that the previous, U.S.-backed regimes in these countries had generated because of entrenched official corruption and widespread human rights abuses, notably in South Vietnam," for instance. (WK 2014s)

Fourthly, an additional main criticism of the study on effect, politics, and domino theory is that the domino theory had failed in its predictions.

For instance, as the critics are quick to point out, after mainland China, North Korea, South Vietnam, Laos, and Cambodia fell into communism, there was a prediction at the time that Thailand, Malaysia, Indonesia, Burma, and India would be next, as the domino effect "had been predicted in Asia," but it never happened, so "the primary evidence against the domino theory is the failure of Communism to take hold in Thailand, Indonesia, and other large Southeast Asian countries after the end of the Vietnam War, as Eisenhower's speech warned it could." (WK 2014s)

And fifthly, another additional main criticism of the study on effect, politics, and domino theory is that whether the domino effect is bad or not is relative.

For instance, the spread of Communism is something to be fought against by its opponents like U.S. President Eisenhower but something to celebrate for its proponents like Argentine revolutionary Che Guevara.

Beyond Domino Theory

These criticisms of the analysis of effect, politics, and domino theory do not mean a total rejection of its usefulness but serve to show us the two opposing sides of the debate, such that the possibility (or impossibility) and desirability (or undesirability) of effect (from the perspective of society with effect, politics, and domino theory as a case study here) are not to the extent that the respective defenders would like us to believe.

In fact, the analysis of effect, politics, and domino theory can teach us valuable on the ontological principles in existential dialectics, and good examples include the formalness-informalness principle, the absoluteness-relativeness principle, the partiality-totality principle, the predictability-unpredictability principle, the explicability-inexplicability principle, the fiction-reality principle, the cognitiveness-noncognitiveness principle, the finiteness-transfiniteness principle, the preciseness-vagueness principle, the simpleness-complicatedness principle, the openness-hiddenness principle, the denseness-emptiness principle, the rule-exception principle, the indispensability-dispensability principle, the prototypicality-variation principle, the change-constancy principle, the order-chaos principle, the slowness-quickness principle, the expansion-contraction principle, the optimality-nonoptimality principle, the simultaneity-nonsimultaneity principle, the isolation-interaction principle, the theory-praxis principle, the convention-novelty principle, the evolution-transformation principle, the symmetry-asymmetry principle, the softness-hardness principle, the seriousness-playfulness principle, the activeness-inactivess principle, the selfness-otherness principle, the regression-progression principle, the same-difference principle, the stability-reaction principle, the functionality-nonfunctionality principle, the intentionality-nonintentionality principle. the survivability-non-survivability principle, and the materiality-nonmateriality principle.

For instance, in relation to the formalness-informalness principle, if there is formalness (e.g., the formal logical requirement of soundness and completeness in a system of ideas, as in the argument on the domino theory), there is informalness (e.g., the non-formal existence of unsoundness and incompleteness in the argument on the domino theory, as shown in the criticisms that the domino theory rests on some false assumptions, that the domino theory neglects "nationalist" causes, that domino theory also ignores the cancerous problem of domesic corruption, that the domino theory had failed in its predictions, and that whether the domino effect is bad or not is relative). And the reverse direction also holds true.

In relation to the absoluteness-relativeness principle, if there is absoluteness (e.g., the absolute view on the domino theory by the advocates like U.S. President Eisenhower), there is relativeness (e.g., what is bad for the advocates in regard to the domino theory to fight against the spread of communism is not necessarily so for the proponents like Argentine revolutionary Che Guevara). And the reverse direction also holds true.

In relation to the partiality-totality principle, if there is partiality (e.g., the partial view on the domino theory by the advocates like U.S. President Eisenhower), there is totality (e.g., the more holistic view on the domino theory, such that the whole is not the sum of its parts, that is, it cannot be reduced to the sum of opposing views by the advocates, the skeptics, the critics, etc., since there will emerge new views in the future not yet known today, just as there are already alternative views nowadays which do not side exclusively with any of them, as is the analysis here). And the reverse direction also holds true.

In relation to the predictability-unpredictability principle, if there is predictability (e.g., the predictable tendency of the advocates of the domino theory to argue in the 1960s and early 1970s that, if South Vietnam, Laos, and Cambodia fell to communism, other surrounding countries like Thailand, Malaysia, Indonesia, Burma, and India would be next). there is unpredictability (e.g., the more difficult task to predict when exactly, after South Vietnam, Laos, and Cambodia fell into communism in the 1970s, other surrounding countries like Thailand, Malaysia, Indonesia, Burma, and India would be next, since, as the history later unfolded, this did not happen at all as predicted). And the reverse direction also holds true.

In relation to the explicability-inexplicability principle, if there is explicability (e.g., the explanation, by those advocates of the domino theory, on the basis of the force of "world communism," such that "if one state in a region came under the influence of communism, then the surrounding countries would follow in a domino effect"), there is inexplicability (e.g., the lack of sufficient explanation, by those advocates of the domino theory, of why it is necessarily true, since the critics pointed out that the domino theory rests on some false assumptions, that the domino theory neglects "nationalist" causes, that domino theory also ignores the cancerous problem of domesic corruption, that the domino theory had failed in its predictions, and that whether the domino effect is bad or not is relative). And the reverse direction also holds true.

In relation to the fiction-reality principle, if there is fiction (e.g., the fictional aspect of the domino theory, insofar as that "no such monolithic force as 'world communism' existed"), there is reality (e.g., the realistic aspect of the domino theory, insofar as, according to some proponents, there is some truth to it, because "the efforts during the containment [i.e. Domino Theory] period, ultimately led the demise of the Soviet Union and the end of the Cold War"). (WK 2014s) And the reverse direction also holds true.

In relation to the cognitiveness-noncognitiveness principle, if there is cognitiveness (e.g., a view of things on the basis of reason and evidences, as shown in the empirical finding that South Vietnam, Laos, and Cambodia fell to communism in the 1970s), there is noncognitiveness (e.g., a view of things on the basis of non-cognitive factors like envy, jealousy, power, nationality, race, gender, age, class, greed, lust, status, faith, anger, sadness, joy, fear, wish, etc.—as shown in the ideological conviction by some proponents who continued to apply the domino theory in regard to the potential spread of "Islamic theocracy" in the Middle East near the end of the 20th century and beyond, even though this did not happen, and even though, in addition, the domino theory had also failed in its prediction about the fall of "Thailand, Indonesia, and other large Southeast Asian countries after the end of the Vietnam War" in the 1970s). And the reverse direction also holds true.

In relation to the finiteness-transfiniteness principle, if there is finiteness (e.g., the finite number of the categories of countries during the Cold War, that is, "the free world" vs. "the communist bloc," when the domino theory was popular), there is transfiniteness (e.g., the transfinite number of all the individuals that have ever lived in history, regardless of whether their countries are "free," "communist," or something else). And the reverse direction also holds true.

In relation to the preciseness-vagueness principle, if there is preciseness (e.g., the precise identification of two different worlds that is, "the free world" and "the communist bloc," during the Cold War, when the domino theory was popular), there is vagueness (e.g., the vagueness in the identification of the two different worlds that is, "the free world" and "the communist bloc," during the Cold War, when the domino theory was popular, since it is not clear why there must be only 2, not 3, 4, and so on, as some countries regarded themselves as "the Third World," especially those in the "non-aligned movement"). And the reverse direction also holds true.

In relation to the simpleness-complicatedness principle, if there is simpleness (e.g., the relatively simple analysis of the domino theory by the advocates), there is complicatedness (e.g., the relatively more complicated analysis of the domino theory, by challenging the claims and assumptions, as shown in the problems pointed out by the critics as cited). And the reverse direction also holds true.

In relation to the openness-hiddenness principle, if there is openness (e.g., the open exploration of the domino effect in Southeast Asia, by U.S. President Eisenhower and others later on), there is hiddenness (e.g., the hidden bias in the open exploration of the domino effect in Southeast Asia, by U.S. President Eisenhower and others later on, since the critics pointed out that the domino theory rests on some false assumptions, that the domino theory neglects "nationalist" causes, that domino theory also ignores the cancerous problem of domesic corruption, that the domino theory had failed in its predictions, and that whether the domino effect is bad or not is relative). And the reverse direction also holds true.

In relation to the denseness-emptiness principle, if there is denseness (e.g., the relatively denser concentration of concerns with the spread of "world communism" by the U.S. during the Cold War), there is emptiness (e.g., the relatively less dense, or more empty, concentration of concerns with the spread of "world communism" by Switzerland during the Cold War, as it was "neutral"). And the reverse direction also holds true.

In relation to the rule-exception principle, if there are rules (e.g., the usual generalization, procedure, habit, or tendency that the domino theory refers to the spread of "world communism"), there are exceptions (e.g., a case to which a rule does not apply, such as the exceptional case of the use of the domino theory to refer to the spread of "liberal democracy," because "in the 2003 invasion of Iraq, some neoconservatives argued that when a democratic government is implemented, it would then help spread democracy and liberalism across the Middle East, and a war can install a democratic government. This has often been referred to as a 'reverse domino theory'"). (WK 2014s; R. Wright 2003) And the reverse direction also holds true.

In relation to the indispensability-dispensability principle, if there is indispensability (e.g., the need for something or someone, like the necessary inclusion of President Eisenhower in the history of the domino theory, since he "was the first to refer to countries in danger of Communist takeover as dominoes" in 1954), there is dispensability (e.g., the superfluity of something or someone, like the dispensable inclusion of the "neocons" in the history of the domino theory, since they were more concerned with the "reverse domino theory" in the Middle East during the 2000s). And the reverse direction also holds true.

In relation to the prototypicality-variation principle, if there is prototypicality (e.g., the prototype, like the example about the original formation of the domino theory by U.S. President Dwight D. Eisenhower in 1954), there is variation (e.g., different variants of the prototptye, as shown in many works since the original formation of the domino theory by U.S. President Dwight D. Eisenhower in 1954—like the later ones by John F. Kennedy, Richard Nixon, etc., though each with its own variation, contribution, and disagreement). And the reverse direction also holds true.

In relation to the change-constancy principle, if there is change (e.g., the ever new ways to study effect, as shown in the work on domino theory), there is constancy (e.g., the ever constant existence of different problems with the ever new ways to study effect, as shown in the problems with the work on domino theory pointed out by the critics). And the reverse direction also holds true.

In relation to the order-chaos principle, if there is order (e.g., the more or less orderly view on the situation in Southeast Asia in the 1970s, if looked from the sole vantage point of the domino theory by the advocates, in that "Thailand, Malaysia, Indonesia, Burma, and India would be next" to fall, after South Vietnam, Laos, and Cambodia became Communist), there is chaos (e.g., the more or less chaotic view on the situation in Southeast Asia in the 1970s and afterwards, if looked from the multiple, conflicting vantage points of both the advocates and the critics of the domino theory, especially in regard to the different problems and disagreements aforecited, such that they do not add up to much of anything coherent). And the reverse direction also holds true.

In relation to the slowness-quickness principle, if there is slowness (e.g., the relatively slower speed of surrounding countries to ever fall to Communism, according to the domino theory, if there is a "containment" policy to prevent the first dominoes from falling), there is quickness (e.g., the relatively quicker speed of surrounding countries to fall to Communism, according to the domino theory by U.S. President Eisenhower, when he said in 1954 that "you have a row of dominoes set up, you knock over the first one, and what will happen to the last one is the certainty that it will go over very quickly"). (WK 2014s) And the reverse direction also holds true.

In relation to the expansion-contraction principle, if there is expansion (e.g., the relative spread of communism in Indochina in the 1970s), there is contraction (e.g., the relative decline of communism in Thailand, Malaysia, Indonesia, the Philippines, etc. after the 1970s and beyond). And the reverse direction also holds true.

In relation to the optimality-nonoptimality principle, if there is optimality (e.g., the search for highly favorable options, like the quest for the effective way to stop "world communism" by way of the "containment policy," later reinforced by the domino theory, during the Cold War), there is nonoptimality (e.g., the existence of non-optimal alternatives to optimality, like the argument for more realistic studies by the critics, who pointed out different problems with the domino theory aforecited). And the reverse direction also holds true.

In relation to the simultaneity-nonsimultaneity principle, if there is simultaneity (e.g., the occurrence of different things more or less at the same time, such as the simultaneous existence of different versions of domino theory, like the older "domino theory" and the recent "reverse domino theory"), there is nonsimultaneity (e.g., the occurrence of something after something else, such as the development of the older "domino theory" before the development of the recent "reverse domino theory"). And the reverse direction also holds true.

In relation to the isolation-interaction principle, if there is isolation (e.g., the state of a situation that is separate from others, such as the isolation of Indochina from communism in the 19th century), there is interaction (e.g., the influence of entities on one another, such as the interaction between Indochina and the communist movement in the later part of the 20th century and its fall to communism in the 1970s). And the reverse direction also holds true.

In relation to the theory-praxis principle, if there is theory (e.g., the theoretical construction of the "domino theory" in regard to the spread of communism in Indochina), there is praxis (e.g., the practical application of the "domino theory" in regard to the spread of communism in Indochina to the region in Latin America, as shown by Che Guevara's call for "two, three… many Vietnams" in 1967). And the reverse direction also holds true.

In relation to the convention-novelty principle, if there is convention (e.g., the conventional wisdom about the "domino theory" in Indochina), there is novelty (e.g., the alternative novel challenge to the conventional wisdom about the "domino theory" in Indochina —by the new idea of the "reverse domino theory" in the Middle East). And the reverse direction also holds true.

In relation to the evolution-transformation principle, if there is evolution (e.g., the natural evolution of humans to encounter chain reactions in the state of nature, like the chain reaction in an energy system to increase entropy), there is transformation (e.g., the technical transformation of human ability to understand chain reactions by the invention of the "domino theory" in politics and other fields). (WK 2014uu) And the reverse direction also holds true.

In relation to the symmetry-asymmetry principle, if there is symmetry (e.g., the co-existence of different countries in Southeast Asia), there is asymmetry (e.g., South Vietnam, Laos, and Cambodia in Southeast Asia fell to communism in the 1970s—but Thailand, Malaysia, Indonesia, and the Philippines did not). And the reverse direction also holds true.

In relation to the softness-hardness principle, if there is softness (e.g., "the 'prestige' interpretation of the [domino] theory, meaning that the success of Communist revolutions in some countries, though it did not provide material support to revolutionary forces in other countries, did contribute morale and rhetorical support"), there is hardness (e.g., the "military" interpretation of the domino theory, in that Che Guevara called for "two, three … many Vietnams" outside Indochina with military aid, not just morale and rhetorical support). And the reverse direction also holds true.

In relation to the seriousness-playfulness principle, if there is seriousness (e.g., the serious business of those who try to understand the nature of the domino effect), there is playfulness (e.g., the playful part of those who try to understand the nature of the domino effect, when they play around with different interpretations and versions over the decades, like the older "domino theory," the recent "reverse domino theory," etc.). And the reverse direction also holds true.

In relation to the activeness-inactivess principle, if there is activeness (e.g., the relative activeness of communists in Vietnam nowadays in the 2010s, as they are now in power), there is inactiveness (e.g., the relative inactiveness of communists in Malaysia nowadays in the 2010s, as they are now banned). And the reverse direction also holds true.

In relation to the selfness-otherness principle, if there is selfness (e.g., the tendency to be mostly centered on one's self or group, as shown in "the rivalry between the Soviet Union and China, known as the Sino-Soviet split, which began in the 1950s," which contributed to the breakup of "world communism"), there is otherness (e.g., the tendency to be mostly centered on others, as shown in the academic analysis of both sides of the debate on the validity of the domino theory, as an advancement in the knowledge of political science for humanity). And the reverse direction also holds true.

In relation to the regression-progression principle, if there is regression (e.g., the regression made by the domino theory, as shown in the problems pointed out by the critics), there is progression (e.g., the progress made by the domino theory, as shown in the contribution to the containment of communism in other Southeast Asian countries which did not fall to communism, as discussed earlier). And the reverse direction also holds true.

In relation to the same-difference principle, if there is similarity in outcome (e.g., the contribution to the molding and control of beliefs, values, and behaviors, regardless of whether this be done by way of the acceptance of the spread of "world communism" by the Soviet Union, or by way of the rejection of the spread of "world communism" by the U.S.A.), there is difference in outcome (e.g., the contribution to the molding and control of beliefs, values, and behaviors by way of the acceptance of the spread of "world communism" by the Soviet Union for a relatively more left-wing lifeworld—but the contribution to the molding and control of beliefs, values, and behaviors by way of the rejection of the spread of "world communism" by the U.S.A. for a relatively more right-wing lifeworld). And the reverse direction also holds true.

In relation to the stability-reaction principle, if there is stability (e.g., the relatively more stable condition of the domino theory in the older days, when it focused on Indochina), there is reaction (e.g., the domino theory in the older days, when it focused on Indochina, then led to further changes later on, when in the 2000s, the neocons proposed the "reverse domino theory" for the Middle East). And the reverse direction also holds true.

In relation to the functionality-nonfunctionality principle, if there is functionality (e.g., the presence of action for which something or someone is fitted, as shown in the domino theory, which serves the function of justifying the need "for American intervention around the world" during the Cold War), there is nonfunctionality (e.g., the relative lack of action for which something or someone is fitted, as shown in the different problems with the domino theory, such that it is not as functional as the advocates would like us to believe). And the reverse direction also holds true.

In relation to the intentionality-nonintentionality principle, if there is intentionality (e.g., the planning or design of something for a certain outcome, as shown in the intended consequences in regard to the U.S. involvement in Indochina in the 1960s and 1970s so as to stop the spread of communism in South Vietnam, Laos, and Cambodia, in accordance to the domino theory), there is nonintentionality (e.g., the relative absence of planning or design of something for a certain outcome, such that the outcome can even be counter-intentional in being the opposite of what was originally planned, as shown in the fall of South Vietnam, Laos, and Cambodia to communism in the 1970s—contrary to the original intention of the U.S. involvement in Indochina in the 1960s and 1970s to stop communism). And the reverse direction also holds true.

In relation to the survivability-nonsurvivability principle, if there is survivability (e.g., the relative survival, nowadays, of the "reverse domino theory" in regard to the situation in the Middle East), there is non-survivability (e.g., the relative non-survival, nowadays, of the "domino theory" in regard to the situation in Southeast Asia). And the reverse direction also holds true.

And in relation to the materiality-nonmateriality principle, if there is materiality (e.g., the material outcome in relation to space-time, matter-energy, Having, etc., like the application of the domino effect to understand chain reactions in the state of nature, like the chain reaction in an energy system to increase entropy), there is non-materiality (e.g., the nonmaterial outcome in relation to the quest for Being, Belonging, etc., like the spiritual search among humans for "freedom," as in the use of the domino theory to justify the U.S. involvement around the world to stop the spread of communism during the Cold War). And the reverse direction also holds true.

Effect, Business, and Effectuation

Another good way to evaluate the possibility (or impossibility) and desirability (or undesirability) of effect from the perspective of society is to explore effect, business, and effectuation.

An argument in the literature is that there is a way of thinking known as "effectuation," which "serves entrepreneurs in starting businesses. Effectuation includes a set of decision-making principles expert entrepreneurs are observed to employ in situations of uncertainty. Situations of uncertainty are situations in which the future is unpredictable, goals are not clearly known and there is no independent environment that serves as the ultimate selection mechanism." (WK 2014vv; SOC 2012; S. Sarasvathy 2001)

Concept of Effectuation

Saras Sarasvathy (2014) in "What Makes Entrepreneurs Entrepreneurial?" proposes "effectuation," with the word "effectual" to be "the inverse of 'causal.' In general, in MBA programs across the world, students are taught causal or predictive reasoning—in every functional area of business. Causal rationality begins with a pre-determined goal and a given set of means, and seeks to identify the optimal—fastest, cheapest, most efficient, etc.—alternative to achieve the given goal. The make-vs.-buy decision in production, or choosing the target market with the highest potential return in marketing, or picking a portfolio with the lowest risk in finance, or even hiring the best person for the job in human resources management, are all examples of problems of causal reasoning. A more interesting variation of causal reasoning involves the creation of additional alternatives to achieve the given goal. This form of creative causal reasoning is often used in strategic thinking."

By contrast, Sarasvathy (2014) prefers "effectual reasoning," which "does not begin with a specific goal. Instead, it begins with a given set of means and allows goals to emerge contingently over time from the varied imagination and diverse aspirations of the founders and the people they interact with. While causal thinkers are like great generals seeking to conquer fertile lands (Genghis Khan conquering two thirds of the known world), effectual thinkers are like explorers setting out on voyages into uncharted waters (Columbus discovering the new world)."

As an illustration, "the simple task of cooking dinner may be used to contrast the two types of reasoning. A chef who is given a specific menu and has only to pick out his or her favorite recipes for the items on the menu, shop for ingredients and cook the meal in their own well equipped kitchens is an example of causal reasoning. An example of effectual reasoning would involve a chef who is not given a menu in advance, and is escorted to a strange kitchen where he or she has to explore the cupboards for unspecified ingredients and cook a meal with them." (S. Sarasvathy (2014)

Process of Effectuation

Sarasvathy (2014) then addresses the process of effectuation in terms of three categories, that is, "(1) Who they are—their traits, tastes and abilities; (2) What they know—their education, training, expertise, and experience; and, (3) Whom they know—their social and professional networks."

With these means, "the entrepreneurs begin to imagine and implement possible effects that can be created with them. Most often, they start very small with the means that are closest at hand, and move almost directly into action without elaborate planning. Unlike causal reasoning that comes to life through careful planning and subsequent execution, effectual reasoning lives and breathes execution. Plans are made and unmade and revised and recast through action and interaction with others on a daily basis. Yet at any given moment, there is always a meaningful picture that keeps the team together, a compelling story that brings in more stakeholders and a continuing journey that maps out uncharted territories. Through their actions, the effectual entrepreneurs' set of means and consequently the set of possible effects change and get reconfigured. Eventually, certain of the emerging effects coalesce into clearly achievable and desirable goals—landmarks that point to a discernible path beginning to emerge in the wilderness." (S. Sarasvathy (2014)

As an illustration, "imagine an entrepreneur who wants to start an Indian restaurant....In the effectual process, it would all depend on who our entrepreneur is, what she knows, and whom she knows. For the sake of understanding the process here, let us say she is a good Indian chef who is considering starting an independent business. Assuming she has very little money of her own, what are some of the ways she can bring her idea to market? When used as a class exercise, students usually suggest courses of action such as partnering with an existing restaurant, participating in ethnic food fairs, setting up a catering service and so on. Let us say that the actual course of action she decides to pursue is to persuade friends who work downtown to allow her to bring lunch for their office colleagues to sample. Let us further say that some customers then sign up for a lunch service and she begins preparing the food at home and delivering lunches personally. Eventually, she could save up enough money to rent a location and start a restaurant. But it could equally be plausible that the lunch business does not take off beyond the first few customers, but instead our entrepreneur discovers that the customers are actually interested in her ethnic philosophy and life experiences or Indian culture or other aspects of her personality or expertise or contacts or interests. She could then decide to go into any one of several different businesses contingent upon the ensuing feedback. To cite but a few possibilities, her eventual successful enterprise could turn out to be in any one or all of the following industries —education, entertainment, travel, manufacturing and packaging, retail, interior decoration, or even self-help and motivation!" (S. Sarasvathy (2014)

Principles of Effectuation

Then, Sarasvathy (2014) proposes three main principles of effectuation, as discussed below (and summarized in *Table 3.5*).

(a) The Affordable Loss Principle
In accordance to this first principle, "effectual reasoning emphasizes affordable loss," unlike the riskier focus on "the highest potential return" in causal reasoning. (S. Sarasvathy (2014)

This first principle then means that, instead of analyzing "the market and choose target segments with the highest potential return"—the effectual "entrepreneurs tend to find ways to reach the market with minimum expenditure of resources such as time, effort, and money. In the extreme case, the affordable loss principle translates into the zero resources to market principle." (S. Sarasvathy (2014)

For instead, "in finding the first customer within their immediate vicinity, whether within their geographic vicinity, within their social network, or within their area of professional expertise, entrepreneurs do not tie themselves to any theorized or pre-conceived 'market' or strategic universe for their idea. Instead, they open themselves to surprises as to which market or markets they will eventually end up building their business in or even which new markets they will end up creating." (S. Sarasvathy (2014)

(b) The Strategic Partnerships Principle
In accordance to this second principle, "since entrepreneurs tend to start the process without assuming the existence of a predetermined market for their idea, detailed competitive analyses do not seem to make any sense to them at the startup phase....Instead entrepreneurs focus on building partnerships right from the start. In fact, the ideal beginning for a

successful startup seemed to be the induction of customers into strategic partnerships." (S. Sarasvathy (2014)

Indeed, "the strategic partnerships principle dovetails very well with the affordable loss principle to bring the entrepreneurs' idea to market at really low levels of capital outlay. Furthermore, obtaining pre-commitments from key stakeholders helps reduce uncertainty in the early stages of creating an enterprise. Finally, since the entrepreneur is not wedded to any particular market for their idea, the expanding network of strategic partnerships determines to a great extent which market or markets the company will eventually end up in." (S. Sarasvathy (2014)

(c) The Leveraging Contingencies Principle

In accordance to this third principle, "the heart of entrepreneurial expertise" is "the ability to turn the unexpected into the profitable. As one of the subjects in the study put it, 'I always live by the motto of *Ready-fire-aim*. I think if you spend too much time doing ready-aim-aim-aim-aim, you're never gonna see all the good things that would happen if you actually start doing it and then aim. And find out where your target is.'" (S. Sarasvathy (2014)

Instead, "great entrepreneurial firms are products of contingencies. Their structure, culture, core competence, and endurance are all residuals of particular human beings striving to forge and fulfill particular aspirations through interactions with the space, time and technologies they live in. For example, we could speculate whether Wedgwood pottery would have been possible if the potter Josiah Wedgwood had not met the gentleman philosopher Thomas Bentley and wooed him into a partnership that created a brand and a great company that has lasted over two centuries. The key to the Wedgwood fortune was the realization that people put their money where their aspirations are and that pots and vases could become vehicles of social mobility. Similarly, in our time, researchers speculate what Microsoft would have been if IBM had written a different type of a contract or if Gary Kildahl had not been out flying his airplane the day IBM came calling. Yet, it is not the contingencies themselves that shaped the companies in the foregoing examples. It is how the entrepreneurs *leveraged* the contingencies that came upon them that has to form the core of models of effectual reasoning. The realization that not all surprises are bad and that surprises, whether good or bad, can be used as inputs into the new venture creation process differentiates effectual reasoning from causal reasoning which tends to focus on the avoidance of surprises as far as possible." (S. Sarasvathy (2014)

Problems with the Study on Business and Effectuation

However, to the critics, this study on effect, business, and effectuation has some major problems. Consider, for illustration, a few examples below (as summarized in *Table 3.5*).

Firstly, one main criticism of the study on effect, business, and effectuation is that it does not give sufficient attention to "optimality."

For example, although Sarasvathy (2014) acknowledges that "the best entrepreneurs are capable of both and do use both modes well" but claims that "they prefer effectual reasoning over causal reasoning in the early stages of a new venture, and arguably, most entrepreneurs do not transition well into latter stages requiring more causal reasoning"—the focus of effectuation is therefore not on optimality.

Secondly, another main criticism of the study on effect, business, and effectuation is that Sarasvathy's analysis often portrays "effectuation" in more favorable light than "causal reasoning" in a biased way.

For instance, here are some passages which shows the bias of Sarasvathy to time and again portray "effectual reasoning" in a more favorable light than "causal reasoning": (a) "the best entrepreneurs are capable of both and do use both modes well. But they prefer effectual reasoning over causal reasoning in the early stages of a new venture, and arguably, most entrepreneurs do not transition well into latter stages requiring more causal reasoning," and (b) "while both causal and effectual reasoning call for domain-specific skills and training, effectual reasoning demands something more—imagination, spontaneity, risk-taking, and salesmanship." (S. Sarasvathy (2014)

Thirdly, still another main criticism of the study on effect, business, and effectuation is that it is msileading to say that effectual reasoning, unlike causal reasoning, does not start with any goal in mind.

For instance, in the illustration above about "an entrepreneur who wants to start an Indian restaurant," the effectual process here already begins with the pre-determined goal of "starting an Indian restaurant," and this is a huge given in the effectual process, even if the outcome may not be successful (but this is true for both types of reasoning).

Fourthly, an additional main criticism of the study on effect, business, and effectuation is that it is more risk-adverse than the alternative causal process and thus can impose a greater limit on potential return.

For instance, the "affordable loss principle" focuses more on preventing loss (for an affordable loss instead) than on risking loss for the "highest potential return" (in causal reasoning).

Fifthly, another additional main criticism of the study on effect, business, and effectuation is that effectuation is more subjectively disposed towards "cooperation" than towards "competition."

For instance, the strategic partnerships principle suggests that "detailed competitive analyses do not seem to make any sense to them at the startup phase" and thus prefers "building partnerships right from the start. In fact, the ideal beginning for a successful startup seemed to be the induction of customers into strategic partnerships." (S. Sarasvathy (2014)

Sixthly, still another additional main criticism of the study on effect, business, and effectuation is that it is inherently more concerned with "people" than with outcome ("effect").

For instance, as Sarasvathy (2014) admits, "effectual logic is people-dependent, unlike causal logic, which is effect-dependent."

And seventhly, one last main criticism of the study on effect, business, and effectuation is that its application is more relevant for business startups (than for established businesses).

For instance, "effectuation serves entrepreneurs in starting businesses," where the situations they have to face are often most "uncertain," but it is not chear how much relevant it is for big established businesses, with their goals and institutions already firmly set up.

Beyond Effectuation

These criticisms of the analysis of effect, business, and effectuation should not be mistaken as a total rejection of its usefulness but serve to show us the two opposing sides of the debate, such that the possibility (or impossibility) and desirability (or undesirability) of effect (from the perspective of society with effect, business, and effectuation as a case study here) are not to the extent that the respective defenders would like us to believe.

In fact, the analysis of effect, business, and effectuation can illuminate the ontological principles in existential dialectics, and good examples include the formalness-informalness principle, the absoluteness-relativeness principle, the partiality-totality principle, the predictability-unpredictability principle, the explicability-inexplicability principle, the fiction-reality principle, the cognitiveness-noncognitiveness principle, the finiteness-transfiniteness principle, the preciseness-vagueness principle, the simpleness-complicatedness principle, the openness-hiddenness principle, the denseness-emptiness principle, the rule-exception principle, the indispensability-dispensability principle, the prototypicality-variation principle, the change-constancy principle, the order-chaos principle, the slowness-quickness principle, the expansion-contraction principle, the optimality-nonoptimality principle, the simultaneity-nonsimultaneity principle, the isolation-interaction principle, the theory-praxis principle, the convention-novelty principle, the evolution-transformation principle, the symmetry-asymmetry principle, the softness-hardness principle, the seriousness-playfulness principle, the activeness-inactivess principle, the selfness-otherness principle, the regression-progression principle, the same-difference principle, the stability-reaction principle, the functionality-nonfunctionality principle, the intentionality-nonintentionality principle. the survivability-non-survivability principle, and the materiality-nonmateriality principle.

For instance, in relation to the formalness-informalness principle, if there is formalness (e.g., the formal logical requirement of soundness and completeness in a system of ideas, as in the argument on effectuation), there is informalness (e.g., the non-formal existence of unsoundness and incompleteness in the argument on effectuation, as shown in the criticisms that it does not give sufficient attention to "optimality," that Sarasvathy's analysis often portrays "effectuation" in a more favorable light than "causal reasoning" in a biased way, that it is msileading to say that effectual reasoning [unlike causal reasoning] does not start with any goal, that it is more risk-adverse than the alternative causal process and thus can impose a greater limit on potential return, that effectuation is more subjectively disposed towards "cooperation" than towards "competition," that it is inherently more concerned with "people" than with outcome ["effect"], and that its application is more relevant for business startups). And the reverse direction also holds true.

In relation to the absoluteness-relativeness principle, if there is absoluteness (e.g., the absolute view on "people" by the advocates of effectual logic), there is relativeness (e.g., what is right for the advocates of effectual logic in regard to "people" is not necessarily so for those of "causal logic," since they are more concerned with "effect" or "outcome" instead). And the reverse direction also holds true.

In relation to the partiality-totality principle, if there is partiality (e.g., the partial view on effectual logic by the advocates), there is totality (e.g., the more holistic view on effectual logic, such that the whole is not the sum of its parts, that is, it cannot be reduced to the sum of opposing views by its advocates, the critics like those for causal logic, etc., since there will emerge new views in the future not yet known today, just as there are already alternative views nowadays which do not side exclusively with any of them, as is the analysis here). And the reverse direction also holds true.

In relation to the predictability-unpredictability principle, if there is predictability (e.g., the focus on "predictive models" by those for causal logic), there is unpredictability (e.g., the focus on "contingencies" or "uncertainty" by those for effectual logic). And the reverse direction also holds true.

In relation to the explicability-inexplicability principle, if there is explicability (e.g., the explanation, by those advocates of effectual logic, of the desirability on the basis of "affordable loss," besides other two principles), there is inexplicability (e.g., the lack of sufficient explanation, by those advocates of effectual logic, of why focusing on "affordable loss" is necessarily desirable, since the critics like those for causal logic prefer riskier loss for the "highest potential return" instead). And the reverse direction also holds true.

In relation to the fiction-reality principle, if there is fiction (e.g., the fictional aspect of effectual logic, insofar as there are "contingencies" or "uncetainty" as shown in the example about someone trying to start a lunch business but discovering later that "the lunch business does not take off beyond the first few customers"), there is reality (e.g., the realistic aspect of effectual logic, insofar as there are more realistic possibilities, as shown in the example that, even though "the lunch business does not take off beyond the first few customers,...our entrepreneur discovers that the customers are actually interested in her ethnic philosophy and life experiences or Indian culture or other aspects of her personality or expertise or contacts or interests"). And the reverse direction also holds true.

In relation to the cognitiveness-noncognitiveness principle, if there is cognitiveness (e.g., a view of things on the basis of reason and evidences, as shown in the empirical finding that there are different logics, like "causal logic" and "effectual logic"), there is noncognitiveness (e.g., a view of things on the basis of non-cognitive factors like envy, jealousy, power, nationality, race, gender, age, class, greed, lust, status, faith, anger, sadness, joy, fear, wish, etc.—as shown in the personal preference of Sarasvathy for "effectual logic," in spite of the problems and biases in the model as discussed earlier). And the reverse direction also holds true.

In relation to the finiteness-transfiniteness principle, if there is finiteness (e.g., the finite number of principles in effectual logic, like the 3 examples aforecited), there is transfiniteness (e.g., the transfinite number of all the individuals that have ever existed in history and have used different logics, regardless of whether they are "effectual," "causal," or something else). And the reverse direction also holds true.

In relation to the preciseness-vagueness principle, if there is preciseness (e.g., the precise identification of 3 principles of effectual logic in the article aforecited), there is vagueness (e.g., the vagueness in the identification of the 3 principles of effectual logic by Sarasvathy in the article aforecited, since it is not clear why there must be only 3, not 4, 5, 6, 7 ,8, 9, and so on, since there are 5 principles in a Wikipedia article on effectuation). (WK 2014vv) And the reverse direction also holds true.

In relation to the simpleness-complicatedness principle, if there is simpleness (e.g., the relatively simple analysis of effectuation by the advocates), there is complicatedness (e.g., the relatively more complicated analysis of effectuation, by challenging the claims and assumptions, as shown in the problems pointed out by the critics as cited). And the reverse direction also holds true.

In relation to the openness-hiddenness principle, if there is openness (e.g., the open exploration of effectual logic as an alternative to causal logic by Sarasvathy), there is hiddenness (e.g., the hidden bias in the open exploration of effectual logic as an alternative to causal logic by Sarasvathy, because of the biased problems as discussed earlier). And the reverse direction also holds true.

In relation to the denseness-emptiness principle, if there is denseness (e.g., the relatively denser concentration of concerns with "affordable loss" by the advocates of effectuation), there is emptiness (e.g., the relatively less dense, or more empty, concentration of concerns with "optimality" by the advocates of effectuation). And the reverse direction also holds true.

In relation to the rule-exception principle, if there are rules (e.g., the usual generalization, procedure, habit, or tendency that "the best entrepreneurs…prefer effectual reasoning over causal reasoning in the early stages of a new venture"), there are exceptions (e.g., a case to which a rule does not apply, such as the exceptional case that a small number of entrepreneurs "transition well into latter stages requiring more causal reasoning"). (S. Sarasvathy 2014) And the reverse direction also holds true.

In relation to the indispensability-dispensability principle, if there is indispensability (e.g., the need for something or someone, like the necessary classification of the principles of effectual logic in terms of 3 by Sarasvathy in the article aforecited), there is dispensability (e.g., the superfluity of something or someone, like the dispensable classification of the principles of effectual logic in terms of 5 in the Wikipedia article on effectuation, but it is not accepted in the article by Sarasvathy as discussed earlier). (WK 2014vv) And the reverse direction also holds true.

In relation to the prototypicality-variation principle, if there is prototypicality (e.g., the prototype, like the example about the original work on effectuation by Sarasvathy in 2001), there is variation (e.g., different variants of the protoptye, as shown in many studies since the original work on effectuation by Sarasvathy in 2001—like the later one with 5 principles by The Society for Effectual Action, though with its own variation, contribution, and disagreement). (SOC 2012) And the reverse direction also holds true.

In relation to the change-constancy principle, if there is change (e.g., the ever new ways to study causation, as shown in the research on effectuation), there is constancy (e.g., the ever constant existence of different problems with the ever new ways to study causation, as shown in the problems with the research on effectuation pointed out by the critics). And the reverse direction also holds true.

In relation to the order-chaos principle, if there is order (e.g., the more or less orderly view on reality, if looked from the sole vantage point of the advocates of "predictive models" in causal reasoning), there is chaos (e.g., the more or less chaotic view on reality, if looked from the alternative conflicting vantage point of "contingencies" or "uncertainty" by the advocates in effectual reasoning)). And the reverse direction also holds true.

In relation to the slowness-quickness principle, if there is slowness (e.g., the relatively slower speed to do business in accordance to effectual logic, which refuses to seek "optimality" for the "fastest, cheapest, most efficient, etc." but instead works with "contingencies" or "uncertainty"), there is quickness (e.g., the relatively quicker speed to do business in accordance to causal logic, which seeks "optimality" for the "fastest, cheapest, most efficient, etc."). And the reverse direction also holds true.

In relation to the expansion-contraction principle, if there is expansion (e.g., the relatively more developed ability to deal with "optimality" among those for causal logic), there is contraction (e.g., the relatively less developed ability to deal with "contingencies" among those for causal logic). And the reverse direction also holds true.

In relation to the optimality-nonoptimality principle, if there is optimality (e.g., the search for highly favorable options, like the quest for "optimality" for the "fastest, cheapest, most efficient, etc." by those in causal logic), there is nonoptimality (e.g., the existence of non-optimal alternatives to optimality, like the argument for more realistic studies by the critics, who pointed out an alternative logic known as "effectual logic"). And the reverse direction also holds true.

In relation to the simultaneity-nonsimultaneity principle, if there is simultaneity (e.g., the occurrence of different things more or less at the same time, such as the simultaneous existence of different logics, like "causal logic" and "effectual logic" nowadays), there is nonsimultaneity (e.g., the occurrence of something after something else, such as the formal development of "causal logic" before the formal development of "effectual logic" in history, or more precisely, in 2001). And the reverse direction also holds true.

In relation to the isolation-interaction principle, if there is isolation (e.g., the state of a situation that is separate from others, such as the isolation of "predictive models" from the focus on "situations of uncertainty" in causal logic), there is interaction (e.g., the influence of entities on one another, such as the interaction between "people" and "contngencies" in effectual logic). And the reverse direction also holds true.

In relation to the theory-praxis principle, if there is theory (e.g., the theoretical construction of "logic" in the field of philosophy), there is praxis (e.g., the practical application of "logic" in the field of philosophy to the field of business management, like "effectual logic"). And the reverse direction also holds true.

In relation to the convention-novelty principle, if there is convention (e.g., the conventional wisdom about "causal logic" for optimality), there is novelty (e.g., the alternative novel challenge to the conventional wisdom about "causal logic" for optimality—by the new idea of "effectual logic" for "contingencies"). And the reverse direction also holds true.

In relation to the evolution-transformation principle, if there is evolution (e.g., the natural evolution of humans to encoutner "uncertainty" in the state of nature), there is transformation (e.g., the technical transformation of human ability to deal with "uncertainty" by the invention of "effectual logic" for "continegencies"). And the reverse direction also holds true.

In relation to the symmetry-asymmetry principle, if there is symmetry (e.g., the co-existence of different logics, like "causal logic" and "effectual logic"), there is asymmetry (e.g., the popularity of "causal logic" is due to its being more "effect-dependent"—but the popularity of "effectual logic" is due to its being more "people-dependent"). And the reverse direction also holds true.

In relation to the softness-hardness principle, if there is softness (e.g., the defense of effectual logic by the advocates aforecited), there is hardness (e.g., the critique of effectual logic, as shown in the different problems pointed out by the critics aforecited). And the reverse direction also holds true.

In relation to the seriousness-playfulness principle, if there is seriousness (e.g., the serious business of those who try to understand the nature of effectual logic), there is playfulness (e.g., the playful part of those who try to understand the nature of effectual logic, when they play around with different principles over the years, like the 3 principles by Sarasvathy, the 5 principles in a Wikipedia article on effectuation, etc.). And the reverse direction also holds true.

In relation to the activeness-inactivess principle, if there is activeness (e.g., the relative active presence of "people" in effectual reasoning, since the focus in this logic is "finding and leading the right people" as "the key to creating an enduring venture"), there is inactiveness (e.g., the relative inactive presence of "predictive models" in effectual reasoning, since it is based on the motto that *"To the extent that we can control the future, we do not need to predict it"*). (S. Sarasvathy (2014) And the reverse direction also holds true.

In relation to the selfness-otherness principle, if there is selfness (e.g., the tendency to be mostly centered on one's self or group, as shown in the focus on "competition" and "highest potential return" by those for "causal reasoning"), there is otherness (e.g., the tendency to be mostly centered on others, as shown in the academic analysis of both sides of the debate on "causal logic" and "effectual logic," as an advancement in the knowledge of business management for humanity). And the reverse direction also holds true.

In relation to the regression-progression principle, if there is regression (e.g., the regression made by the work on effectuation, as shown in the problems pointed out by the critics), there is progression (e.g., the progress made by the work on effectuation, as shown in the contribution to the understanding of doing business in "situations of uncertainty" aforecited). And the reverse direction also holds true.

In relation to the same-difference principle, if there is similarity in outcome (e.g., the contribution to the molding and control of beliefs, values, and behaviors, regardless of whether this be done by way of causal reasoning, or by way of effectual reasoning), there is difference in outcome (e.g., the contribution to the molding and control of beliefs, values, and behaviors by way of causal reasoning for a relatively more predictive worldview—but the contribution to the molding and control of beliefs, values, and behaviors by way of effectual reasoning for a relatively more unpredictive worldview). And the reverse direction also holds true.

In relation to the stability-reaction principle, if there is stability (e.g., the relatively more stable condition of the formal framework of causal reasoning in the older days), there is reaction (e.g., the formal framework of causal reasoning in the older days then led to further changes later on, when nowadays, there is the alternative formal development of effectual reasoning). And the reverse direction also holds true.

In relation to the functionality-nonfunctionality principle, if there is functionality (e.g., the presence of action for which something or someone is fitted, as shown in the formal development of effectual logic, which serves the function of providing principles for decision-making in situations of uncertainty), there is nonfunctionality (e.g., the relative lack of action for which something or someone is fitted, as shown in the different problems with the formal development of effectual logic, such that it is not as functional as the advocates would like us to believe). And the reverse direction also holds true.

In relation to the intentionality-nonintentionality principle, if there is intentionality (e.g., the planning or design of something for a certain outcome, as shown in the intended consequences in regard to the mainstream use of causal reasoning, as those who used it intended to achieve optimality, for example), there is nonintentionality (e.g., the relative absence of planning or design of something for a certain outcome, such that the outcome can even be counter-intentional in being the opposite of what was originally planned, as shown in the recent proposal of effectual reasoning for decision-making in situations of uncertainty, as an alternative to causal reasoning—contrary to the original intention of those who used causal reasoning to achieve optimality, for example). And the reverse direction also holds true.

In relation to the survivability-nonsurvivability principle, if there is survivability (e.g., the relative survival, nowadays, of effectual logic), there is non-survivability (e.g., the relative non-survival, nowadays, of the focus on causal logic without any attention to alternative logics like effectual logic). And the reverse direction also holds true.

And in relation to the materiality-nonmateriality principle, if there is materiality (e.g., the material outcome in relation to space-time, matter-energy, Having, etc., like the use of causal reasoning to seek "the highest potential return" or "profit"), there is non-materiality (e.g., the nonmaterial outcome in relation to the quest for Being, Belonging, etc., like the spiritual search among humans "to achieve their best potential" by the use of effectual logic, which helps "people" create that which "will embody their deepest passions and aspirations while enabling them to achieve their best potential"). (S. Sarasvathy (2014) And the reverse direction also holds true.

Effect and Culture

Effect, when examined from the perspective of culture, can cast an illuminating light on its possibility (or impossibility) and desirability (or undesirability), and this can be shown by way of two case studies, namely, (3.5.1) effect, philosophy, and determinism, and (3.5.2) effect, the chicken-and-egg problem, and eternal return—to be addressed hereafter, in that order.

Effect, Philosophy, and Determinism

An excellent case study here to understand effect from the perspective of culture has to do with effect, philosophy, and determinism.

An argument in the literature is that, in accordance to "determinism," "for every event exist conditions that could cause no other event." (WK 2014u)

Philosopical Connections of Causal Determmism

The idea of determinism "often is taken to mean causal determinism, which in physics is known as cause-and-effect. It is the concept that events within a given paradigm are so causally bound that prior states of any object or event completely determine its later states."(WK 2014u)

In philosophy, the idea of "causal determinism" has been used for different debates on some controversial issues. For illustration, consider three main examples (about these philosophical connections) below (as summarized in *Table 3.6*).

(a) With the Nature/Nurture Controversy

Causal determinism has been used "to explain how the interaction of both nature and nurture is entirely predictable." (WK 2014u)

On the genetic side, "the concept of heritability has been helpful to make this distinction. Biological determinism, sometimes called Genetic determinism, is the idea that each of our behaviors, beliefs, and desires are fixed by our genetic nature." (WK 2014u)

And on the environmental side, "behaviorism is the idea that all behavior can be traced to specific causes—either environmental or reflexive. This Nurture-focused determinism was developed by John B. Watson and B. F. Skinner. Cultural determinism or social determinism is the nurture-focused theory that it is the culture in which we are raised that determines who we are. Environmental determinism is also known as climatic or geographical determinism. It holds the view that the physical environment, rather than social conditions, determines culture. Supporters often also support Behavioral determinism. Key proponents of this notion have included Ellen Churchill Semple, Ellsworth Huntington, Thomas Griffith Taylor and possibly Jared Diamond, although his status as an environmental determinist is debated." (WK 2014u; S. Andrew 2003)

(b) With a Particular Factor

Other versions of causal determinism have been used instead "to highlight the importance of a particular factor in predicting the future. These theories often use the factor as a sort of guide or constraint on the future. They need not suppose that complete knowledge of that one factor would allow us to make perfect predictions." (WK 2014u)

For instance, "psychological determinism can mean that humans must act according to reason, but it can also be synonymous with some sort of Psychological egoism. The latter is the view that humans will always act according to their perceived best interest."(WK 2014u)

In "linguistic determinism," the proponents claim that "our language determines (at least limits) the things we can think and say and thus know. The Sapir–Whorf hypothesis argues that individuals experience the world based on the grammatical structures they habitually use." (WK 2014u)

In "economic determinism," the focus here is on "the economic structure over politics in the development of human history. It is associated with the dialectical materialism of Karl Marx." (WK 2014u)

And in "technological determinism," the reductionistic viewpoint here is that "a society's technology drives the development of its social structure and cultural values. Media determinism, a subset of technological determinism, is a philosophical and sociological position which posits the power of the media to impact society. Two leading media determinists are the Canadian scholars Harold Innis and Marshall McLuhan." (WK 2014u)

(c) With Ethics

Causal determinism has also been used to defend "compatibilism," which "refers to the view that free will is, in some sense, compatible with determinism," especially in the context of ethics.

For instance, "a compatibilist who centers around plans for the future might posit" the following: (WK 2014u)

- "The moral judgment that you shouldn't have done X implies that you can do something else instead."

- "That you can do something else instead implies that there is something else for you to do."
- "That there is something else for you to do implies that you can do something else."
- "That you can do something else implies that you have free will for planning future recourse."
- "If you have free will to do other than X we can make the moral judgment that you should do other than X, and punishing you as a responsible party for having done X that you know you should not have done can help you remember to not do X in the future."

Of course, not everyone agrees with this position, and a good example is Peter van Inwagen (2009), who proposed the opposite position known as "incompatibilism." (WK 2014u)

Cultural Traditions of Causal Determinism

In any event, there are different cultural traditions of causal determinism. For illustration, consider two main traditions below (as summarized in *Table 3.6*).

(a) In the Eastern Tradition
In the Eastern tradition, "the idea that the entire universe is a deterministic system has been articulated in...Eastern...religion, philosophy, and literature." (WK 2014u)

For instance, "in *I Ching* and Philosophical Taoism, the ebb and flow of favorable and unfavorable conditions suggests the path of least resistance is effortless." (WK 2014u)

And "in the philosophical schools of India, the concept of precise and continual effect of laws of Karma on the existence of all sentient beings is analogous to Western deterministic concept. Karma is the concept of 'action' or 'deed' in Indian religions. It is understood as that which causes the entire cycle of cause and effect (i.e., the cycle called saṃsāra) originating in ancient India and treated in Hindu, Jain, Sikh and Buddhist philosophies. Karma is considered predetermined and deterministic in the universe, and in combination with the decisions (free will) of living beings, accumulates to determine futuristic situations that the living being encounters." (WK 2014u)

(b) In the Western Tradition
And in the Western tradition, "determinism...is often associated with Newtonian physics, which depicts the physical matter of the universe as operating according to a set of fixed, knowable laws. The 'billiard ball'

hypothesis, a product of Newtonian physics, argues that once the initial conditions of the universe have been established, the rest of the history of the universe follows inevitably. If it were actually possible to have complete knowledge of physical matter and all of the laws governing that matter at any one time, then it would be theoretically possible to compute the time and place of every event that will ever occur (Laplace's demon). In this sense, the basic particles of the universe operate in the same fashion as the rolling balls on a billiard table, moving and striking each other in predictable ways to produce predictable results." (WK 2014u)

However, "Newtonian physics...fails spectacularly as velocities become some substantial fraction of the speed of light and when interactions at the atomic scale are studied. Before the discovery of quantum effects and other challenges to Newtonian physics, 'uncertainty' was always a term that applied to the accuracy of human knowledge about causes and effects, and not to the causes and effects themselves." (WK 2014u)

Scientific Perspectives of Causal Determmism

Causal determinism has also been examined from different scientific perspectives. For illustration, consider four main examples below (as summarized in *Table 3.6*).

(a) Generative Processes

In the context of "generative processes," some proponents "of emergentist or generative philosophy, cognitive sciences and evolutionary psychology, argue that determinism is true. They suggest instead that an illusion of free will is experienced due to the generation of infinite behaviour from the interaction of finite-deterministic set of rules and parameters. Thus the unpredictability of the emerging behaviour from deterministic processes leads to a perception of free will, even though free will as an ontological entity does not exist." (WK 2014u; D. Kenrick 2003; A. Nowak 2000; J. Epstein 1996)

For example, "the strategy board-games chess and Go have rigorous rules in which no information (such as cards' face-values) is hidden from either player and no random events (such as dice-rolling) happen within the game. Yet, chess and especially Go with its extremely simple deterministic rules, can still have an extremely large number of unpredictable moves. By this analogy, it is suggested, the experience of free will emerges from the interaction of finite rules and deterministic parameters that generate nearly infinite and practically unpredictable behaviourial responses. In theory, if all these events could be accounted for, and there were a known way to evaluate these events, the seemingly unpredictable behaviour would become predictable." (WK 2014u; D. Kenrick 2003; A. Nowak 2000; J. Epstein 1996)

(b) Mathematical Models

In mathematical models, say, "of physical systems," determinism is often the case, and "this is true of most models involving differential equations (notably, those measuring rate of change over time). Mathematical models that are not deterministic because they involve randomness are called stochastic. Because of sensitive dependence on initial conditions, some deterministic models may appear to behave non-deterministically; in such cases, a deterministic interpretation of the model may not be useful due to numerical instability and a finite amount of precision in measurement. Such considerations can motivate the consideration of a stochastic model even though the underlying system is governed by deterministic equations." (WK 2024u Werndl, Charlotte. 2009a; J. Glimm 1999.)

(c) Day-to-Day Physics

In day-to-day physics, "taken in isolation (rather than as an approximation to quantum mechanics), Newtonian physics depicts a universe in which objects move in perfectly determined ways. At the scale where humans exist and interact with the universe, Newtonian mechanics remain useful, and make relatively accurate predictions (e.g. calculating the trajectory of a bullet),...[I]n theory, absolute knowledge of the forces accelerating a bullet would produce an absolutely accurate prediction of its path...." (WK 2014u)

(d) Quantum Realm

And in the quantum realm, "a particle's path simply cannot be exactly specified in its full quantum description. 'Path' is a classical, practical attribute in our every day life, but one which quantum particles do not meaningfully possess. The probabilities discovered in quantum mechanics do nevertheless arise from measurement (of the perceived path of the particle). As Stephen Hawking [2010] explains, the result is not traditional determinism, but rather determined probabilities....In fact, as far as prediction goes, the quantum development is at least as predictable as the classical motion, but the key is that it describes wave functions that cannot be easily expressed in ordinary language. As far as the thesis of determinism is concerned, these probabilities, at least, are quite determined." (WK 2014u)

Problems with the Study on Philosophy and Determinism

However, to the critics, this argument on effect, philosophy, and determinism has some major problems. Consider, for illustration, a few examples below (as summarized in *Table 3.6*).

Firstly, one main criticism of this argument on effect, philosophy, and determinism is that there are alternative theories to determinism.

For instance, to the critics, "opposing determinism is some kind of indeterminism (otherwise called nondeterminism). Determinism is often contrasted with free will." (WK 2014t)

Secondly, another main criticism of this argument on effect, philosophy, and determinism is that there are competing (even opposing) versions of determinism among the proponents themselves.

For instance, even the proponents of determinism often debate among themselves "the scope of determined systems, with some maintaining that the entire universe is a single determinate system and others identifying other more limited determinate systems (or multiverse). Numerous historical debates involve many philosophical positions and varieties of determinism, some concerning determinism and free will, technically denoted as compatibilistic (allowing the two to coexist) and incompatibilistic (denying their coexistence is a possibility)." (WK 2014t)

Thirdly, still another main criticism of the study on effect, philosophy, and determinism is that causal determinism has been criticized as empirically false.

For instance, to the critics, although there are different "forms of determinism" which "concern human behaviors and cognition"—"these theories have been widely rejected as a single cause fallacy," especially "as scientific understanding has grown." (WK 2014u; I. de Melo-Martín 2005) And also "relevant is the fact that certainty is never absolute in practice (and not just because of David Hume's problem of induction). The equations of Newtonian mechanics can exhibit sensitive dependence on initial conditions. This is an example of the butterfly effect, which is one of the subjects of chaos theory." (WK 2014u)

Fourthly, an additional main criticism of the study on effect, philosophy, and determinism is that causal determinism is too "materialistic."

For instance, to the critics, "materialism" in causal determinism "does not present a complete understanding of the universe, because while it can describe determinate interactions among material things, it ignores the minds or souls of conscious beings"; so "a number of non-materialistic positions" have been proposed, such as the claims that "immaterial souls are all that exist (Idealism)" and that "immaterial souls exist and exert a non-deterministic causal influence on bodies. (Traditional free-will, interactionist dualism)." (WK 2014u; STAN 2010)

And fifthly, another additional main criticism of the study on effect, philosophy, and determinism is that the idea of determinism has been misused for religious purposes.

For instance, to the critics, a good illustration is "theological determinism," which states that "all events that happen are pre-ordained, or predestined to happen, by a monotheistic deity, or that they are destined to occur given its omniscience. Two forms of theological determinism exist, here referenced as strong and weak theological determinism. The first one, strong theological determinism, is based on the concept of a creator deity dictating all events in history: 'everything that happens has been predestined to happen by an omniscient, omnipotent divinity.' The second form, weak theological determinism, is based on the concept of divine foreknowledge—'because God's omniscience is perfect, what God knows about the future will inevitably happen, which means, consequently, that the future is already fixed.'" (WK 2014u; A. Iannone 2001; W. van Huyssteen 2003)

Beyond Determinism

These criticisms of the analysis of effect, philosophy, and determinism, however, do not entail a total rejection of its usefulness but serve to show us the two opposing sides of the debate, such that the possibility (or impossibility) and desirability (or undesirability) of effect (from the perspective of culture with effect, philosophy, and determinism as a case study here) are not to the extent that the respective defenders would like us to believe.

In fact, the analysis of effect, philosophy, and determinism can teach us a good lesson on the ontological principles in existential dialectics, and good examples include the formalness-informalness principle, the absoluteness-relativeness principle, the partiality-totality principle, the predictability-unpredictability principle, the explicability-inexplicability principle, the fiction-reality principle, the cognitiveness-noncognitiveness principle, the finiteness-transfiniteness principle, the preciseness-vagueness principle, the simpleness-complicatedness principle, the openness-hiddenness principle, the denseness-emptiness principle, the rule-exception principle, the indispensability-dispensability principle, the prototypicality-variation principle, the change-constancy principle, the order-chaos principle, the slowness-quickness principle, the expansion-contraction principle, the optimality-nonoptimality principle, the simultaneity-nonsimultaneity principle, the isolation-interaction principle, the theory-praxis principle, the convention-novelty principle, the evolution-transformation principle, the symmetry-asymmetry principle, the softness-hardness principle, the seriousness-playfulness principle, the activeness-inactivess principle, the selfness-otherness principle, the regression-progression principle, the same-difference principle, the stability-reaction principle, the functionality-nonfunctionality principle, the intentionality-nonintentionality principle. the survivability-non-survivability principle, and the materiality-nonmateriality principle.

For instance, in relation to the formalness-informalness principle, if there is formalness (e.g., the formal logical requirement of soundness, completeness, and consistency in a system of ideas, as in the argument on causal determinism), there is informalness (e.g., the non-formal existence of unsoundness, incompleteness, and inconsistency in the argument on causal determinism, as shown in the criticisms that there are alternative theories to determinism, that there are competing [even opposing] versions of determinism among the proponents themselves, that causal determinism has been criticized as empirically false, that causal determinism is too "materialistic," and that the idea of determinism has been misused for religious purposes). And the reverse direction also holds true.

In relation to the absoluteness-relativeness principle, if there is absoluteness (e.g., the absolute view on certainty by the advocates of Newtonian mechanics), there is relativeness (e.g., what is right for the advocates of Newtonian mechanics in regard to certainty is not necessarily so for the critics, who pointed out that "certainty is never absolute in practice [and not just because of David Hume's problem of induction]" and "the equations of Newtonian mechanics can exhibit sensitive dependence on initial conditions," and "this is an example of the butterfly effect, which is one of the subjects of chaos theory"). And the reverse direction also holds true.

In relation to the partiality-totality principle, if there is partiality (e.g., the partial view on "certainty" by the advocates of Newtonian mechanics), there is totality (e.g., the more holistic view on "certainty," such that the whole is not the sum of its parts, that is, it cannot be reduced to the sum of opposing views by the advocates of Newtonian mechanics, the advocates of quantum mechanics, the advocates of the Humean problem of induction, etc., since there will emerge new views in the future not yet known today, just as there are already alternative views nowadays which do not side exclusively with any of them, as is the analysis here). And the reverse direction also holds true.

In relation to the predictability-unpredictability principle, if there is predictability (e.g., the predictable tendency that "Newtonian mechanics...make relatively accurate predictions [e.g. calculating the trajectory of a bullet]"), there is unpredictability (e.g., "quantum mechanics casts reasonable doubt on this main thesis of determinism," that is, on "accurate predictions"). (WK 2014u) And the reverse direction also holds true.

In relation to the explicability-inexplicability principle, if there is explicability (e.g., the explanation, by those advocates of "causal determinism," on the basis that "every event is necessitated by antecedent events and conditions together with the laws of nature"), there is inexplicability (e.g., the lack of sufficient explanation, by those advocates of "causal determinism," of why it is necessarily true, since, to the critics, "opposing determinism is some kind of indeterminism [otherwise called nondeterminism]"). (WK 2014u) And the reverse direction also holds true.

In relation to the fiction-reality principle, if there is fiction (e.g., the fictional aspect of causal determinism, insofar as "the equations of Newtonian mechanics can exhibit sensitive dependence on initial conditions" and "this is an example of the butterfly effect, which is one of the subjects of chaos theory"), there is reality (e.g., the realistic aspect of causal determinism, insofar as "Newtonian mechanics remain useful, and make relatively accurate predictions [e.g. calculating the trajectory of a bullet]" in day-to-day physics). And the reverse direction also holds true.

In relation to the cognitiveness-noncognitiveness principle, if there is cognitiveness (e.g., a view of things on the basis of reason and evidences, as shown in the empirical finding that there are different forms of determinism aforecited), there is noncognitiveness (e.g., a view of things on the basis of non-cognitive factors like envy, jealousy, power, nationality, race, gender, age, class, greed, lust, status, faith, anger, sadness, joy, fear, wish, etc.—as shown in the rigid ideological conviciton by those for Marxist "economic determinism," even after the collapse of the Communist bloc in the 1990s and after "these theories have been widely rejected as a single cause fallacy," especially "as scientific understanding has grown"). And the reverse direction also holds true.

In relation to the finiteness-transfiniteness principle, if there is finiteness (e.g., the finite number of different forms of determinism with "one particular factor," like "psychological determinism," "linguistic determinism," "economic determinism," and "technological determinism"), there is transfiniteness (e.g., the transfinite number of all the particular events that have ever occurred in history, regardless of whether they can fit in any of the different forms of determinism as discussed earlier). And the reverse direction also holds true.

In relation to the preciseness-vagueness principle, if there is preciseness (e.g., the precise identification of 4 different forms of determinism with "one particular factor" in the article aforecited), there is vagueness (e.g., the vagueness in the identification of the 4 different forms of determinism with "one particular factor" in the article aforecited, since it is not clear why there must be only 4, not 5, 6, 7, and so on). And the reverse direction also holds true.

In relation to the simpleness-complicatedness principle, if there is simpleness (e.g., the relatively simple analysis of causal determinism by the advocates), there is complicatedness (e.g., the relatively more complicated analysis of causal determinism, by challenging the claims and assumptions, as shown in the problems pointed out by the critics as cited). And the reverse direction also holds true.

In relation to the openness-hiddenness principle, if there is openness (e.g., the open exploration of a "materialistic" interpretation of the universe by those for causal determinism), there is hiddenness (e.g., the hidden bias in the open exploration of a "materialistic" interpretation of the universe by those for causal determinism, because, to the critics, "it ignores the minds or souls of conscious beings"). And the reverse direction also holds true.

In relation to the denseness-emptiness principle, if there is denseness (e.g., the relatively denser concentration of concerns with "materialism" by those for causal determinism), there is emptiness (e.g., the relatively less dense, or more empty, concentration of concerns with "minds or souls" by those for causal determinism). And the reverse direction also holds true.

In relation to the rule-exception principle, if there are rules (e.g., the usual generalization, procedure, habit, or tendency that "the probabilities discovered in quantum mechanics," as Stephen Hawking explains, are not those of "traditional determinism, but rather determined probabilities"), there are exceptions (e.g., a case to which a rule does not apply, such as the exceptional situation, in which "in some cases, a quantum particle may indeed trace an exact path, and the probability of finding the particles in that path is one [certain]"). (WK 2014u) And the reverse direction also holds true.

In relation to the indispensability-dispensability principle, if there is indispensability (e.g., the need for something or someone, like the necessary inclusion of the idea that "for every event…exist conditions that could cause no other event" in the definition of "causal determinism"), there is dispensability (e.g., the superfluity of something or someone, like the dispensable inclusion of "linguistic determinism" in an analysis of "causal determinism," since there are other forms of determinism, like "economic determinism," "technological determinism," etc., which can be used instead). And the reverse direction also holds true.

In relation to the prototypicality-variation principle, if there is prototypicality (e.g., the prototype, like the example about the original work on "causal determinism" by the Stoics in the history of the Western philosophical tradition), there is variation (e.g., different variants of the protoptye, as shown in many studies since the original work on "causal determinism" by the Stoics in the history of the Western philosophical tradition—like the later ones by Thomas Hobbes, Baruch Spinoza, Gottfried Leibniz, David Hume, Arthur Schopenhauer, William James, Friedrich Nietzsche, etc., though each with its own variation, contribution, and disagreement). (WK 2014u) And the reverse direction also holds true.

In relation to the change-constancy principle, if there is change (e.g., the ever new ways to study cause and effect, as shown in the research on "causal determinism"), there is constancy (e.g., the ever constant existence of different problems with the ever new ways to study cause and effect, as shown in the problems with the research on "causal determinism" pointed out by the critics). And the reverse direction also holds true.

In relation to the order-chaos principle, if there is order (e.g., the more or less orderly view on the universe, if looked from the sole vantage point of Newtonian mechanics with its view on certainty in causal determinism), there is chaos (e.g., the more or less chaotic view on the universe, if looked from the alternative vantage point of chaos theory with its focus on "sensitive dependence on initial conditions" as in "the example of the butterfly effect"). And the reverse direction also holds true.

In relation to the slowness-quickness principle, if there is slowness (e.g., the relatively slower speed of "the trajectory of a bullet" as measured by Newtonian mechanics, when contrasted with the speed of light), there is quickness (e.g., the relatively quicker speed of light, as nothing can travel faster, according to the theory of relativity). And the reverse direction also holds true.

In relation to the expansion-contraction principle, if there is expansion (e.g., the relative spread, nowadays, of quantum mechanics, which "casts reasonable doubt on th[e]...main thesis of determinism" in regard to "certainty"), there is contraction (e.g., the relative decline, nowadays, of the old-fashioned view of Newtonian physics which "depicts a universe in which objects move in perfectly determined ways," although "Newtonian mechanics remain useful, and make relatively accurate predictions [e.g. calculating the trajectory of a bullet]"). And the reverse direction also holds true.

In relation to the optimality-nonoptimality principle, if there is optimality (e.g., the search for highly favorable options, like the quest for certainty in "Newtonian physics," which "depicts a universe in which objects move in perfectly determined ways"), there is nonoptimality (e.g., the existence of non-optimal alternatives to optimality, like the argument for more realistic studies by the critics, who pointed out different problems with Newtonian physics, since "modern quantum mechanics casts reasonable doubt on this main thesis of determinism" in Newtonian physics). And the reverse direction also holds true.

In relation to the simultaneity-nonsimultaneity principle, if there is simultaneity (e.g., the occurrence of different things more or less at the same time, such as the simultaneous existence of different physical theories nowadays, like Newtonian physics, quantum mechanics, etc.), there is nonsimultaneity (e.g., the occurrence of something after something else, such as the develoment of Newtonian physics in history before that of quantum mechanics). And the reverse direction also holds true.

In relation to the isolation-interaction principle, if there is isolation (e.g., the state of a situation that is separate from others, such as the isolation of Newtonian physics in the older days before the rise of quantum mechanics, when, "taken in isolation [rather than as an approximation to quantum mechanics], Newtonian physics depicts a universe in which objects move in perfectly determined ways"), there is interaction (e.g., the influence of entities on one another, such as the interaction between quantum mechanics and Newtonian physics in the 20th century, since "modern quantum mechanics casts reasonable doubt on this main thesis of determinism"). And the reverse direction also holds true.

In relation to the theory-praxis principle, if there is theory (e.g., the theoretical construction of "determined probabilities" in the field of quantum mechanics), there is praxis (e.g., the practical application of "determined probabilities" in the field of quantum mechanics to the field of everyday technologies, as "these findings from quantum mechanics...allow us to build transistors and lasers,...personal computers, Blu-ray players and the internet"). WK 2014u) And the reverse direction also holds true.

In relation to the convention-novelty principle, if there is convention (e.g., the conventional wisdom about Newtonian mechanics in the older days), there is novelty (e.g., the alternative novel challenge to the conventional wisdom about Newtonian mechanics in the older days —by the new idea of quantum mechanics in the 20th century). And the reverse direction also holds true.

In relation to the evolution-transformation principle, if there is evolution (e.g., the natural evolution of humans to experience causation in the state of nature), there is transformation (e.g., the technical transformation of human ability to understand causation by the invention of "causal determinism"). And the reverse direction also holds true.

In relation to the symmetry-asymmetry principle, if there is symmetry (e.g., the co-existence of different theories in physics, like classical mechanics and quantum mechanics), there is asymmetry (e.g., classical mechanics can be applied better to the macroscopic world—but quantum mechanics can be applied better to the microscopic world). And the reverse direction also holds true.

In relation to the softness-hardness principle, if there is softness (e.g., the defense of causal determinism by the advocates aforecited), there is hardness (e.g., the critique of causal determinism, as shown in the problems pointed out by the critics aforecited). And the reverse direction also holds true.

In relation to the seriousness-playfulness principle, if there is seriousness (e.g., the serious business of those who try to understand the nature of causal determinism), there is playfulness (e.g., the playful part of those who try to understand the nature of causal determinism, when they play around with different versions and possibilities over the centuries, as shown in the different examples aforediscussed). And the reverse direction also holds true.

In relation to the activeness-inactivess principle, if there is activeness (e.g., the relative activeness of classical mechanics when applied to the macroscopic world), there is inactiveness (e.g., the relative inactiveness of classical mechanics when applied to the microscopic world, since quantum mechanics is more useful here). And the reverse direction also holds true.

In relation to the selfness-otherness principle, if there is selfness (e.g., the tendency to be mostly centered on one's self or group, as shown by those who misuse causal determinism for religious purposes, as discussed earlier), there is otherness (e.g., the tendency to be mostly centered on others, as shown in the academic analysis of both sides of the debate on causal determinism, as an advancement in the knowledge of science for humanity). And the reverse direction also holds true.

In relation to the regression-progression principle, if there is regression (e.g., the regression made by the research on causal determinism, as shown in the problems pointed out by the critics), there is progression (e.g., the progress made by the research on causal determinism, as shown in the contribution to the understanding of "day-today physics" by Newtonian physics aforecited). And the reverse direction also holds true.

In relation to the same-difference principle, if there is similarity in outcome (e.g., the contribution to the molding and control of beliefs, values, and behaviors, regardless of whether this be done by way of the belief in classical mechanics, or by way of the belief in quantum mechanics), there is difference in outcome (e.g., the contribution to the molding and control of beliefs, values, and behaviors by way of the belief in classical mechanics for a relatively more certain worldview—but the contribution to the molding and control of beliefs, values, and behaviors by way of the belief in quantum mechanics for a relatively more uncertain worldview). And the reverse direction also holds true.

In relation to the stability-reaction principle, if there is stability (e.g., the relatively more stable condition of Newtonian mechanics in the older days), there is reaction (e.g., Newtonian mechanics in the older days then led to further changes later on, when it was later challenged by quantum mechanics in the 20th century). And the reverse direction also holds true.

In relation to the functionality-nonfunctionality principle, if there is functionality (e.g., the presence of action for which something or someone is fitted, as shown in the development of Newtonian physics, which serves the function of providing a deterministic worldview), there is nonfunctionality (e.g., the relative lack of action for which something or someone is fitted, as shown in the problems with Newtonian physics challenged by quantum mechanics, such that it is not as functional as the advocates would like us to believe). And the reverse direction also holds true.

In relation to the intentionality-nonintentionality principle, if there is intentionality (e.g., the planning or design of something for a certain outcome, as shown in the intended consequences in regard to "accurate predictions" like "calculating the trajectory of a bullet" by Newtonian physics, as those who used it intended to explain causal determinism in day-to-day physics aforediscussed), there is nonintentionality (e.g., the relative absence of planning or design of something for a certain outcome, such that the outcome can even be counter-intentional in being the opposite of what was originally planned, as shown in the re-interpretation of Newtonian mechanics on the basis of "sensitive dependence on initial conditions" known as "the butterfly effect, which is one of the subjects of chaos theory"—contrary to the original intention of those who used Newtonian physics to explain causal determinism). And the reverse direction also holds true.

In relation to the survivability-nonsurvivability principle, if there is survivability (e.g., the relative survival, nowadays, of quantum mechanics), there is non-survivability (e.g., the relative non-survival, nowadays, of classical mechanics to be applied to the microscopic world, although it remains "useful" and makes "relatively accurate predictions" for day-to-day physics like "calculating the trajectory of a bullet"). And the reverse direction also holds true.

And in relation to the materiality-nonmateriality principle, if there is materiality (e.g., the material outcome in relation to space-time, matter-energy, Having, etc., like the use of causal determinism to explain a "materialistic" world), there is non-materiality (e.g., the nonmaterial outcome in relation to the quest for Being, Belonging, etc., like the spiritual search among humans for "God," as shown by the use of causal determinism for "theological determinism" aforecited). And the reverse direction also holds true.

Effect, the Chicken-and-Egg Problem, and Eternal Return

Another way to evaluate the possibility (or impossibility) and desirability (or undesirability) of effect from the perspective of culture concerns effect, the chicken-and-egg problem, and eternal return.

An argument in the literature is that the idea of "eternal return" can be used to resolve "the chicken or the egg causality dilemma" in the question stated as "which came first, the chicken or the egg?" (WK 2014ww)

Introduction to the Chicken-and-Egg Problem

The Chicken-and-Egg Problem can be described in terms of (a) its concept and (b) its history (as summarized in *Table 3.7*).

(a) Concept

Conceptually, the term "chicken-and-egg problem" refers to a philosophical dilemma known as "the chicken or the egg causality dilemma," which asks: "Which came first, the chicken or the egg?" (WK 2014ww)

In philosophy, "the question about the first chicken or egg also evoked the questions of how life and the universe in general began," but "cultural references to the Chicken and Egg intend to point out the futility of identifying the first case of a circular cause and consequence. It could be considered that in this approach lies the most fundamental nature of the question....To better understand its metaphorical meaning, the question could be reformulated as: 'Which came first, X that can't come without Y, or Y that can't come without X?'"(WK 2014ww)

In fact, "an equivalent situation arises in engineering and science known as circular reference, in which a parameter is required to calculate that parameter itself. Examples are Van der Waals equation and the Colebrook equation." (WK 2014ww; THEO 1939)

In addition, "the term 'chicken-and-egg problem' is further commonly used to describe a situation that is not a philosophical dilemma, but one in which it is impossible to reach a certain desired outcome because a necessary precondition is not satisfied, while to meet that precondition in turn requires that the desired outcome has already been realized. For example, it has been argued that the transformation to alternative fuels for vehicles faces a chicken-and-egg problem: 'it is not economical for individuals to purchase alternative fuels absent sufficient refueling stations, and it is not economical for fuel dealers to open stations absent sufficient alternative fuel vehicles.' This is closely related to the economic concept of vicious circle, but in this kind of situation one that becomes a virtuous circle upon reaching a tipping point." (WK 2014ww; USCOTA 1994)

(b) History

Historically, "ancient references to the dilemma are found in the writings of classical philosophers. Their writings indicate that the proposed problem was perplexing to them and was commonly discussed by others of their time as well." (WK 2014ww)

For instance, "Aristotle (384–322 BC) was puzzled by the idea that there could be a first bird or egg and concluded that both the bird and egg must have always existed: 'If there has been a first man he must have been born without father or mother—which is repugnant to nature. For there could not have been a first egg to give a beginning to birds, or there should have been a first bird which gave a beginning to eggs; for a bird comes from an egg.'" (WK 2014ww)

Later, "Plutarch (46–126) referred to a hen rather than simply a bird. Plutarch discussed a series of arguments based on questions posed in a symposium. Under the section entitled 'Whether the hen or the egg came first,' the discussion is introduced in such a way suggesting that the origin of the dilemma was even older," as he wrote: "[T]he problem about the egg and the hen, which of them came first, was dragged into our talk, a difficult problem which gives investigators much trouble. And Sulla my comrade said that with a small problem, as with a tool, we were rocking loose a great and heavy one, that of the creation of the world..." (WK 2014ww; Plutarch 1976; G. Renaud 2005)

In modern times, "Stephen Hawking [2012] and Christopher Langan argue that the egg came before the chicken, though the real importance of the question has faded since Darwin's *On the Origin of Species* and the accompanying *Theory of Evolution*, under which the egg must have come first," but this is question-begging, since the answer assumes "the question intended 'egg' to mean an egg in general rather than an egg that hatches into a chicken." (WK 2014ww)

Eternal Return and the Chicken-and-Egg Problem

In any event, in philosophy, "the question about the first chicken or egg also evoked the questions of how life and the universe in general began," and a good illustration here concerns the age-old idea of "eternal return."

For instance, "in Buddhism, Hinduism, as well as other Dharmic religions, there is the belief of the wheel of time which regards time as cyclical and with repeating ages, as some other cultures such as Mesoamerican (Aztecs, Mayan) and some native American Indians believe. Their idea of time gives a different answer to the question of 'who is first.' The concept of *eternal return*, which is well known in the Western culture through the writings of Nietzsche indicates that there is repetition of time. The assumption is that time is eternally repetitive, and therefore, there is no 'first' in eternity; there is no creation. The answer then becomes: neither the egg nor the chicken is first. There is no 'first' in a cyclical view of time." (WK 2014ww)

For illustration, let's consider how the idea of "eternal return" can resolve the chicken-and-egg problem from the three perspectives of (a) religion, (b) philosophy, and (c) cosmology (as summarized in *Table 3.7*).

(a) In Religion
In religion, there are different answers to the question.
(a1) Indian Religions
For instance, in Indian religions, "the concept of cyclical patterns is very prominent in...Jainism, Hinduism, Sikhism and Buddhism among others. The wheel of life represents an endless cycle of birth, life, and death from which one seeks liberation. In Tantric Buddhism, a wheel of time concept known as the Kalachakra expresses the idea of an endless cycle of existence and knowledge." (WK 2014aa; A. Thalheimer 2012)
(a2) Judaism
And in Judaism, there is "a creation narrative 'In the beginning' and a redeemed 'Olam Haba' at the end, which means Judaism has a linear, not a cyclical, view of time. But cyclical time and return are reflected in Jewish

traditions such as: The history of the Jewish people is said to repeat events that occurred in the lives of its biblical forefathers; people's lives in the next world, or after death, are to some extent spiritual repetitions of what they did in this world; and some kabbalists wrote that time is composed of seven cycles, which repeat every seven thousand years (a view rejected by Isaac Luria). These concepts give human choices to do good deeds in *Olam HaZeh*—'this world'—some of what Nietzsche called the eternal recurrence's 'infinite weight.'" (WK 2014aa; Z. Golan 2007)

(b) In Philosophy

In philosophy, one of the most influential pieces on "eternal return" is the work by Friedrich Nietzsche.

(b1) The Work of Friedrich Nietzsche

Martin Heidegger (1984) once pointed out in his lectures on Nietzsche that "Nietzsche's first mention of eternal recurrence, in aphorism 341 of *The Gay Science,*...presents this concept as a hypothetical question rather than postulating it as a fact. According to Heidegger, it is the burden imposed by the question of eternal recurrence—whether or not such a thing could possibly be true—that is so significant in modern thought," because "the way Nietzsche here patterns the first communication of the thought of the 'greatest burden' [of eternal recurrence] makes it clear that this 'thought of thoughts' is at the same time 'the most burdensome thought.'" (WK 2014aa)

More specifically, "Nietzsche sums up his thought most succinctly when he addresses the reader with: 'Everything has returned. Sirius, and the spider, and thy thoughts at this moment, and this last thought of thine that all things will return.'" (WK 2014aa)

But "Nietzsche calls the idea 'horrifying and paralyzing,' referring to it as a burden of the 'heaviest weight' ('das schwerste Gewicht') imaginable. He professes that the wish for the eternal return of all events would mark the ultimate affirmation of life." (WK 2014aa; M. Kundera 1999)

In the end, to Nietzsche, "to comprehend eternal recurrence in his thought, and to not merely come to peace with it but to embrace it, requires *amor fati*, 'love of fate.'" (WK 2014aa; W. Dudley 2002)

(c) In Cosmology

And in cosmology, there are likewise different speculaive answers to the question.

For instance, in quantum cosmology, "there are now many different speculative big bang scenarios...which actually imply eternal return—although based on other assumptions than Nietzsche's." (WK 2014aa) (c1) The Oscillating Universe Theory

A good case in point is "the oscillating universe theory" dating from the 1930, which states "that the universe will end in a collapse or 'big crunch' followed by another big bang, and so on....Cosmologists such as professor Alexander Vilenkin from Tufts University and Massachusetts Institute of Technology professor Max Tegmark suggest that if space is sufficiently large and uniform, or infinite as some theories suggest, and if quantum theory is true such that there is only a finite number of configurations within a finite volume possible, due to Heisenberg's uncertainty principle, then identical instances of the history of Earth's entire Hubble volume occur every so often, *simply by chance.*" (WK 2014aa; A. Vilenkin 2006)

(c2) The Steinhardt–Turok Model

And in another cosmological theory known as the Steinhardt–Turok model, "two parallel orbifold planes or M-branes collide periodically in a higher dimensional space. The visible four-dimensional universe lies on one of these branes. The collisions correspond to a reversal from contraction to expansion, or a big crunch followed immediately by a big bang. The matter and radiation we see today were generated during the most recent collision in a pattern dictated by quantum fluctuations created before the branes. After billions of years the universe reached the state we observe today; after additional billions of years it will ultimately begin to contract again. Dark energy corresponds to a force between the branes, and serves the crucial role of solving the monopole, horizon, and flatness problems. Moreover the cycles can continue indefinitely into the past and the future, and the solution is an attractor, so it can provide a complete history of the universe." (WK 2014xx; P. Steinhardt 2004)

Problems with the Study on Eternal Return

However, to the critics, this study on effect, chicken-and-egg problem, and eternal return has some major problems. Consider, for illustration, a few examples below (as summarized in *Table 3.7*).

Firstly, one main criticism of the study on effect, the chicken-and-egg problem, and eternal return is that there are conflicting answers to the question over the centuries.

For example, on the one hand, "a literal answer is an egg according to some people, as egg-laying species pre-date the existence of chickens"; on the other hand, "to others, the chicken came first, seeing as chickens are merely domesticated Red Junglefowls." (WK 2014ww) And those who believe in "eternal return" simply assume that "time is eternally repetitive, and therefore, there is no 'first' in eternity; there is no creation. The answer then becomes: neither the egg nor the chicken is first." (WK 2014ww)

Secondly, another main criticism of the study on effect, the chicken-and-egg problem, and eternal return is that an eternally recurrent life is not necessarily desirable.

For instance, according to an interpretation of Nietzsche's thought, even Nietzsche himself was turned off by this potentially negative implicaiton of an eternally recurrent life, because "a late 1880s comment by Nietzsche, 'In an infinite period of time, every possible combination would at some time be attained,' has been cited to argue that Nietzsche dropped his plans to try to scientifically prove the theory because he realized that if he would have to eventually repeat life as it is, his presumption of infinite time means 'he' would also have to 'repeat' life differently, since every configuration of atoms and events will occur." (WK 2014aa; Z. Golan 2007)

Thirdly, still another main criticism of the study on effect, the chicken-and-egg problem, and eternal return is that the answers are often highly speculative, without any proof.

For instance, in regard to "the oscillating universe theory" aforediscussed, "it would be impossible to scientifically verify an identical Hubble volume" as needed, and "science would consider a multiverse theory that posits neither a common point of causation, nor the possibility of interaction between universes, to be an ideal speculation." (WK 2014aa) And in regard to the Steinhardt–Turok model, "there remain major open issues in the model. Foremost among them is that colliding branes are not understood by string theorists, and nobody knows if the scale invariant spectrum will be destroyed by the big crunch. Moreover, as with cosmic inflation, while the general character of the forces (in the ekpyrotic scenario, a force between branes) required to create the vacuum fluctuations is known, there is no candidate from particle physics." (WK 2014xx; P. Woit 2006)

Fourthly, an additional main criticism of the study on effect, the chicken-and-egg problem, and eternal return is that the idea of eternal return has been misused for religious purposes.

For instance, to the critics, "in their book *Godhead*, authors Griffin [2011] and Tyrrell present the ancient idea of the oscillating universe—oscillating between the poles of pure awareness and pure energy—in a manner that is not inconsistent with the modern understanding of physics. They state the problem thus: '...physicists say the singularity came out of nothing, but cannot explain how both energy and information can arise out of nothing.' They explain nothingness as total energy restrained by total information, summed up in the expression: ti + te = 0; where energy is defined as omnidirectional force and information as that which restrains energy. Nothing, therefore, contains within it all energy and all information; the state of nothing continuously deconstructs into fields of energy and information even as everything continues to return to the state of nothing: '...the totality of all knowledge restraining the totality of all energy would cancel each other out. That would leave us with nothing...This is the answer to where information and energy come from: the nothing state has always contained them. It's when this nothing state automatically deconstructs...that the different levels of information and energy—the visible and invisible forces of the Universe—manifest.' The Godhead, they claim, is the religio-mystical representation of this nothing out of which all things continuously emerge." (WK 2014aa)

And fifthly, another additional main criticism of the study on effect, the chicken-and-egg problem, and eternal return is that the idea of "eternal return" has been proved to be implausible.

For instance, to the critics, "Nietzsche scholar Walter Kaufmann [1974] has described an argument originally put forward by Georg Simmel, which rebuts the claim that a finite number of states must repeat within an infinite amount of time," because, as he wrote, "even if there were exceedingly few things in a finite space in an infinite time, they would not have to repeat in the same configurations. Suppose there were three wheels of equal size, rotating on the same axis, one point marked on the circumference of each wheel, and these three points lined up in one straight line. If the second wheel rotated twice as fast as the first, and if the speed of the third wheel was $1/\pi$ of the speed of the first, the initial line-up would never recur." (WK 2014aa) Therefore, "a system could have an infinite number of distinct physical configurations that never recur. However the example presupposes the possibility of perfect continuity: for instance, if the universe proves to have a quantum foam nature, then the exact quantity of an irrational number cannot be expressed by any physical object." (WK 2014aa)

Beyond Eternal Return

These criticisms of the analysis of effect, the chicken-and-egg problem, and eternal return should not be misunderstood as a total rejection of its usefulness but serve to show us the two opposing sides of the debate, such that the possibility (or impossibility) and desirability (or undesirability) of effect (from the perspective of culture with effect, the chicken-and-egg problem, and eternal return as a case study here) are not to the extent that the respective defenders would like us to believe.

Moreover, the analysis of effect, the chicken-and-egg problem, and eternal return is useful for the understanding of the ontological principles in existential dialectics, and good examples include the formalness-informalness principle, the absoluteness-relativeness principle, the partiality-totality principle, the predictability-unpredictability principle, the explicability-inexplicability principle, the fiction-reality principle, the cognitiveness-noncognitiveness principle, the finiteness-transfiniteness principle, the preciseness-vagueness principle, the simpleness-complicatedness principle, the openness-hiddenness principle, the denseness-emptiness principle, the rule-exception principle, the indispensability-dispensability principle, the prototypicality-variation principle, the change-constancy principle, the order-chaos principle, the slowness-quickness principle, the expansion-contraction principle, the optimality-nonoptimality principle, the simultaneity-nonsimultaneity principle, the isolation-interaction principle, the theory-praxis principle, the convention-novelty principle, the evolution-transformation principle, the symmetry-asymmetry principle, the softness-hardness principle, the seriousness-playfulness principle, the activeness-inactivess principle, the selfness-otherness principle, the regression-progression principle, the same-difference principle, the stability-reaction principle, the functionality-nonfunctionality principle, the intentionality-nonintentionality principle. the survivability-non-survivability principle, and the materiality-nonmateriality principle.

For instance, in relation to the formalness-informalness principle, if there is formalness (e.g., the formal logical requirement of soundness, completeness, and consistency in a system of ideas, as in the argument on eternal return), there is informalness (e.g., the non-formal existence of unsoundness, incompleteness, and inconsistency in the argument on eternal return, as shown in the criticisms that there are conflicting answers to the question over the centuries, that an eternally recurrent life is not necessarily desirable, that the answers are often highly speculative without any proof, that the idea of eternal return has been misused for religious purposes, and that the idea of "eternal return" has been proved to be implausible). And the reverse direction also holds true.

In relation to the absoluteness-relativeness principle, if there is absoluteness (e.g., the absolute view on "Godhead" by the advocates of a different version of eternal return), there is relativeness (e.g., what is right for the advocates of a different version of eternal return in regard to "Godhead" is not necessarily so for the critics, because it is "not inconsistent with the modern understanding of physics"). And the reverse direction also holds true.

In relation to the partiality-totality principle, if there is partiality (e.g., the partial view on "the chicken-and-egg problem" by the advocates of "the egg comes first"), there is totality (e.g., the more holistic view on "the chicken-and-egg problem," such that the whole is not the sum of its parts, that is, it cannot be reduced to the sum of opposing views by the advocates of "the egg comes first," the advocates of "the chicken comes first," and the advocates of "neither comes first," as discussed earlier, since there will emerge new views in the future not yet known today, just as there are already alternative views nowadays which do not side exclusively with any of them, as is the analysis here). And the reverse direction also holds true.

In relation to the predictability-unpredictability principle, if there is predictability (e.g., the predictable tendency that there are different answers to "the chicken-and-egg problem" in the foreseeable future), there is unpredictability (e.g., the more difficult task to predict exactly the extent to which a particular answer to "the chicken-and-egg problem" will become dominant in a particular future era). And the reverse direction also holds true.

In relation to the explicability-inexplicability principle, if there is explicability (e.g., the explanation, by those advocates of "Godhead," of its validity on the basis of "ti + te = 0," in that "nothing, therefore, contains within it all energy and all information; the state of nothing" at the beginning), there is inexplicability (e.g., the lack of sufficient explanation, by those advocates of "Godhead," of why "ti + te = 0," is necessarily true, since, to the critics, it "is not inconsistent with the modern understanding of physics"). And the reverse direction also holds true.

In relation to the fiction-reality principle, if there is fiction (e.g., the fictional aspect of eternal return, insofar as "Georg Simmel...rebuts the claim that a finite number of states must repeat within an infinite amount of time," because, "if the second wheel rotated twice as fast as the first, and if the speed of the third wheel was $1/\pi$ of the speed of the first, the initial line-up would never recur"), there is reality (e.g., the realistic aspect of eternal return, insofar as, "related to the concept of eternal return is the Poincaré recurrence theorem in mathematics," which "states that a system whose dynamics are volume-preserving and which is confined to a finite spatial volume will, after a sufficiently long time, return to an arbitrarily small neighborhood of its initial state"). (WK 2014aa) And the reverse direction also holds true.

In relation to the cognitiveness-noncognitiveness principle, if there is cognitiveness (e.g., a view of things on the basis of reason and evidences, as shown in the empirical finding that there are different answers to "the chicken-and-egg problem" aforecited), there is noncognitiveness (e.g., a view of things on the basis of non-cognitive factors like envy, jealousy, power, nationality, race, gender, age, class, greed, lust, status, faith, anger, sadness, joy, fear, wish, etc.—as shown in the continued "faith" in "Godhead" by the believers, in spite of the fact that it is "not inconsistent with the modern understanding of physics" and has been rejected by mainstream scientists). And the reverse direction also holds true.

In relation to the finiteness-transfiniteness principle, if there is finiteness (e.g., the finite number of the categories of things in the universe, like "energy," "information," "matter," etc., which can recur, in according to the idea of eternal return), there is transfiniteness (e.g., the transfinite number of all the individual bits, joules, and objects, in respect to info, energy, and matter, that have ever existed in history, regardless of whether they will recur or not in future returns). And the reverse direction also holds true.

In relation to the preciseness-vagueness principle, if there is preciseness (e.g., the precise identification of 2 types of entities in "nothing," like "info" and "energy," by the authors of "Godhead"), there is vagueness (e.g., the vagueness in the identification of the 2 types of entities in "nothing," like "info" and "energy," by the authors of "Godhead," since it is not clear why there must be only 2, not 3, 4, 5, 6, and so on). And the reverse direction also holds true.

In relation to the simpleness-complicatedness principle, if there is simpleness (e.g., the relatively simple analysis of "eternal return" by the advocates), there is complicatedness (e.g., the relatively more complicated analysis of "eternal return," by challenging the claims and assumptions, as shown in the problems pointed out by the critics as cited). And the reverse direction also holds true.

In relation to the openness-hiddenness principle, if there is openness (e.g., the open exploration of "eternal return" by cosmological theories like "the oscillating universe theory" and "the Steinhardt–Turok model"), there is hiddenness (e.g., the hidden bias in the open exploration of "eternal return" by cosmological theories like "the oscillating universe theory" and "the Steinhardt–Turok model," since these theories have been critcized as highly speculative without any proof). And the reverse direction also holds true.

In relation to the denseness-emptiness principle, if there is denseness (e.g., the relatively denser concentration of concerns with "eternal return" by Nietzsche), there is emptiness (e.g., the relatively less dense, or more empty, concentration of concerns with the second law of thermodynamics for increasing entropy in the universe by Nietzsche). And the reverse direction also holds true.

In relation to the rule-exception principle, if there are rules (e.g., the usual generalization, procedure, habit, or tendency that, in general, "with the decline of antiquity and the spread of Christianity, the concept [of eternal return] fell into disuse in the Western world"), there are exceptions (e.g., a case to which a rule does not apply, such as "the exception of Friedrich Nietzsche, who connected the thought to many of his other concepts, including *amor fati*," even though at the time, "with the decline of antiquity and the spread of Christianity, the concept [of eternal return] fell into disuse in the Western world"). (WK 2014aa) And the reverse direction also holds true.

In relation to the indispensability-dispensability principle, if there is indispensability (e.g., the need for something or someone, like the necessary inclusion of *"amor fati,* 'love of fate'" to deal with "eternal return," according to Nietzsche), there is dispensability (e.g., the superfluity of something or someone, like the dispensable inclusion of the proof for "eternal return," since, "according to Heidegger, it is the burden imposed by the question of eternal recurrence," but not "whether or not such a thing could possibly be true," that is so important for Nietzsche). And the reverse direction also holds true.

In relation to the prototypicality-variation principle, if there is prototypicality (e.g., the prototype, like the example about the original work on eternal return by Nietzsche), there is variation (e.g., different variants of the protoptye, as shown in many studies since the original work on eternal return by Nietzsche—like the later ones by Martin Heidegger, Rudolf Steiner, Walter Kaufmann, etc., commenting on Nietzsche's work, though each with its own variation, contribution, and disagreement). And the reverse direction also holds true.

In relation to the change-constancy principle, if there is change (e.g., the ever new ways to study cause and effect, as shown in the research on eternal return), there is constancy (e.g., the ever constant existence of different problems with the ever new ways to study cause and effect, as shown in the problems with the research on eternal return pointed out by the critics). And the reverse direction also holds true.

In relation to the order-chaos principle, if there is order (e.g., the more or less orderly view on the universe, if looked from the sole vantage point of "eternal return" by the advocates), there is chaos (e.g., the more or less chaotic view on the universe, if looked from the multiple conflicting vantage points of "eternal return," "increasing entropy" in the 2nd law of thermodynamics, etc., by both the advocates and the critics, especially in regard to the different problems aforecited, such that they do not add up to much of anything coherent). And the reverse direction also holds true.

In relation to the slowness-quickness principle, if there is slowness (e.g., the relatively slower speed of the universe to end in a collapse or "big crunch" in our time, because there is still a long way to go before its final acceleration, according to "the oscillating universe theory"), there is quickness (e.g., the relatively quicker speed of the universe to end in a collapse or "big crunch" in its final moments of acceleration, according to "the oscillating universe theory"). And the reverse direction also holds true.

In relation to the expansion-contraction principle, if there is expansion (e.g., the expansion of the universe after the "big bang," according to the "big bang" theory), there is contraction (e.g., according to the oscillating universe theory, "the universe will end in a collapse or 'big crunch'"). And the reverse direction also holds true.

In relation to the optimality-nonoptimality principle, if there is optimality (e.g., the search for highly favorable options, like the quest for the understanding of "every possible combination [of life events]" which "would at some time be attained" in "an infinite period of time," in the "eternal return" as proposed by Nietzsche), there is nonoptimality (e.g., the existence of non-optimal alternatives to optimality, like the argument for more realistic studies by the critics, who pointed out different probems with the "eternal return" as proposed by Nietzsche, as discussed earlier). And the reverse direction also holds true.

In relation to the simultaneity-nonsimultaneity principle, if there is simultaneity (e.g., the occurrence of different things more or less at the same time, such as the simultaneous existence of "two parallel orbifold planes or M-branes," which "collide periodically in a higher dimensional space," according to the Steinhardt–Turok model), there is nonsimultaneity (e.g., the occurrence of something after something else, such as "the collision" between "two parallel orbifold planes or M-branes," such that there will be "a big crunch followed immediately by a big bang," according to the Steinhardt–Turok model). And the reverse direction also holds true.

In relation to the isolation-interaction principle, if there is isolation (e.g., the state of a situation that is separate from others, such as the isolation of "the visible four-dimensional universe" of ours prior to its collision with other "parallel orbifold planes or M-branes" in due time, according to the Steinhardt–Turok model), there is interaction (e.g., the influence of entities on one another, such as the interaction between "two parallel orbifold planes or M-branes" when they collide, according to the Steinhardt–Turok model). And the reverse direction also holds true.

In relation to the theory-praxis principle, if there is theory (e.g., the theoretical construction of "eternal return" in the field of cosmology), there is praxis (e.g., the practical application of "eternal return" in the field of cosmology to the field of religion, like "Godhead" by Griffin and Tyrrell for a "religio-mystical representation" of the fate of the universe). And the reverse direction also holds true.

In relation to the convention-novelty principle, if there is convention (e.g., the conventional wisdom about the big bang theory," which "in the framework of relativistic cosmology seems to be at odds with eternal return" in the older days), there is novelty (e.g., the alternative novel challenge to the conventional wisdom about the big bang theory," which "in the framework of relativistic cosmology seems to be at odds with eternal return" in the older days—by the new ideas nowadays, in terms of "many different speculative big bang scenarios in quantum cosmology which actually imply eternal return"). And the reverse direction also holds true.

In relation to the evolution-transformation principle, if there is evolution (e.g., the natural evolution of humans to live on this planet Earth as part of the larger universe), there is transformation (e.g., the technical transformation of human ability to deal with the fate of the universe by the invention of "cosmology" like different ideas of "eternal return"). And the reverse direction also holds true.

In relation to the symmetry-asymmetry principle, if there is symmetry (e.g., the co-existence of different versions of "eternal return," like Jainism in India and modern scientific cosmologies in the U.S. as discussed earlier), there is asymmetry (e.g., the Jainist version of "eternal return" is more accepted in India—but the modern scientific cosmological versions of "eternal return" as discussed earlier are more accepted in the U.S.). And the reverse direction also holds true.

In relation to the softness-hardness principle, if there is softness (e.g., the defense of "eternal return" by the advocates like Nietzsche), there is hardness (e.g., the critique of "eternal return," as shown in the problems pointed out by the critics aforecited). And the reverse direction also holds true.

In relation to the seriousness-playfulness principle, if there is seriousness (e.g., the serious business of those who try to understand the fate of the universe), there is playfulness (e.g., the playful part of those who try to understand the fate of the universe, when they play around with different versions of "eternal return" over the centures in philosophy, religion, and cosmology, as discussed earlier). And the reverse direction also holds true.

In relation to the activeness-inactivess principle, if there is activeness (e.g., the relative activeness of the idea of "eternal return" in the modern Western philosopical tradition, when Friedrich Nietzsche contributed to its re-introduction by connecting "the thought to many of his other concepts, including *amor fati*"), there is inactiveness (e.g., the relative inactiveness of the idea of "eternal return," when, "with the decline of antiquity and the spread of Christianity, the concept [of eternal return] fell into disuse in the Western world" until the modern era). (WK 2014aa) And the reverse direction also holds true.

In relation to the selfness-otherness principle, if there is selfness (e.g., the tendency to be mostly centered on one's self or group, as shown in the self-interest of Nietzsche when he "dropped his plans to try to scientifically prove the theory because he realized that if he would have to eventually repeat life as it is, his presumption of infinite time means 'he' would also have to 'repeat' life differently"), there is otherness (e.g., the tendency to be mostly centered on others, as shown in the academic analysis of both sides of the debate on "eternal return," as an advancement in the knowledge of the fate of the universe for humanity). And the reverse direction also holds true.

In relation to the regression-progression principle, if there is regression (e.g., the regression made by the idea of "eternal return," as shown in the problems pointed out by the critics), there is progression (e.g., the progress made by the idea of "eternal return," as shown in the contribution to the understanding of the fate of the universe aforecited). And the reverse direction also holds true.

In relation to the same-difference principle, if there is similarity in outcome (e.g., the contribution to the molding and control of beliefs, values, and behaviors, regardless of whether this be done by way of the acceptance of the "oscillating universe theory," or by way of the acceptance of the "Godhead" theory), there is difference in outcome (e.g., the contribution to the molding and control of beliefs, values, and behaviors by way of the acceptance of the "oscillating universe theory" for a relatively more scientific worldview—but the contribution to the molding and control of beliefs, values, and behaviors by way of the acceptance of the "Godhead" theory for a relatively more religio-mystical worldview). And the reverse direction also holds true.

In relation to the stability-reaction principle, if there is stability (e.g., the relatively more stable condition of "the big bang theory in the framework of relativistic cosmology" which "seems to be at odds with eternal return" in the older days), there is reaction (e.g., "the big bang theory in the framework of relativistic cosmology" which "seems to be at odds with eternal return" in the older days then led to further changes later on, when "there are now many different speculative big bang scenarios in quantum cosmology which actually imply eternal return"). And the reverse direction also holds true.

In relation to the functionality-nonfunctionality principle, if there is functionality (e.g., the presence of action for which something or someone is fitted, as shown in the idea of "eternal return," which serves the function of accounting for the future fate of the universe), there is nonfunctionality (e.g., the relative lack of action for which something or someone is fitted, as shown in the different problems with the idea of "eternal return," such that it is not as functional as the advocates would like us to believe). And the reverse direction also holds true.

In relation to the intentionality-nonintentionality principle, if there is intentionality (e.g., the planning or design of something for a certain outcome, as shown in the intended consequences, in regard to the big bang theory about "the singularity point" coming "out of nothing" at the beginning of the universe, as those who used it intended to explain the origin of the universe and its subsequent expansion in this way), there is nonintentionality (e.g., the relative absence of planning or design of something for a certain outcome, such that the outcome can even be counter-intentional in being the opposite of what was originally planned, as shown in the re-interpretation, by Griffin and Tyrrell, of "nothing" with "all energy and all information" for a "religio-mysical view of "Godhead"—contrary to the original intention of those who proposed the big bang theory for a more secular interpretation). And the reverse direction also holds true.

In relation to the survivability-nonsurvivability principle, if there is survivability (e.g., the relative survival, nowadays, of the big bang theory, as shown in "different speculative big bang scenarios in quantum cosmology which actually imply eternal return"), there is non-survivability (e.g., the relative non-survival, nowadays, of the faith in the "scarab [or dung beetle]," which "was viewed as a sign of eternal renewal and reemergence of life, a reminder of the life to come," in ancient Egypt). (WK 2014aa) And the reverse direction also holds true.

And in relation to the materiality-nonmateriality principle, if there is materiality (e.g., the material outcome in relation to space-time, matter-energy, Having, etc., like the use of the big bang theory on the basis of the oscillating universe model by Vilenkin and Tegmark, to provide a secular interpretation of the fate of the universe), there is non-materiality (e.g., the nonmaterial outcome in relation to the quest for Being, Belonging, etc., like the spiritual search among humans for supernatural entities, like the re-interpretation, by Griffin and Tyrrell, of the big bang theory on the basis of coming out of "nothing" with "all energy and all information" for a "religio-mysical view of "Godhead"). And the reverse direction also holds true.

The Impotency of Effect

This comprehensive analysis of the possibility (or impossibility) and desirability (or undesirability) of effect in the context of etiology, from the perspectives of the mind, nature, society, and culture, is important to show us the different ways in which effect is both possible and desirable, but not to the extent that the spokespersons from each side would like us to believe.

Thus, effect thus has its potency, just as it has its impotency too, as the other side of the same coin.

And the other side of the story concerns cause, the opposite of effect, but it was already dealt with in the previous chapter (chapter Two).

Again, these dual analyses should not be underestimated, because those on the side of cause often downgrade effect merely as the receiving end of causation without really appreciating it from the vantage point of effect too—and vice versa.

Now that this long treatise on cause and effect comes to an end, what then can be concluded about their future? This is the question, whose answer is to be given in the concluding chapter, Chapter Four, for the future of etiology—for which we now turn to next chapter.

Table 3.1. Effect and its Ambivalence

• **Effect and the Mind**
  —Ex: effect, medicine, and adverse effect
  —Ex: effect, intentionality, and consequences

• **Effect and Nature**
  —Ex: effect, nature, and chaos theory
  —Ex: effect, quantum physics, and Zeno effect

• **Effect and Society**
  —Ex: effect, politics, and domino theory
  —Ex: effect, business, and effectuation

• **Effect and Culture**
  —Ex: effect, philosophy, and determinism
  —Ex: effect, the chicken-and-egg problem, and eternal return

Notes: The examples in the categories are solely illustrative (not exhaustive), and the comparison is relative (not absolute), nor are they necessarily mutually exclusive. And some can be easily re-classified elsewhere. As generalities, they allow exceptions.
Source: A summary of Ch.3 of *FPHETIO*

Table 3.2. Effect, Medicine, and Adverse Effect

• **Reporting Systems of Adverse Effects**
  —Ex: United Kingdom
  —Ex: United States
  —Ex: Australia
  —Ex: New Zealand
  —Ex: Canada

• **Situations of Adverse Effects**
  —Ex: medical procedures
  —Ex: drug reaction

• **Problems with the Study on Medicine and Adverse Effect**
  —Firstly, the claim for "adverse effect" can be controversially false.
  —Secondly, the claim for "adverse effect" can be exaggerated, without putting the cost-benefit analysis in a proper perspective.
  —Thirdly, adverse effects can be psychological.
  —Fourthly, adverse effects can be ambiguous.
  —Fifthly, there can be beneficial side-effects too.
  —Sixthly, there is no universal definition of "adverse effect."
  —And seventhly, reporting systems of adverse effects are not often effective.

Notes: The examples in the categories are solely illustrative (not exhaustive), and the comparison is relative (not absolute), nor are they necessarily mutually exclusive. And some can be easily re-classified elsewhere. As generalities, they allow exceptions.
Source: From *Sec. 3.2.1* of *FPHETIO*. See book for citations.

Table 3.3. Effect, Intentionality, and Consequences

- **Causes of Unintended Consequences**
    —Ex: "ignorance"
    —Ex: "error"
    —Ex: "immediate interest"
    —Ex: "basic values"
    —Ex: "self-defeating prophecy"

- **Types of Unintended Consequences**
    —Ex: "unexpected benefits"
    —Ex: "unexpected drawbacks"
    —Ex: "perverse effects"

- **Problems with the Study on Intentionality and Consequences**
    —Firstly, one main criticism of the study on effect, intentionality, and consequences is that Merton did not focus enough on what exactly is meant by "intentionality," since "unintentional" in "unintended
    —Secondly, another main criticism of the study on effect, intentionality, and consequences is that it does not distinguish between something ("non- intentional") and something ('unintentional'), so what is "not intentional" does not necessarily mean "unintentional."
    —Thirdly, still another main criticism of the study on effect, intentionality, and consequences is that Merton's conception of social action is narrow.
    —Fourthly, an additional main criticism of the study on effect, intentionality, and consequences is that the world is too complex to have only 5 causes of unintended consequences as suggested by Merton.
    —And fifthly, another additional main criticism of the study on effect, intentionality, and consequences is that it is not clear if the third type, "perverse results," is redundant.

Notes: The examples in the categories are solely illustrative (not exhaustive), and the comparison is relative (not absolute), nor are they necessarily mutually exclusive. And some can be easily re-classified elsewhere. As generalities, they allow exceptions.
Source: From *Sec. 3.2.2* of *FPHETIO*. See book for citations.

Table 3.4. Effect, Nature, and Chaos Theory

• **History of Two Classics of Chaos Theory**
—Ex: the work of Edward Lorenz
—Ex: the work of Benoit Mandelbrot

• **Properties of Chaotic Dynamics**
—Ex: sensitivity to initial conditions
—Ex: topological mixing
—Ex: density of periodic orbits
—Ex: strange attractors
—Ex: minimum complexity of a chaotic system

• **Problems with the Study on Nature and Chaos theory**
—Firstly, one main criticism of the argument on effect, nature, and chaos theory is that the so-called "butterfly effect" is much exaggerated.
—Secondly, another main criticism of the argument on effect, nature, and chaos theory is that the so-called "butterfly effect" misleadingly exclude some other effects in its analysis.
—Thirdly, still another main criticism of the study on effect, nature, and chaos theory is that the property of "sensitivity to initial conditions" can be redundant.
—Fourthly, an additional main criticism of the study on effect, nature, and chaos theory is that the butterfly effect can be countered by more complicated forecasting systems.
—Fifthly, another additional main criticism of the study on effect, nature, and chaos theory is that the butterfly effect does not apply in some situations.
—And sixthly, still another additional main criticism of the study on effect, nature, and chaos theory is that there is no universal definition of "chaos" in chaos theory.

Notes: The examples in the categories are solely illustrative (not exhaustive), and the comparison is relative (not absolute), nor are they necessarily mutually exclusive. And some can be easily re-classified elsewhere. As generalities, they allow exceptions.
Source: From *Sec. 3.3.1* of *FPHETIO*. See book for citations.

Table 3.5. Effect, Business, and Effectuation

• **Process of Effectuation**
—Ex: "who they are—their traits, tastes and abilities"
—Ex: "what they know—their education, training, expertise, and experience"
—Ex: "whom they know—their social and professional networks"

• **Principles of Effectuation**
—Ex: "the affordable loss principle"
—Ex: "the strategic partnerships principle"
—Ex: "the leveraging contingencies principle"

• **Problems with the Study on Business and Effectuation**
—Firstly, it does not give sufficient attention to "optimality."
—Secondly, Sarasvathy's analysis often portrays "effectuation" in more favorable light than "causal reasoning" in a biased way.
—Thirdly, it is msileading to say that effectual reasoning, unlike causal reasoning, does not start with any goal in mind.
—Fourthly, it is more risk-adverse than the alternative causal process and thus can impose a greater limit on potential return.
—Fifthly, effectuation is more subjectively disposed towards "cooperation" than towards "competition."
—Sixthly, it is inherently more concerned with "people" than with outcome ("effect").
—And seventhly, its application is more relevant for business startups (than for established businesses).

Notes: The examples in the categories are solely illustrative (not exhaustive), and the comparison is relative (not absolute), nor are they necessarily mutually exclusive. And some can be easily re-classified elsewhere. As generalities, they allow exceptions.
Source: From *Sec. 3.4.2* of *FPHETIO*. See book for citations.

Table 3.6. Effect, Philosophy, and Determinism

• **Philosopical Connections of Causal Determnism**
  —Ex: with the nature/nurture controversy
  —Ex: with a particular factor
  —Ex: with ethics

• **Cultural Traditions of Causal Determnism**
  —Ex: in the Eastern tradition
  —Ex: in the Western tradition

• **Scientific Perspectives of Causal Determnism**
  — Ex: generative processes
  — Ex: mathematical models
  — Ex: day-to-day physics
  — Ex: quantum realm

• **Problems with the Study on Philosophy and Determinism**
  —Firstly, one main criticism of this argument on effect, philosophy, and determinism is that there are alternative theories to determinism.
  —Secondly, another main criticism of this argument on effect, philosophy, and determinism is that there are competing (even opposing) versions of determinism among the proponents themselves.
  —Thirdly, still another main criticism of the study on effect, philosophy, and determinism is that causal determinism has been criticized as empirically false.
  —Fourthly, an additional main criticism of the study on effect, philosophy, and determinism is that causal determinism is too "materialistic."
  —And fifthly, another additional main criticism of the study on effect, philosophy, and determinism is that the idea of determinism has been misused for religious purposes.

Notes: The examples in the categories are solely illustrative (not exhaustive), and the comparison is relative (not absolute), nor are they necessarily mutually exclusive. And some can be easily re-classified elsewhere. As generalities, they allow exceptions.
Source: From *Sec. 3.5.1* of *FPHETIO*. See book for citations.

Table 3.7. Effect, the Chicken-and-Egg Problem, and Eternal Return

• **Introduction to the Chicken-and-Egg Problem**
—Ex: concept
—Ex: history

• **Eternal Return and the Chicken-and-Egg Problem**
—In religion
  • Ex: Indian Religions
  • Ex: Judaism
—In philosophy
  • Ex: the work of Friedrich Nietzsche
—In cosmology
  • Ex: the Oscillating Universe theory
  • Ex: the Steinhardt–Turok model

• **Problems with the Study on Eternal Return**
—Firstly, one main criticism of the study on effect, the chicken-and-egg problem, and eternal return is that there are conflicting answers to the question over the centuries.
—Secondly, another main criticism of the study on effect, the chicken-and-egg problem, and eternal return is that an eternally recurrent life is not necessarily desirable.
—Thirdly, still another main criticism of the study on effect, the chicken-and-egg problem, and eternal return is that the answers are often highly speculative, without any proof.
—Fourthly, an additional main criticism of the study on effect, the chicken-and-egg problem, and eternal return is that the idea of eternal return has been misused for religious purposes.
—And fifthly, another additional main criticism of the study on effect, the chicken-and-egg problem, and eternal return is that the idea of "eternal return" has been proved to be implausible.

Notes: The examples in the categories are solely illustrative (not exhaustive), and the comparison is relative (not absolute), nor are they necessarily mutually exclusive. And some can be easily re-classified elsewhere. As generalities, they allow exceptions.
Source: From *Sec. 3.5.2* of *FPHETIO*. See book for citations.

• PART FOUR •

Conclusion

CHAPTER 4
CONCLUSION—THE FUTURE
OF ETIOLOGY

Today is yesterday's effect and tomorrow's cause
__Phillip Gribble (TH 2014b)

Beyond Cause and Effect

The analyses of cause (in Chapter Two) and effect (in Chapter Three) are valuable for the evaluation of the opposing views on etiology (and other views as already introduced in *Sec. 1.5* and the rest of the book), such that etiology (in relation to both cause and effect) are neither possible (or impossible) nor desirable (or undesirable) to the extent that the respective ideologues (on different sides) would like us to believe.

As already indicated in *Sec. 1.1*, this questioning of different opposing views on cause and effect does not mean that the study of etiology is useless, or that those diverse fields (related to etiology)—like physics, engineering, biology, philosophy, medicine, epidemiology, government, geography, spatial analysis, psychology, statistics, mathematics, economics, management, history, law, sociology, theology, and so on—are worthless. (WK 2014b & 2014c) In fact, neither of these extreme views is plausible.

Rather, this book offers an alternative (better) way to understand the future of etiology in regard to the dialectic relationship between cause and effect—while learning from different approaches in the literature but without favoring any one of them (nor integrating them, since they are not necessarily compatible with each other).

More specifically, this book offers a new theory (that is, *the pluralist theory of etiology*) to go beyond the existing approaches in a novel way. My *pluralist theory of etiology* has four major distinct features.

Firstly, my theory makes good use of all theoretical approaches to etiology in relation to cause and effect, be they about the mental argument, the natural argument, the societal argument, or the cultural argument—especially from the most comprehensive combined perspectives of the mind, nature, society, and culture (as already dealt with in Chapter Two and Chapter Three).

Secondly, just like many other theories of mine in my previous books, my theory here does not heavily favor any specific theory over others in the literature, nor trying to integrate them (as they are not necessarily compatible with each other).

Thirdly, my theory re-interprets etiology in the distinctive dialectic context of no analysis of cause without that of effect, and vice versa—to be eventually transcended altogether later.

And fourthly, it contains thirty-eight major theses, namely, (a) the first thesis: the formalness-informalness principle, (b) the second thesis: the absoluteness-relativeness principle, (c) the third thesis: the partiality-totality principle, (d) the fourth thesis: the predictability-unpredictability principle, (e) the fifth thesis: the explicability-inexplicability principle, (f) the sixth thesis: the fiction-reality principle, (g) the seventh thesis: the cognitiveness-noncognitiveness principle, (h) the eighth thesis: the finiteness-transfiniteness principle, (i) the ninth thesis: the preciseness-vagueness principle, (j) the tenth thesis: the simpleness-complicatedness principle, (k) the eleventh thesis: the openness-hiddenness principle, (l) the twelfth thesis: the denseness-emptiness principle, (m) the thirteenth thesis: the rule-exception principle, (n) the fourteenth thesis: the indispensability-dispensability principle, (o) the fifteenth thesis: the prototypicality-variation principle, (p) the sixteenth thesis: the change-constancy principle, (q) the seventeenth thesis: the order-chaos principle, (r) the eighteenth thesis: the slowness-quickness principle, (s) the nineteenth thesis: the expansion-contraction principle, (t) the twentieth thesis: the optimality-nonoptimality principle, (u) the twenty-first thesis: the simultaneity-nonsimultaneity principle, (v) the twenty-second thesis: the isolation-interaction principle, (w) the twenty-third thesis: the theory-praxis principle, (x) the twenty-fourth thesis: the convention-novelty principle, (y) the twenty-fifth thesis: the evolution-transformation principle, (z) the twenty-sixth thesis: the symmetry-asymmetry principle, (aa) the twenty-seventh thesis: the softness-hardness principle, (bb) the twenty-eighth thesis: the seriousness-playfulness principle, (cc) the twenty-ninth thesis: the activeness-inactiveness principle, (dd) the thirtieth thesis: the selfness-otherness principle, (ee) the thirty-first thesis: the regression-progression principle, (ff) the thirty-second thesis: the sameness-difference principle, (gg) the thirty-third thesis: the stability-reaction principle, (hh) the thirty-fourth thesis: the functionality-nonfunctionality principle, (ii) the thirty-fifth thesis: the intentionality-nonintentionality principle, (jj) the thirty-sixth thesis: the survivability-non-survivability principle, (kk) the thirty-seventh thesis: the materiality-nonmateriality principle, (ll) the thirty-eighth thesis: the post-human plurality—to be elaborated in the rest of the book.

Because of the last thesis on "the post-human plurality," the word "plurality" in the title of my theory is suggestive, because it refers to the dual analyses of both cause and effect in the history of etiology—which then require a multi-faceted inquiry of the dialectic relationship between cause and effect, as well as an understanding of the different views regarding the relationships in etiology (together with other debates as already discussed in the book)—and in the end it calls for a need to transcend both cause and effect by future advanced humans and later post-humans in the context of the great transformations of etiology in the future worlds (as will be discussed in this chapter).

With this clarification in mind—the seminal project here will fundamentally change the way that we think about cause and effect (especially, though not solely, in the context of etiology), together with other debates as already discussed in the book, from the combined perspectives of the mind, nature, society, and culture, with enormous implications for the human future and what I originally called its "post-human" fate.

In Relation to Method

The first seven theses are in relation to method in existential dialectics, as shown below.

1st Thesis: The Formalness-Informalness Principle

The first thesis refers to the formalness-informalness principle (on the formal requirements of logical systems) in the category of "method" in existential dialectics, which was first proposed in *FPHML* (and later, *FPHH*, *FPHGAM*, *FPHSEM*, and other books of mine), in that the formal requirements of a logical system (e.g., consistency, soundness, and completeness) have both usefulness and non-usefulness, to the extent that, if there are formal systems requiring them, there are alternative ones which do not.

The formalness-informalness principle reveals something interesting in existential dialectics, in that it goes beyond both classical and non-classical logics (while learning something from both).

Thus, it does *not* exclude classical logics but simply goes beyond both classical and non-classical logics, while learning something from each. There is no formalness without informalness—and vice versa.

For illustration, existential dialectics can make use of both classical logics under certain conditions (e.g., especially, though not exclusively, when they are clear-cut, etc.) and non-classical logics under alternative conditions (especially, though not exclusively, when they are "unknown," "irrelevant," "ambiguous," "possible," with "different degrees of truth," empirically inconsistent in a desirable way, etc.). (WK 2008u)

For instance, on the one hand, there is formalness (e.g., the formal logical requirement of soundness, completeness, and consistency in a system of ideas, as in the argument on cognitive bias and attribution, in *Sec. 2.2.1*; the formal logical requirement of soundness, completeness, and consistency in a system of ideas, as in the argument on self-fulfilling prophecy, in *Sec. 2.2.2*; the formal logical requirement of soundness, completeness, and consistency in a system of ideas, as in the argument on time's arrow and entropy, in *Sec. 2.3.1*; the formal logical requirement of soundness, completeness, and consistency in a system of ideas, as in the argument on "retrocausality," in *Sec. 2.3.2*; the formal logical requirement of soundness, completeness, and consistency in a system of ideas, as in the argument on causation and legal liability, in *Sec. 2.4.1*; the formal logical requirement of soundness and completeness in a system of ideas, as in the argument on RCA, in *Sec. 2.4.2*; the formal logical requirement of soundness, completeness, and consistency in a system of ideas, as in the argument on origin myths, in *Sec. 2.5.1*; the formal logical requirement of soundness and completeness in a system of ideas, as in the argument on Aristotle's "four causes," in *Sec. 2.5.2*; the formal logical requirement of soundness, completeness, and consistency in a system of ideas, as in the argument on adverse effects, in *Sec. 3.2.1*; the formal logical requirement of soundness and completeness in a system of ideas, as in the argument on "unintended consequences," in *Sec. 3.2.2*; the formal logical requirement of soundness and completeness in a system of ideas, as in the argument on the butterfly effect, in *Sec. 3.3.1*; the formal logical requirement of soundness, completeness, and consistency in a system of ideas, as in the argument on the quantum Zeno effect, in *Sec. 3.3.2*; the formal logical requirement of soundness and completeness in a system of ideas, as in the argument on the domino theory, in *Sec. 3.4.1*; the formal logical requirement of soundness and completeness in a system of ideas, as in the argument on effectuation, in *Sec. 3.4.2*; the formal logical requirement of soundness, completeness, and consistency in a system of ideas, as in the argument on causal determinism, in *Sec. 3.5.1*; and the formal logical requirement of soundness, completeness, and consistency in a system of ideas, as in the argument on eternal return, in *Sec. 3.5.2*).

On the other hand, there is also informalness (e.g., the non-formal existence of unsoundness, incompleteness, and inconsistency in the argument on cognitive bias and attribution, as shown in the criticisms that attribution theory is too rationalistic in its assumptions about people, that it does not include non-psychological factors, that there are disgreements about the explanation of a given attribution even among the so-called experts themselves, that there can be individual differences in regard to being susceptible to attributions, that cognitive biases are not necessarily bad, and that cognitive biases are treatable, in *Sec. 2.2.1*; the non-formal existence of unsoundness, incompleteness, and inconsistency in the argument on self-fulfilling prophecy, as shown in the criticisms that there are disagreements about the interpretation of a given story about self-fulfilling prophecy, that the idea of self-fulfilling prophecy is not necessarily true, that it is not necessarily undesirable, and that "self-fulfilling prophecy" can be defeated by "self-defeating prophecy," in *Sec. 2.2.2*; the non-formal existence of unsoundness, incompleteness, and inconsistency in the argument on time's arrow and entropy, as shown in the criticisms that the second law is not consistent with some well-established theorems, that there are uncertainties in regard to the application of the second law to the future scenarios of the universe, that it does not explain its own origin, that the second law is not quite accurate in some small systems, that the second law makes some questionable assumptions which limit its range of application, and that it exaggerates the occurrence of "equilibrium states," in *Sec. 2.3.1*; the non-formal existence of unsoundness, incompleteness, and inconsistency in the argument on "retrocausality," as shown in the criticisms that the idea of retrocausality creates difficult paradoxes, that the effects of retrocausality [even if possible] might not differ from those of normal causality, that the use of retrocausality in certain cases is a misnomer [as it has nothing to do with the traditional understanding of causality], that the idea of retrocausality has not been verified, that the idea of retrocausality can be replaced by the conventional idea of causality in certain cases, and that the idea of retrocausality is not verifiable [not merely that it has not been verified, in *Sec. 2.3.2*; the non-formal existence of unsoundness, incompleteness, and inconsistency in the argument on causation and legal liability, as shown in the criticisms that additional considerations are needed in some legal cases [such that the "two-stage inquiry" about legal liability is not deemed sufficient], that in some legal cases the judge can exercise some discretion [such that a defendant can still be liable even if he successfully passes the "two-stage inquiry" about legal liability], that causation in the "two-stage inquiry" may not be relevant at all in some legal cases, that in some legal cases only one of the two stages in the "two-stage inquiry" about legal liability is observed, and that the appeal to "common sense" in the first stage of establishing "factual" causation has been criticized as unsatisfactory by some legal scholars, in *Sec. 2.4.1*; the non-formal existence of unsoundness and incompleteness in the argument on RCA, as shown in the criticisms that RCA does not guarantee effective corrective action, that RCA does not distinguish between "necessary" and "sufficient" conditions of causation, that RCA focuses too much on gradual [not radical] corrective action, that RCA does not have a systematic process to prevent the adverse effects of "human factors," that RCA is reactive [not proactive enough], and that RCA is not more effective in combating incidents, in *Sec. 2.4.2*; the non-formal existence of unsoundness, incompleteness, and inconsistency in the argument on origin myths, as shown in the criticisms that there is no universal classification of origin myths, that there are conflicting interpretations about the functions of origin myths, that there is also no general agreement about the definition of "origin myth," and that there is no universal interpretation about the meaning of an origin myth, in *Sec. 2.5.1*; the non-formal existence of unsoundness and incompleteness in the argument on Aristotle's "four causes," as shown in the criticisms that Aristotle's analysis of "material cause" is embedded within a questionable metaphysics of "innateness," that Aristotle's analysis of "formal cause" is plagued with the controversial "theory of forms," that Aristotle's analysis of "final cause" uncritically presupposes a misleading teleology of some sort, and that Aristotle does not pay sufficient attention to "chance events," in *Sec. 2.5.1*; the non-formal existence of unsoundness, incompleteness, and inconsistency in the argument on adverse effects, as shown in the criticisms that the claim for "adverse effect" can be controversially false, that the claim for "adverse effect" can be exaggerated without putting the cost-benefit analysis in a proper perspective, that adverse effects can be psychological, that adverse effects can be ambiguous, that there can be beneficial side-effects too, that there is no universal definition of "adverse effect," and that reporting systems of adverse effects are not often effective, in *Sec. 3.2.1*; the non-formal existence of unsoundness and incompleteness in the argument on "unintended consequences," as shown in the criticisms that Merton did not focus enough on what exactly is meant by "intentionality" since "unintentional" in "unintended consequences" is a term relative to "intentionality" [as its opposite], that it does not distinguish between something ["non-intentional"] and something ['unintentional"] so what is "not intentional" does not necessarily mean "unintentional," that Merton's conception of social action is narrow, that the world is too complex to have only 5 causes of unintended consequences as suggested by Merton, and that it is not clear if the third type ["perverse results"] is redundant, in *Sec. 3.2.2*; the non-formal existence of unsoundness and incompleteness in the argument on the butterfly effect, as shown in the criticisms that the so-called "butterfly effect" is much exaggerated, that the so-called "butterfly effect" misleadingly exclude some other effects in its analysis, that the property of "sensitivity to initial conditions" can be redundant, that the butterfly effect can be countered by more complicated forecasting systems, that the butterfly effect does not apply in some situations, and that there is no universal definition of "chaos" in chaos theory, in *Sec. 3.3.1*; the non-formal existence of unsoundness, incompleteness, and inconsistency in the argument on the quantum Zeno effect, as shown in the criticisms that there is a controversy over the interpretation of the quantum Zeno effect, that there is "the time-energy indeterminacy relation" in measuring the quantum Zeno effect such that it can be much harder to violate the exponential decay law than previously thought, that there can be an increase of decay instead under some circumstances, that the limit of "periodic measurements" is still not clear, that the quantum Zeno effect does not apply to all interpretations of quantum theory, and that it has been used by some scholars for their questionable purposes, in *Sec. 3.3.2*; the non-formal existence of unsoundness and incompleteness in the argument on the domino theory, as shown in the criticisms that the domino theory rests on some false assumptions, that the domino theory neglects "nationalist" causes, that domino theory also ignores the cancerous problem of domesic corruption, that the domino theory had failed in its predictions, and that whether the domino effect is bad or not is relative, in *Sec. 3.4.1*; the non-formal existence of unsoundness and incompleteness in the argument on effectuation, as shown in the criticisms that it does not give sufficient attention to "optimality," that Sarasvathy's analysis often portrays "effectuation" in a more favorable light than "causal reasoning" in a biased way, that it is msileading to say that effectual reasoning [unlike causal reasoning] does not start with any goal, that it is more risk-adverse than the alternative causal process and thus can impose a greater limit on potential return, that effectuation is more subjectively disposed towards "cooperation" than towards "competition," that it is inherently more concerned with "people" than with outcome ["effect"], and that its application is more relevant for business startups, in *Sec. 3.4.2*; the non-formal existence of unsoundness, incompleteness, and inconsistency in the argument on causal determinism, as shown in the criticisms that there are alternative theories to determinism, that there are competing [even opposing] versions of determinism among the proponents themselves, that causal determinism has been criticized as empirically false, that causal determinism is too "materialistic," and that the idea of determinism has been misused for religious purposes, in *Sec. 3.5.1*; and the non-formal existence of unsoundness, incompleteness, and inconsistency in the argument on eternal return, as shown in the criticisms that there are conflicting answers to the question over the centuries, that an eternally recurrent life is not necessarily desirable, that the answers are often highly speculative without any proof, that the idea of eternal return has been misused for religious purposes, and that the idea of "eternal return" has been proved to be implausible, in *Sec. 3.5.2*).

And the reverse direction also holds true.

However, it should be stressed (as this is something that I regularly did in my previous books, *almost verbatim*) that there are different shades of gray (or different degrees of truth) in the two opposites, and the classification is not necessarily mutually exclusive either. In fact, even when some combinations of the two occur, they only end up sharing the same dialectic relationship, but in a different degree.

Also, there are some other relationships (as a kind of family resemblance) which have something in common with the principle, but they are not exactly the same but only more or less comparable, which varies from case to case.

Good examples of family resemblance in relation to the principle are logicalness-nonlogicalness, rationality-nonrationality, etc.

2nd Thesis: The Absoluteness-Relativeness Principle

The second thesis refers to the absoluteness-relativeness principle (on the multiplicity of things) in the category of "method" in existential dialectics, which was first proposed in *FPHK*, in that there is the multiplicity of things in reality, be they about entities, qualities (or properties), and relationships. If there is something absolute, there is likewise something relative. And there is no absoluteness without relativeness—and vice versa.

Both absoluteness and relativeness here are also relevant to different modalities often cited in the literature on ontology, such as possibility (e.g., something "can" happen) and its opposite (e.g., impossibility) in alethic modalities, probability (e.g., something "will" happen) and its opposite (e.g., improbability) in temporal modalities, and necessity (e.g., something "should" happen) and its opposite (e.g., contingency) in alethic modalities.

For instance, on the one hand, there is absoluteness (e.g., the absolute view on attribution theory by the advocates like Fritz Heider, in *Sec. 2.2.1*; the absolute view on self-fulfilling prophecy by those who strongly believe in it, in *Sec. 2.2.2*; the absolute view on the 2nd law by the advocates who used the statement "The entropy of the universe tends to a maximum," in *Sec. 2.3.1*; the absolute view on "retrocausality" by its advocates in para-science, in *Sec. 2.3.2*; the absolute view on the appeal to "common sense" in the stage of "factual causation" by the advocates, in *Sec. 2.4.1*; the absolute view on "small" [not "radical"] changes by the advocates of continuous improvement, in *Sec. 2.4.2*;, the absolute view on origin myths by the believers, since, "in many cultures, people are expected to take mythical gods and heroes as their role models, imitating their deeds and upholding the customs they established," in *Sec. 2.5.1*; the absolute view on teleology in "final cause" by Aristotle, in *Sec. 2.5.2*; the absolute view against drug manufacturers in regard to the controversy about autism linked to the MMR vaccine, in *Sec. 3.2.1*; the absolute view on "covert operations" by the CIA, like "covert funding of the Afghan Mujahideen," in *Sec. 3.2.2;* the absolute view on the "butterfly effect" by the advocates, in *Sec. 3.3.1*; the absolute view on "the Quantum Zeno effect" by the advocates on the basis of "the reductionist postulate for reconciling the measurement problem," in *Sec. 3.3.2*; the absolute view on the domino theory by the advocates like U.S. President Eisenhower, in *Sec. 3.4.1*; the absolute view on "people" by the advocates of effectual logic, in *Sec.3.4.2*; the absolute view on certainty by the advocates of Newtonian mechanics, in *Sec.3.5.1*; and the absolute view on "Godhead" by the advocates of a different version of eternal return, in *Sec.3.5.2*).

On the other hand, there is relativeness (e.g., what is right for the advocates like Fritz Heider in regard to attribution theory is not necessarily so for the critics, since "attribution theory has been criticized as being mechanistic and reductionist for assuming that people are rational, logical and systematic thinkers" but "it turns out however that they are cognitive misers and motivated tacticians as demonstrated by the fundamental attribution error," in *Sec. 2.2.1*; what is right for those who strongly believe in self-fulfilling prophecy is not necessarily so for those in "self-defeating prophecy" to counter it instead, in *Sec. 2.2.2*; what is right for the advocates in regard to the statement "The entropy of the universe tends to a maximum" is not necessarily so for the critics, who pointed out that the statement "The entropy of the universe tends to a maximum" is limited due to its assumptions," because, "owing to the general broadness of the terminology used here, e.g. universe, as well as lack of specific conditions, e.g. open, closed, or isolated," it is not true, as shown in the example that, "in thermodynamic systems that are not closed, entropy can decrease with time," in *Sec. 2.3,1*; what is right for the advocates of "retrocausality" in para-science is not necessarily so for the critics like "mainstream scientists," who "generally regarded these explanations as pseudoscientific," in *Sec. 2.3.2*; what is right for the advocates in regard to the appeal to "common sense" in the stage of "factual causation" is not necessarily so for the critics like Hart, Honoré, and Wright, who proposed "a test of sufficiency instead of a test of necessity," because "this arguably gives us a more theoretically satisfying reason to conclude that something was a cause of something else than by appealing to notions of intuition or common sense," in *Sec. 2.4.1*; what is right for the advocates of continuous improvement in regard to "small" [not "radical"] changes is not necessarily so for the critics, who pointed out that it focuses too much on "many small changes rather than the radical changes that might arise from Research and Development," in *Sec. 2.4.2*; what is true or right for the believers of origin myths is not necessarily so for the critics, who pointed out that "they are today seen as symbolic narratives which must be understood in terms of their own cultural context," not "in a literal or logical sense," in *Sec. 2.5.1*; what is right for Aristotle in regard to teleology in "final cause" is not necessarily so for the critics in modern science, who are not receptive to the Aristotelian teleology in "final cause," in *Sec. 2.5.2*; what is right for those against drug manufacturers in regard to the controversy about autism linked to the MMR vaccine is not necessarily so for the critics, who pointed out that "no link has been found in several large studies," in *Sec. 3.2.1*; what is right for the CIA in regard to "covert funding of the Afghan Mujahideen" is not necessarily so for the critics, who pointed out the problem of "blowback," in that "covert funding of the Afghan Mujahideen...contributed to the rise of Al-Qaeda," in *Sec. 3.2.2*; what is right for the advocates in regard to the "butterfly effect" is not necessarily so for the critics, who pointed out that the so-called "butterfly effect" is much exaggerated, that the so-called "butterfly effect" misleadingly exclude some other effects in its analysis, that the butterfly effect can be countered by more complicated forecasting systems, that the butterfly effect does not apply in some situations, etc., in *Sec. 3.3.1*; what is right for the advocates of "the Quantum Zeno effect" on the basis of "the reductionist postulate for reconciling the measurement problem" is not necessarily so for the critics, because "the Quantum Zeno effect does not apply to all interpretations of quantum theory, in particular, the many-worlds interpretation...and the Quantum Logic Interpretation," in *Sec. 3.3.2*; what is bad for the advocates in regard to the domino theory to fight against the spread of communism is not necessarily so for the proponents like Argentine revolutionary Che Guevara, in *Sec. 3.4.1*; what is right for the advocates of effectual logic in regard to "people" is not necessarily so for those of "causal logic," since they are more concerned with "effect" or "outcome" instead, in *Sec. 3.4.2*; what is right for the advocates of Newtonian mechanics in regard to certainty is not necessarily so for the critics, who pointed out that "certainty is never absolute in practice [and not just because of David Hume's problem of induction]" and "the equations of Newtonian mechanics can exhibit sensitive dependence on initial conditions," and "this is an example of the butterfly effect, which is one of the subjects of chaos theory," in *Sec. 3.5.1*; and what is right for the advocates of a different version of eternal return in regard to "Godhead" is not necessarily so for the critics, because it is "not inconsistent with the modern understanding of physics," in *Sec. 3.5.2*).

And the reverse direction also holds true.

However, it should be stressed (as this is something that I regularly did in my previous books, *almost verbatim*) that there are different shades of gray (or different degrees of truth) in the two opposites, and the classification is not necessarily mutually exclusive either. In fact, even when some combinations of the two occur, they only end up sharing the same dialectic relationship, but in a different degree.

Also, there are some other relationships (as a kind of family resemblance) which have something in common with the principle, but they are not exactly the same but only more or less comparable, which varies from case to case.

Good examples of family resemblance in relation to the principle are internalness-externalness, immanence-transcendence, independence-dependence, internality-externality, autonomy-dependency, universalness-relativeness, and so forth.

3rd Thesis: The Partiality-Totality Principle

The third thesis refers to the partiality-totality principle (on the relationships between whole and parts) in the category of "method" in existential dialectics, which was first proposed in *FC* and later *FPHGEOL*, based on earlier works like *FHC* and *FPHC*), in that any analysis of a phenomenon in the world requires both the examination of the individual parts and the whole of them (with the whole as being not the sum of its parts), without privileging the whole as more important than the parts, or vice-versa (that is, the parts as more important than the whole).

In fact, this principle targets two kinds of misleading methodologies as used over the ages, that is, again in the absence of better words, what I called (in *FHC*, *FPHC* and *FC*) "reductionism" and its opposite, "reverse-reductionism," which can take four major forms in relation to concept, theory, methodology, and ontology (as summarized in *Sec. 1.8*).

Thus, reductionism and reverse-reductionism can be (i) conceptual, (ii) theoretical, (iii) methodological, and (iv) ontological. And the whole is not the sum of its parts, and there is no partiality without totality—and vice versa.

Works on emergence (as in *FC*), gestalt psychology (as in *FPHGEOL*), and the hermeneutic circle (as in *FPHDA*), just to name a few of them, have contributed to the understanding of whole and parts.

For instance, on the one hand, there is partiality (e.g., the partial view on attribution by the advocates of attribution theory like Fritz Heider, in *Sec. 2.2.1*; the partial view on "self-fulfilling prophecy" by the believers, in *Sec. 2.2.2*; the partial view on the 2nd law by the advocates, in *Sec. 2.3.1*; the partial view on "retrocausality" by the advocates, in *Sec. 2.3.2*; the partial view on the "two-stage" approach to legal liability by the advocates, in *Sec. 2.4.1*; the partial view on "many small changes" by the advocates of continuous improvement as part of RCA, in *Sec. 2.4.2*; the partial view on origin myths by the believers, in *Sec. 2.5.1*; the partial view on "formal cause" by Aristotle, in *Sec. 2.5.2*; the partial view on the controversy about autism linked to the MMR vaccine by the advocates, in *Sec. 3.2.1*; the partial view on the Soviet war in Afghanistan by the CIA, in *Sec. 3.2.2*; the partial view on the "butterfly effect" by the advocates, in *Sec. 3.3.1*; the partial view on "the Quantum Zeno effect" by the advocates of "the reductionist postulate," in *Sec. 3.3.2*; the partial view on the domino theory by the advocates like U.S. President Eisenhower, in *Sec. 3.4.1*; the partial view on effectual logic by the advocates, in *Sec. 3.4.2*; the partial view on "certainty" by the advocates of Newtonian mechanics, in *Sec. 3.5.1*; and the partial view on "the chicken-and-egg problem" by the advocates of "the egg comes first," in *Sec. 3.5.2*).

On the other hand, there is also totality (e.g., the more holistic view on attribution, such that the whole is not the sum of its parts, that is, it cannot be reduced to the sum of opposing views by the advocates like Fritz Heider, the critics, etc., since there will emerge new views in the future not yet known today, just as there are already alternative views nowadays which do not side exclusively with any of them, as is the analysis here, in *Sec. 2.2.1*; the more holistic view on "self-fulfilling prophecy," such that the whole is not the sum of its parts, that is, it cannot be reduced to the sum of opposing views by the believers, the skeptics, the counter-believers known as those in "self-defeating prophecy," etc., since there will emerge new views in the future not yet known today, just as there are already alternative views nowadays which do not side exclusively with any of them, as is the analysis here, in *Sec. 2.2.2*; the more holistic view on the 2nd law, such that the whole is not the sum of its parts, that is, it cannot be reduced to the sum of opposing views by the advocates, the crtics, etc., since there will emerge new views in the future not yet known today, just as there are already alternative views nowadays which do not side exclusively with any of them, as is the analysis here, in *Sec. 2.3.1*; the more holistic view on "retrocausality," such that the whole is not the sum of its parts, that is, it cannot be reduced to the sum of opposing views by the advocates, the critics, the skeptics, etc., since there will emerge new views in the future not yet known today, just as there are already alternative views nowadays which do not side exclusively with any of them, as is the analysis here, in *Sec. 2.3.2*; the more holistic view on the "two-stage" approach to legal liability, such that the whole is not the sum of its parts, that is, it cannot be reduced to the sum of opposing views by the advocates, the skeptics, the critics, etc., since there will emerge new views in the future not yet known today, just as there are already alternative views nowadays which do not side exclusively with any of them, as is the analysis here, in *Sec. 2.4.1*; the more holistic view on "many small changes," such that the whole is not the sum of its parts, that is, it cannot be reduced to the sum of opposing views by the advocates, the critics, etc., since there will emerge new views in the future not yet known today, just as there are already alternative views nowadays which do not side exclusively with any of them, as is the analysis here, in *Sec. 2.4.2*; the more holistic view on origin myths, such that the whole is not the sum of its parts, that is, it cannot be reduced to the sum of opposing views by the believers, the skeptics, the critics, etc., since there will emerge new views in the future not yet known today, just as there are already alternative views nowadays which do not side exclusively with any of them, as is the analysis here, in *Sec. 2.5.1*; the more holistic view on "formal cause," such that the whole is not the sum of its parts, that is, it cannot be reduced to the sum of opposing views by the advocates, the skeptics, the critics, etc., since there will emerge new views in the future not yet known today, just as there are already alternative views nowadays which do not side exclusively with any of them, as is the analysis here, in *Sec. 2.5.2*; the more holistic view on   the controversy about autism linked to the MMR vaccine, such that the whole is not the sum of its parts, that is, it cannot be reduced to the sum of opposing views by the advocates, the skeptics, the critics, etc., since there will emerge new views in the future not yet known today, just as there are already alternative views nowadays which do not side exclusively with any of them, as is the analysis here, in *Sec. 3.2.1*; the more holistic view on the Soviet war in Afghanistan, such that the whole is not the sum of its parts, that is, it cannot be reduced to the sum of opposing views by the CIA, the Soviet Union, the critics about "blowback," etc., since there will emerge new views in the future not yet known today, just as there are already alternative views nowadays which do not side exclusively with any of them, as is the analysis here, in *Sec. 3.2.2*; the more holistic view on the "butterfly effect," such that the whole is not the sum of its parts, that is, it cannot be reduced to the sum of opposing views by by the advocates, the skeptics, the critics, etc., since there will emerge new views in the future not yet known today, just as there are already alternative views nowadays which do not side exclusively with any of them, as is the analysis here, in *Sec. 3.3.1*; the more holistic view on "the Quantum Zeno effect," such that the whole is not the sum of its parts, that is, it cannot be reduced to the sum of opposing views by the advocates of "the reductionist postulate," the advocates of "the many-worlds interpretation," the advocates of "the Quantum Logic Interpretation," etc., since there will emerge new views in the future not yet known today, just as there are already alternative views nowadays which do not side exclusively with any of them, as is the analysis here, in *Sec. 3.3.2*; the more holistic view on the domino theory, such that the whole is not the sum of its parts, that is, it cannot be reduced to the sum of opposing views by the advocates, the skeptics, the critics, etc., since there will emerge new views in the future not yet known today, just as there are already alternative views nowadays which do not side exclusively with any of them, as is the analysis here, in *Sec. 3.4.1*; the more holistic view on effectual logic, such that the whole is not the sum of its parts, that is, it cannot be reduced to the sum of opposing views by its advocates, the critics like those for causal logic, etc., since there will emerge new views in the future not yet known today, just as there are already alternative views nowadays which do not side exclusively with any of them, as is the analysis here, in *Sec. 3.4.2*; the more holistic view on "certainty," such that the whole is not the sum of its parts, that is, it cannot be reduced to the sum of opposing views by the advocates of Newtonian mechanics, the advocates of quantum mechanics, the advocates of the Humean problem of induction, etc., since there will emerge new views in the future not yet known today, just as there are already alternative views nowadays which do not side exclusively with any of them, as is the analysis here, in *Sec. 3.5.1*; and the more holistic view on "the chicken-and-egg problem," such that the whole is not the sum of its parts, that is, it cannot be reduced to the sum of opposing views by the advocates of "the egg comes first," the advocates of "the chicken comes first," and the advocates of "neither comes first," as discussed earlier, since there will emerge new views in the future not yet known today, just as there are already alternative views nowadays which do not side exclusively with any of them, as is the analysis here, in *Sec. 3.5.2*).

And the reverse direction also holds true.

However, it should be stressed (as this is something that I regularly did in my previous books, *almost verbatim*) that there are different shades of gray (or different degrees of truth) in the two opposites, and the classification is not necessarily mutually exclusive either. In fact, even when some combinations of the two occur, they only end up sharing the same dialectic relationship, but in a different degree.

Also, there are some other relationships (as a kind of family resemblance) which have something in common with the principle, but they are not exactly the same but only more or less comparable, which varies from case to case.

Good examples of family resemblance in relation to the principle are individualisticness-holisticness, partness-wholeness, analysis-synthesis, and the like.

4th Thesis: The Predictability-Unpredictability Principle

The fourth thesis is called the predictability-unpredictability principle (on the occurrence of events) in the category of "method" in existential dialectics (which was first proposed in *FC* and, later, other books of mine), in that both predictability and unpredictability have a major role to play in the occurrence of things, so that neither determinism nor indeterminism wins the centuries-old fight. There is no predictability without unpredictability—and vice versa.

There are events which are predictable, just as there are those which are not. Or what is regarded as unpredictable at one point in time may turn out to be predictable later, and, conversely, what is deemed as predictable may turn out to not be so predictable. Even in predictability, outcomes are subject to uncertainty, the degree of which varies from case to case.

Works on ecological uncertainty (as in *BNR*), complexity theory (as in *FC*), quantum mechanics (as in *FPHST* and *FPHG*), subjective (or Bayesian) probability (as in *FPHPROB*), "special causes" (as in *FPHGAM*), measurement uncertainty (as in *FPHPROB*), the butterfly effect (as in *FPHAERO*), and unintended consequences (as in *FPHAERO*), just to name a few of them, have contributed to the understanding of uncertainity.

The predictability-unpredictability principle is not to be confused with the absoluteness-relativeness principle; although both can address the issue of probability, the former is concerned with the extent of certainty in prediction, whereas the latter focuses on the relativity of viewpoints.

For instance, on the one hand, there is predictability (e.g., the predictable tendency that there are 4 main versions of attribuion theory nowadays, as aforediscussed, in *Sec. 2.2.1*; the predictable tendency that those who are vulnerable to self-fulfilling prophecy tend to "define situations as real," such that they will act on "their consequences" as "real," in *Sec. 2.2.2*; the predictable tendency that, in accordance to the 2nd law, "the entropy of the universe tends to a maximum," in *Sec. 2.3.1*; the predictable tendency that the idea of "retrocausality" will continue to have its proponents in the future, in *Sec. 2.3.2*; the predictable tendency that the examination of legal liability follows the "two-stage" approach in the U.S., in *Sec. 2.4.1*; the predictable tendency that "continuous improvement" as part of RCA focuses on "many small changes rather than the radical changes that might arise from Research and Development," in *Sec. 2.4.2*; the predictable tendency that creation myths can have different types, as shown in the 5 types aforedescribed, in *Sec. 2.5.1*; the predictable tendency that, to Aristotle, "nature is teleological in the sense that he believed that Nature has goals apart from those that humans have," in Sec. *2.5.2*; the predictable tendency that "public outcry" can exaggerate the adverse effects of "hormonal contraception and hormone replacement therapy," like "breast cancer," in *Sec. 3.2.1*; the predictable tendency that people can act "purposively," in *Sec. 3.2.2*; the predictable tendency that "a small change at one place in a deterministic nonlinear system can result in large differences in a later state," in *Sec. 3.3.1*; the predictable tendency that "the Quantum Zeno effect" is dependent on "the reductionist postulate," in *Sec. 3.3.2*; the predictable tendency of the advocates of the domino theory to argue in the 1960s and early 1970s that, if South Vietnam, Laos, and Cambodia fell to communism, other surrounding countries like Thailand, Malaysia, Indonesia, Burma, and India would be next, in *Sec. 3.4.1*; the focus on "predictive models" by those for causal logic in *Sec. 3.4.2*; the predictable tendency that "Newtonian mechanics...make relatively accurate predictions [e.g. calculating the trajectory of a bullet]," in *Sec. 3.5.1*; and the predictable tendency that there are different answers to "the chicken-and-egg problem" in the foreseeable future, in *Sec. 3.5.2*).

On the other hand, there is unpredictability (e.g., the more difficult task to predict exactly the extent to which a particular attribution theory will be influential in a particular future era, in *Sec. 2.2.1*; the more difficult task to predict exactly the extent to which a particualr self-fulfilling prophecy will become real on a particular future occasion, since it is not necessarily true and can be defeated by "self-defeating prophecy," in *Sec. 2.2.2*; the more difficult task to predict exactly the extent to which the statement "The entropy of the universe tends to a maximum" will be true, in the distant future of the universe, since there are uncertainties in regard to the application of the second law to the future scenarios of the universe, in *Sec. 2.3.1*; the more difficult task to predict exactly the extent to which a particular version of "retrocausality" will become influential in a particular future era, in *Sec. 2.3.2*; the more difficult task to predict exactly the extent to which the "two-stage" approach in the U.S. will be followed in a particular future case, because of the "complex amalgam of fact and policy," as shown by the different problems aforediscussed, including the situation that causation in the "two-stage inquiry" may not be relevant at all in some legal cases, in *Sec. 2.4.1*; the more difficult task to predict exactly the extent to which a particular change initiated for "continuous improvement" will become effective on a particular future occasion, since RCA does not guarantee effective corrective action, in *Sec. 2.4.2*; the more difficult task to predict exactly the extent to which a particular type of these creation myths will turn out to be true in a particular distant future era, in *Sec. 2.5.1*; the more difficult task to predict exactly the extent to which a particular natural event will be teleological on a particular future occasion, since Aristotle does not focus on "chance events," in *Sec. 2.5.2*; the more difficult task to predict exactly the extent to which a particular case of "hormonal contraception and hormone replacement therapy" will actually lead to "breast cancer" on a particular occasion, since its probabilities are very marginal, in *Sec. 3.2.1*; the more difficult task to predict exactly the extent to which a particular "purposive action" will yield consequences as intended on a particular future occasion, because of the problems with "unintended consequences" aforediscussed, in Sec. *3.2.2*; "dynamical systems that are highly sensitive to initial conditions...yield widely diverging outcomes..., rendering long-term prediction impossible in general," in *Sec. 3.3.1*; the more difficult task to predict exactly "the limit of "periodic measurements" on a particular future occasion, since, to the critics, "it is still an open question how closely one can approach the limit of an infinite number of interrogations due to the Heisenberg uncertainty involved in shorter measurement times," in *Sec. 3.3.2*; the more difficult task to predict when exactly, after South

Vietnam, Laos, and Cambodia fell into communism in the 1970s, other surrounding countries like Thailand, Malaysia, Indonesia, Burma, and India would be next, since, as the history later unfolded, this did not happen at all as predicted, in *Sec. 3.4.1*; the focus on "contingencies" or "uncertainty" by those for effectual logic, in *Sec. 3.4.2*; "quantum mechanics casts reasonable doubt on this main thesis of determinism," that is, on "accurate predictions," in *Sec. 3.5.1*; and the more difficult task to predict exactly the extent to which a particular answer to "the chicken-and-egg problem" will become dominant in a particular future era, in *Sec. 3.5.2*).

And the reverse direction also holds true.

Again, it should be stressed, however, that there are different shades of gray (or different degrees of truth) in the two opposites, and the classification is not necessarily mutually exclusive either. In fact, even when some combinations of the two occur, they only end up sharing the same dialectic relationship, but in a different degree.

Also, there are some other relationships (as a kind of family resemblance) which have something in common with the principle, but they are not exactly the same but only more or less comparable, which varies from case to case.

Good examples of family resemblance in relation to the principle are sureness-arbitrariness, deterministicness-randomness, likeliness-riskiness, sureness-doubtfulness, deterministicness-indeterministicness, certainty-uncertainty, reliability-unreliability, and so forth.

5th Thesis: The Explicability-Inexplicability Principle

The fifth thesis is called the explicability-inexplicability principle (on the underlying mechanisms of things) in the category of "method" in existential dialectics (which was proposed in *FPHU* and other books of mine), in that both explicability and inexplicability are part of the understanding of things. There is no explicability without inexplicability—and vice versa.

This principle tells us the dual nature of the research dilemma, in that, if reality can be explained in some ways, it also has its other ways which are not quite explainable, at a given point in time.

For instance, on the one hand, there is explicability (e.g., the explanation, by some advocates of self-serving bias, on the basis of the protection of "self-esteem," in *Sec. 2.2.1*; the explanation, by those advocates of self-fulfilling prophecy, of its validity on the basis that "once people convince themselves that a situation really has a certain meaning, regardless of whether it actually does, they will take very real actions in consequence" towards that direction, in *Sec. 2.2.2*; the explanation, by those advocates of the 2nd law, of the "preferred direction of progress" or "time's arrow" on the basis of "entropy," in *Sec. 2.3.1*; the explanation, by those advocates of "the Wheeler–Feynman absorber theory," of the possibility of "retrocausality" on the basis that it is supposed "to explain the absence of a type of converging concentric wave suggested by certain solutions to Maxwell's equations," in *Sec. 2.3.2*; the explanation, by those advocates of the "two-stage" approach in the U.S., of its desirability on the basis of the "complex amalgam of fact and policy," in *Sec. 2.4.1*; the explanation, by those advocates of "incident management," of its desirability on the basis of "limiting the potential disruption caused by...an event, followed by a return to business as usual," in *Sec. 2.4.2*; the explanation, by those advocates of origin myths, of their desirability on the basis of providing "social order," in *Sec. 2.5.1*; the explanation, by Aristotle, of the validity of its philosophy on the basis of a metaphysics of teleology, in *Sec. 2.5.2*; the explanation, by those who carried out "lawsuits against drug manufacturers," on the basis that "autism was linked to the MMR vaccine," in *Sec. 3.2.1*; the explanation, by Merton, of unintended consquences on the basis of 5 causes, in *Sec. 3.2.2*; the explanation, by those advocates of the "butterfly effect," on the basis that "a small change at one place in a deterministic nonlinear system can result in large differences in a later state," in *Sec. 3.3.1*; the explanation, by those advocates of "the quantum Zeno effect," of its possibility on the basis of "the reductionist postulate for reconciling the measurement problem," in *Sec. 3.3.2*; the explanation, by those advocates of the domino theory, on the basis of the force of "world communism," such that "if one state in a region came under the influence of communism, then the surrounding countries would follow in a domino effect," in *Sec. 3.4.1*; the explanation, by those advocates of effectual logic, of the desirability on the basis of "affordable loss," besides other two principles, in *Sec. 3.4.2*; the explanation, by those advocates of "causal determinism," on the basis that "every event is necessitated by antecedent events and conditions together with the laws of nature," in *Sec. 3.5.1*; and the explanation, by those advocates of "Godhead," of its validity on the basis of "ti + te = 0," in that "nothing, therefore, contains within it all energy and all information; the state of nothing" at the beginning, in *Sec. 3.5.2*).

On the other hand, there is inexplicability (e.g., the lack of sufficient explanation, by those advocates of self-serving bias, why the idea about the protection of "self-esteem is necessarily explainable, since, to the critics, there are other researchers who disagreed and suggested instead that, "when the outcomes match people's expectations, they make attributions to internal factors; when the outcome does not match their expectations, they make external attributions," in *Sec. 2.2.1*; the lack of sufficient explanation, by those advocates of self-ulfilling prophecy, of why it is necessarily valid, since, to the critics, "self-fulfilling prophecy" can be defeated by "self-defeating prophecy," in *Sec. 2.2.2*; the lack of sufficient explanation, by those advocates of the 2nd law, of why "entropy" is necessarily explainable, since the critics pointed out different problems, in that the second law is not consistent with some well-established theorems, that there are uncertainties in regard to the application of the second law to the future scenarios of the universe, that it does not explain its own origin, that the second law makes some questionable assumptions which limit its range of application, and that it exaggerates the occurrence of "equilibrium states, etc., in *Sec. 2.3.1*; the lack of sufficient explanation, by those advocates of "the Wheeler–Feynman absorber theory," of why "retrocausality" is really true, since, to the critics, "these advanced waves don't have anything to do with cause and effect" as conventionally understood, in *Sec. 2.3.2*; the lack of sufficient explanation, by those advocates of the "two-stage" approach in the U.S., of why it is necessarily desirable, since the critics pointed out the problems that additional considerations are needed in some legal cases, that in some legal cases the judge can exercise some discretion beyond the "two-stage inquiry," that causation in the "two-stage inquiry" may not be relevant at all in some legal cases, that in some legal cases only one of the two stages in the "two-stage inquiry" is observed, and that the appeal to "common sense" in the first stage of establishing "factual" causation has been criticized as unsatisfactory by some legal scholars, in *Sec. 2.4.1*; the lack of sufficient explanation, by those advocates of "incident management," of why it is necessarily desirable, since, to the critics, RCA like "incident management" is too reactive, not proactive enough, in *Sec. 2.4.2*; the lack of sufficient explanation, by those advocates of origin myths, of why the provision of "social order" is necessarily explainable, since, to the critics, there are conflicting interpretations about the functions of origin myths, like "philosophy of life," "sense of place in the world," etc., in *Sec. 2.5.1*; the lack of sufficient explanation, by Aristotle, of why his metaphysics of teleology is necessarily true, since, to the critics, "Aristotle's metaphysics, his account of nature and causality, was for the most part rejected by the early modern philosophers," in *Sec. 2.5.2*; the lack of sufficient explanation, by those who carried out "lawsuits against drug manufacturers," of why the claim that "autism was linked to the MMR vaccine" is necessarily true, since, to the critics, "no link has been found in several large studies, and despite removal of thimerosal from vaccines a decade ago the rate of autism has not decreased as would be expected if it had been the causative," in *Sec. 3.2.1*; the lack of sufficient explanation, by Merton, of why his list of 5 causes is necessarily complete, since, to the critics, the world is too complex to have only 5 causes of unintended consequences as suggested by Merton, in *Sec. 3.2.2*; the lack of sufficient explanation, by those advocates of the "butterfly effect," of why it is necessarily valid, since the critics pointed out different problems, in that the so-called "butterfly effect" is much exaggerated, that the so-called "butterfly effect" misleadingly exclude some other effects in its analysis, that the property of "sensitivity to initial conditions" can be redundant, that the butterfly effect can be countered by more complicated forecasting systems, that the butterfly effect does not apply in some situations, etc., in *Sec. 3.3.1*; the lack of sufficient explanation, by those advocates of "the quantum Zeno effect," of why it is necessarily possible, since, to the critics, "the quantum Zeno effect does not apply to all interpretations of quantum theory, in particular, the many-worlds interpretation...and the Quantum Logic Interpretation," in *Sec. 3.3.2*; the lack of sufficient explanation, by those advocates of the domino theory, of why it is necessarily true, since the critics pointed out that the domino theory rests on some false assumptions, that the domino theory neglects "nationalist" causes, that domino theory also ignores the cancerous problem of domesic corruption, that the domino theory had failed in its predictions, and that whether the domino effect is bad or not is relative, in *Sec. 3.4.1*; the lack of sufficient explanation, by those advocates of effectual logic, of why focusing on "affordable loss" is necessarily desirable, since the critics like those for causal logic prefer riskier loss for the "highest potential return" instead, in *Sec. 3.4.2*; the lack of sufficient explanation, by those advocates of "causal determinism," of why it is necessarily true, since, to the critics, "opposing determinism is some kind of indeterminism [otherwise called nondeterminism]," in *Sec. 3.5.1*; and the lack of sufficient explanation, by those advocates of "Godhead," of why "ti + te = 0," is necessarily true, since, to the critics, it "is not inconsistent with the modern understanding of physics," in *Sec. 3.5.2*).

And the reverse direction also holds true.

Once more, it should be stressed, however, that there are different shades of gray (or different degrees of truth) in the two opposites, and the classification is not necessarily mutually exclusive either. In fact, even when some combinations of the two occur, they only end up sharing the same dialectic relationship, but in a different degree.

Also, there are some other relationships (as a kind of family resemblance) which have something in common with the principle, but they are not exactly the same but only more or less comparable, which varies from case to case.

Good examples of family resemblance in relation to the principle are underlyingness-regularness, causation-regularity, causation-correlation, explanation-description, explanation-narration, explanation-interpretation, relation-nonrelation, and so forth.

6th Thesis: The Fiction-Reality Principle

The sixth thesis is called the fiction-reality principle (on the different faces of reality) in the category of "method" in existential dialectics (as first proposed in *FPHLIT*), in that both fiction and reality co-exist. There is no reality without fiction—and vice versa.

This principle tells us the different categories of reality, in that, if there is reality, there is also some fiction in it—just as, if there is fiction, there is also some reality in it.

For instance, on the one hand, there is fiction (e.g., the fictional aspect of attribution, insofar as people who make "attributions" often "fall into many traps of biases and errors," in *Sec. 2.2.1*; the fictional aspect of "self-fulfilling prophecy," insofar as people's behavior is "determined in part by their perception and the meaning they ascribe to the situations they are in," even when they are actually false, in *Sec. 2.2.2*; the fictional aspect of the 2nd law, insofar as it relies on some questionable assumptions as discussed earlier, in *Sec. 2.3.1*; the fictional aspect of "retrocausality," insofar as "mainstream scientists generally regarded these explanations as pseudoscientific" in para-science, in *Sec. 2.3.2*; the fictional aspect of the "two-stage" approach, insofar as causation in the "two-stage inquiry" is not relevant at all in some legal cases, like the case about "a contract of indemnity insurance," in *Sec. 2.4.1*; the fictional aspect of RCA, insofar as it does not guarantee effective corrective action, in *Sec. 2.4.2*; the fictional aspect of origin myths, insofar as they are symbolic, not to be taken literally, in *Sec. 2.5.1*; the fictional aspect of Aristotle's "four causes," insofar as "Aristotle's metaphysics, his account of nature and causality, was for the most part rejected by the early modern philosophers," in *Sec. 2.5.2*; the fictional aspect of "hormonal contraception and hormone replacement therapy," insofar as "even marginal probabilities of adverse effects of a severe nature, such as breast cancer, have led to public outcry and changes in medical therapy, although its benefits largely surpassed the statistical risks," in *Sec. 3.2.1*; the fictional aspect of the benefits of "safety helmets" required by the Australian state of Victoria in 1990, insofar as "the decrease in exercise caused by reduced cycling as a result of helmets laws is counterproductive in terms of net health," in *Sec. 3.2.2*; the fictional aspect of the "butterfly effect," insofar as that the so-called "butterfly effect" is much exaggerated, that the so-called "butterfly effect" misleadingly exclude some other effects in its analysis, that the property of "sensitivity to initial conditions" can be redundant, that the butterfly effect can be countered by more complicated forecasting systems, that the butterfly effect does not apply in some situations, etc., in *Sec. 3.3.1*; the fictional aspect of "the quantum Zeno effect," insofar as Stapp's application of the quantum Zeno effect for his claim about "quantum mind" is rejected by the critics as false, in that "'Stapp's model does not build upon 'the prevailing principles of physics,' but negates them," in *Sec. 3.3.2*; the fictional aspect of the domino theory, insofar as that "no such monolithic force as 'world communism' existed," in *Sec. 3.4.1*; the fictional aspect of effectual logic, insofar as there are "contingencies" or "uncetainty" as shown in the example about someone trying to start a lunch business but discovering later that "the lunch business does not take off beyond the first few customers," in *Sec. 3.4.2*; the fictional aspect of causal determinism, insofar as "the equations of Newtonian mechanics can exhibit sensitive dependence on initial conditions" and "this is an example of the butterfly effect, which is one of the subjects of chaos theory," in *Sec. 3.5.1*; and the fictional aspect of eternal return, insofar as "Georg Simmel…rebuts the claim that a finite number of states must repeat within an infinite amount of time," because, "if the second wheel rotated twice as fast as the first, and if the speed of the third wheel was $1/\pi$ of the speed of the first, the initial line-up would never recur," in *Sec. 3.5.2*).

On the other hand, there is reality (e.g., the realistic aspect of attribution, insofar as "some cognitive biases are presumably adaptive" and "may lead to more effective actions in a given context" and, "furthermore, cognitive biases enable faster decisions when timeliness is more valuable…, as illustrated in heuristics," in *Sec. 2.2.1*; the realistic aspect of "self-fulfilling prophecy," insofar a "If men define situations as real, they are real in their consequences," in *Sec. 2.2.2*; the realistic aspect of the 2nd law, insofar as "the key concept for the explanation of this phenomenon [i.e., a preferred direction of progress]" is "entropy" in an isolated system, in *Sec. 2.3.1*; the realistic aspect of "retrocausality," insofar as the Wheeler–Feynman absorber theory, proposed by John Archibald Wheeler [1945] and Richard Feynman, uses retrocausality and a temporal form of destructive interference to explain the absence of a type of converging concentric wave suggested by certain solutions to Maxwell's equations," in *Sec. 2.3.2*; the realistic aspect of the "two-stage" approach, insofar as it was observed in some legal cases, like the case about the "Summers v. Tice rule," in *Sec. 2.4.1*; the realistic aspect of RCA, insofar as it can be helpful to "limit...the potential disruption caused by...an event, followed by a return to business as usual," under certain circumstances, in *Sec. 2.4.2*; the realistic aspect of origin myths, insofar as they serve the social function of providing "social order," in *Sec. 2.5.1*; the realistic aspect of Aristotle's "four causes," insofar as, "in the case of a statue, it is the person chiseling away which transforms a block of marble into a statue," in *Sec. 2.5.2*; the realistic aspect of "hormonal contraception and hormone replacement therapy," insofar as there are "probabilities of adverse effects of a severe nature, such as breast cancer," although they are marginal, in *Sec. 3.2.1*; the realistic aspect of the benefits of "safety helmets" required by the Australian state of Victoria in 1990, insofar as "helmet use reduces 'the risk of head or brain injury by approximately two-thirds or more,'" in *Sec. 3.2.2*; the realistic aspect of the "butterfly effect," insofar as, under certain limited conditions, a small change at one place in a deterministic nonlinear system can result in large differences in a later state," in *Sec. 3.3.1*; the realistic aspect of "the Quantum Zeno effect," insofar as it was tested experimentally over the years, like ones by David J. Wineland and his group at NIST in 1989 and by Mark G. Raizen and his group at the University of Texas at Austin in 2001, in *Sec. 3.3.2*; the realistic aspect of the domino theory, insofar as, according to some proponents, there is some truth to it, because "the efforts during the containment [i.e. Domino Theory] period, ultimately led the demise of the Soviet Union and the end of the Cold War," in *Sec. 3.4.1*; the realistic aspect of effectual logic, insofar as there are more realistic possibilities, as shown in the example that, even though "the lunch business does not take off beyond the first few customers,...our entrepreneur discovers that the customers are actually interested in her ethnic philosophy and life experiences or Indian culture or other aspects of her personality or expertise or contacts or interests," in *Sec. 3.4.2*; the realistic aspect of causal determinism, insofar as "Newtonian mechanics remain useful, and make relatively accurate predictions [e.g. calculating the trajectory of a bullet]" in day-to-day physics, in *Sec. 3.5.1*; and the realistic aspect of eternal return, insofar as, "related to the concept of eternal return is the Poincaré recurrence theorem in mathematics," which "states that a system whose dynamics are volume-preserving and which is confined to a finite spatial volume will, after a sufficiently long time, return to an arbitrarily small neighborhood of its initial state," in *Sec. 3.5.2*).

And the reverse direction also holds true.

Once more, it should be stressed, however, that there are different shades of gray (or different degrees of truth) in the two opposites, and the classification is not necessarily mutually exclusive either. In fact, even when some combinations of the two occur, they only end up sharing the same dialectic relationship, but in a different degree.

Also, there are some other relationships (as a kind of family resemblance) which have something in common with the principle, but they are not exactly the same but only more or less comparable, which varies from case to case.

Good examples of family resemblance in relation to the principle are fiction-nonfiction, fiction-fact, imagination-fact, imagination-nonfiction, subjectivity-objectivity, inaccuracy-accuracy, arbitrariness-reality, error-reality, misunderstanding-correctness, speculation-reality, and so forth.

7th Thesis: The Cognitiveness-Noncognitiveness Principle

The seventh thesis is called the cognitiveness-noncognitiveness principle (on the understanding of meaning) in the category of "method" in existential dialectics (as first proposed in *BNR*), in that, if a view of things is based on reason and evidences, it is also affected by non-cognitive factors (such that it is neither true nor false in the latter case)—and vice versa. In other words, there is no cognitiveness without noncognitiveness—and vice versa.

Noncognitive factors can come in all shapes and sizes, and good examples include envy, jealousy, power, nationality, race, gender, age, class, greed, lust, status, faith, anger, sadness, joy, fear, wish, etc.

Communication, even in its ideal type, is seldom based on reason and evidences only, as falsely assumed during the Age of the Enlightenment and its continued supporters nowadays. What is understood about something is often twisted on the basis of something else too. In these cases, what is at stake is often neither true nor false (which is something that classical logic has sidelined and ignored).

For instance, on the one hand, there is cognitiveness (e.g., a view of things on the basis of reason and evidences, as shown in the finding that, as told by Aristotle, "the most intelligent minds are those that can entertain an idea without necessarily believing it," in *Sec. 2.2.1*; a view of things on the basis of reason and evidences, as shown in the finding that there are individuals who are vulnerable to "self-fulfilling prophecy," in *Sec. 2.2.2*; a view of things on the basis of reason and evidences, as shown in the finding about the 2nd law that "the key concept for the explanation of this phenomenon [i.e., a preferred direction of progress]" is "entropy" in an isolated system, in *Sec. 2.3.1*; a view of things on the basis of reason and evidences, as shown in the finding that there are different works on "retrocausality" in physics, philosophy of science, and para-science aforediscussed, in *Sec. 2.3.2*; a view of things on the basis of reason and evidences, as shown in the finding that legal liability generally requires the examination of "facts" for "factual causation," in *Sec. 2.4.1*; a view of things on the basis of reason and evidences, as shown in the finding that RCA can "solve problems by attempting to identify and correct the root causes of events," in *Sec. 2.4.2*; a view of things on the basis of reason and evidences, as shown in the finding that "many cultures have stories set after the cosmogonic myth, which describe the origin of natural phenomena and human institutions within a preexisting universe," in *Sec. 2.5.1*; a view of things on the basis of reason and evidences, as shown in the finding that "Aristotle's metaphysics, his account of nature and causality, was for the most part rejected by the early modern philosophers," in *Sec. 2.5.2*; a view of things on the basis of reason and evidences, as shown in the empirical finding about the possible adverse effects of "the MMR vaccine," in *Sec. 3.2.1*; a view of things on the basis of reason and evidences, as shown in the empirical finding that there are unintended consequences, even if people act purposively, in *Sec. 3.2.2*; a view of things on the basis of reason and evidences, as shown in the empirical finding that there were early studies on chaos theory, like those by Henri Poincaré, G. D. Birkhoff, A. N. Kolmogorov, M.L. Cartwright, J.E. Littlewood, Stephen Smale, and so on, in *Sec. 3.3.1*; a view of things on the basis of reason and evidences, as shown in the empirical finding that the quantum Zeno effect was tested experimentally by David J. Wineland and his group at NIST in 1989 and by Mark G. Raizen and his group at the University of Texas at Austin in 2001, in *Sec. 3.3.2*; a view of things on the basis of reason and evidences, as shown in the empirical finding that South Vietnam, Laos, and Cambodia fell to communism in the 1970s, in *Sec. 3.4.1*; a view of things on the basis of reason and evidences, as shown in the empirical finding that there are different logics, like "causal logic" and "effectual logic," in *Sec. 3.4.2*; a view of things on the basis of reason and evidences, as shown in the empirical finding that there are different forms of determinism aforecited, in *Sec. 3.5.1*; and a view of things on the basis of reason and evidences, as shown in the empirical finding that there are different answers to "the chicken-and-egg problem" aforecited, in *Sec. 3.5.2*).

On the other hand, there is noncognitiveness (e.g., a view of things on the basis of non-cognitive factors like envy, jealousy, power, nationality, race, gender, age, class, greed, lust, status, faith, anger, sadness, joy, fear, wish, etc.—as shown in the emotional and intellectual underdevelopment of children, such that they are "the most susceptible to influence" by adults, regardless of whether what they are told is true or false, in *Sec. 2.2.1*; a view of things on the basis of non-cognitive factors like envy, jealousy, power, nationality, race, gender, age, class, greed, lust, status, faith, anger, sadness, joy, fear, wish, etc.—as shown in the faith of some people, in that when they "convince themselves that a situation really has a certain meaning, regardless of whether it actually does, they will take very real actions in consequence," in *Sec. 2.2.2*; a view of things on the basis of non-cognitive factors like envy, jealousy, power, nationality, race, gender, age, class, greed, lust, status, faith, anger, sadness, joy, fear, wish, etc.—as shown in the "conventional" acceptance that, "by convention, for the purposes of thermodynamic analysis,…any arbitrary occasion of space-time is said to be in thermodynamic equilibrium," even though "nothing in the entire universe is or has ever been truly in exact thermodynamic equilibrium," in *Sec. 2.3.1*; a view of things on the basis of non-cognitive factors like envy, jealousy, power, nationality, race, gender, age, class, greed, lust, status, faith, anger, sadness, joy, fear, wish, etc.—as shown in the politics of para-science by the advocates to continue their belief in "retrocausality," in spite of the fact that "mainstream scientists generally regarded these explanations as pseudoscientific," in *Sec. 2.3.2*; a view of things on the basis of non-cognitive factors like envy, jealousy, power, nationality, race, gender, age, class, greed, lust, status, faith, anger, sadness, joy, fear, wish, etc.—as shown in the discretionary power of the judge in Chester v Afshar, where the defendant was found liable even though he successfully passed the "two-stage inquiry" about legal liability, in *Sec. 2.4.1*; a view of things on the basis of non-cognitive factors like envy, jealousy, power, nationality, race, gender, age, class, greed, lust, status, faith, anger, sadness, joy, fear, wish, etc.—as shown in the preference for RCA by the advocates, in spite of the problems that that RCA does not guarantee effective corrective action, that RCA focuses too much on gradual [not radical] corrective action, that RCA does not have a systematic process to prevent the adverse effects of "human factors," that RCA is reactive [not proactive enough], etc., in *Sec. 2.4.2*; a view of things on the basis of non-cognitive factors like envy, jealousy, power, nationality, race, gender, age, class, greed, lust, status, faith, anger, sadness, joy, fear, wish, etc.—as shown in the faith of the believers in creation myths, in spite of the criticisms that they are not verifiable or simply mythical, not to be taken "in a literal or logical sense," in *Sec. 2.5.1*; a view of things on the basis of non-cognitive factors like envy, jealousy, power, nationality, race, gender, age, class, greed, lust, status, faith, anger, sadness, joy, fear, wish, etc.—as shown in the continued support of Aristotle's metaphysics by some people nowadays, like the misleading use of evolutionary theory for its defense, in spite of its incorrection, in *Sec. 2.5.2*; a view of things on the basis of non-cognitive factors like envy, jealousy, power, nationality, race, gender, age, class, greed, lust, status, faith, anger, sadness, joy, fear, wish, etc.—as shown in emotions surrounding the "public outcry" and "lawsuits against drug manufacturers" in regard to the claim about "autism…linked to the MMR vaccine," even though "no link has been found in several large studies, and despite removal of thimerosal from vaccines a decade ago the rate of autism has not decreased as would be expected if it had been the causative agent," in *Sec. 3.2.1*; a view of things on the basis of non-cognitive factors like envy, jealousy, power, nationality, race, gender, age, class, greed, lust, status, faith, anger, sadness, joy, fear, wish, etc.—as shown in the persistence of "cognitive or emotional biases" among some people, such that unintended consequences continue to occur, in spite of their being informed about their biases as causes of these consequences, in *Sec. 3.2.2*; a view of things on the basis of non-cognitive factors like envy, jealousy, power, nationality, race, gender, age, class, greed, lust, status, faith, anger, sadness, joy, fear, wish, etc.—as shown in the personal prejudice of the advisor of a graduate student in Chihiro Hayashi's laboratory at Kyoto University, Yoshisuke Ueda, because, when his student "was experimenting with analog computers and noticed, on Nov. 27, 1961, what he called 'randomly transitional phenomena,'" the "advisor…did not allow him to report his findings until 1970," even though it was correct, in *Sec. 3.3.1*; a view of things on the basis of non-cognitive factors like envy, jealousy, power, nationality, race, gender, age, class, greed, lust, status, faith, anger, sadness, joy, fear, wish, etc.—as shown in personal faith by Stapp in the application of the quantum Zeno effect for his claim about "quantum mind," in spite of the rejection by the critics as false, in that "'Stapp's model does not build upon 'the prevailing principles of physics,' but negates them," in *Sec. 3.3.2*; a view of things on the basis of non-cognitive factors like envy, jealousy, power, nationality, race, gender, age, class, greed, lust, status, faith, anger, sadness, joy, fear, wish, etc.—as shown in the ideological conviction by some proponents who continued to apply the domino theory in regard to the potential spread of "Islamic theocracy" in the Middle East near the end of the 20th century and beyond, even though this did not happen, and even though, in addition, the domino theory had also failed in its prediction about the fall of "Thailand, Indonesia, and other large Southeast Asian countries after the end of the Vietnam War" in the 1970s, in *Sec. 3.4.1*; a view of things on the basis of non-cognitive factors like envy, jealousy, power, nationality, race, gender, age, class, greed, lust, status, faith, anger, sadness, joy, fear, wish, etc.—as shown in the personal preference of Sarasvathy for "effectual logic," in spite of the problems and biases in the model as discussed earlier, in *Sec. 3.4.2*; a view of things on the basis of non-cognitive factors like envy, jealousy, power, nationality, race, gender, age, class, greed, lust, status, faith, anger, sadness, joy, fear, wish, etc.—as shown in the rigid ideological conviciton by those for Marxist "economic determinism," even after the collapse of the Communist bloc in the 1990s and after "these theories have been widely rejected as a single cause fallacy," especially "as scientific understanding has grown," in *Sec. 3.5.1*; and a view of things on the basis of non-cognitive factors like envy, jealousy, power, nationality, race, gender, age, class, greed, lust, status, faith, anger, sadness, joy, fear, wish, etc.—as shown in the continued "faith" in "Godhead" by the believers, in spite of the fact that it is "not inconsistent with the modern understanding of physics" and has been rejected by mainstream scientists, in *Sec. 3.5.2*).

And the reverse direction also holds true.

Once more, it should be stressed, however, that there are different shades of gray (or different degrees of truth) in the two opposites, and the classification is not necessarily mutually exclusive either. In fact, even when some combinations of the two occur, they only end up sharing the same dialectic relationship, but in a different degree.

Also, there are some other relationships (as a kind of family resemblance) which have something in common with the principle, but they are not exactly the same but only more or less comparable, which varies from case to case.

Good examples of family resemblance in relation to the principle are proposition-attitude, cognition-emotion, cognition-prescription, theory-extratheory, justification-nonjustification, recognition-nonrecogntion, reason-perception, reason-emotion, and so forth.

In Relation to Structure

The next six theses are in relation to structure in existential dialectics, as shown below.

8th Thesis: The Finiteness-Transfiniteness Principle

The eighth thesis is called the finiteness-transfiniteness principle (on the nature of numbers) in the category of "structure" in existential dialectics (as first proposed in *FPHG*), in that, if there are finite things, there are likewise transfinite ones—and vice versa.

To avoid confusion, my usage of the word "transfinite" here differs radically from the one used by Cantor (and other mathematicians) for "relative" infinity—and is more limited, in light of the problems confronting any attempt to understand the idea of infinity, be it by intuition, imagination, and conception (as detailedly analyzed in *Sec. 2.2.3* of *FPHG*).

Instead, by "transfinity," I allow numbers which can be many times larger—or smaller, for that matter—than the finite things that we encounter in daily life, but they do not have to be related to the idea of infinity at all (which may not exist).

Of course, there may be some *borderline* cases, in which it is not clear whether the number in question is transfinite (in my usage) or simply a mathematical convenience. A good example of a borderline case is the Planck unit of length for "the smallest space possibly measured in nature," which is "less than billionths of trillionths of trillionths of an inch" (or something like 1.6×10^{-35} meters). (P. Baofu 2006a; N. McAleer 1987: 219; WKV 2008; D. Corbett 2008a)

That said—my usage of "transfinity" can also resolve (or better, dissolve) an age-old problem in philosophy known as "Zeno's paradoxes" (as already explained in *Sec. 2.2.3* of *FPHG*).

In any event, in relation to the finiteness-transfiniteness principle, on the other hand, there is finiteness (e.g., the finite number of the types of attribution, like the 2 types known as "explanatory attribution" and "interpersonal attribution," in *Sec. 2.2.1*; the finite number of the works on "self-fulfilling prophecy" in history aforecited, in *Sec. 2.2.2*; the finite number of laws in thermodynamics, like "conservation of energy" in the 1st law and "entropy" in the 2nd law, in *Sec. 2.3.1*; the finite number of the cateogries of properties in retrocausality, like "effect" and "cause," in *Sec. 2.3.2*; the finite number of the categories of causation in legal liability, like "factual causation" and "legal causation," in *Sec. 2.4.1*; the finite number of the fields of origin of RCA, like "safety-based, production-based, process-based, failure-based, and systems-based," in *Sec. 2.4.2*; the finite number of the types of creation myths, as shown in the 5 types aforedescribed, in *Sec. 2.5.1*; the finite number of the categories of causes, like the 4 ones suggested by Aristotle, in *Sec. 2.5.2*; the finite number of the types of situations in regard to adverse effects, as shown in the two types as discussed earlier, in *Sec. 3.2.1*; the finite number of types of unintended consequences, like the 3 types aforecited, in *Sec. 3.2.2*; the finite number of the properties of chaotic dynamics, like the 5 aforediscussed, in *Sec. 3.3.1*; the finite number of the experiments with the quantum Zeno effect, like the two by David J. Wineland and his group at NIST in 1989 and by Mark G. Raizen and his group at the University of Texas at Austin in 2001 aforecited, in *Sec. 3.3.2*; the finite number of the categories of countries during the Cold War, that is, "the free world" vs. "the communist bloc," when the domino theory was popular, in *Sec. 3.4.1*; the finite number of principles in effectual logic, like the 3 examples aforecited, in *Sec. 3.4.2*; the finite number of different forms of determinism with "one particular factor," like "psychological determinism," "linguistic determinism," "economic determinism," and "technological determinism," in *Sec. 3.5.1*; and the finite number of the categories of things in the universe, like "energy," "information," "matter," etc., which can recur, in according to the idea of eternal return, in *Sec. 3.5.2*).

On the other hand, there is transfinitty (e.g., the transfinite number of all the individual instances of attribution that have ever been made by all peoples in history, regardless of which types they actually belong to, in *Sec. 2.2.1*; the transfinite number of all the individual instances of "self-fulfilling prophecy" that have ever existed in history, in *Sec. 2.2.2*; the transfinite number of all the individual instances of "conservation of energy" and "entropy" that have ever occurred in history, in *Sec. 2.3.1*; the transfinite number of all the individual instances of "cause" and "effect" that have ever occurred in history, regardless of whether they belong to "causality" or "retrocausality," in *Sec. 2.3.2*; the transfinite number of all the individual instances of causation under the law that have ever occurred in history, regardless of whether they are "factual" or "legal," in *Sec. 2.4.1*; the transfinite number of all the individual instances of incidents that have ever occurred in history and required problem solving, regardless of which fileds of origin they belong to, in *Sec. 2.4.2*; the transfinite number of all the individual entities that have ever existed in the history of the universe, regardless of which creation myths can be used to understand their origins, in *Sec. 2.5.1*; the transfinite number of all the individual instances of causes that have ever ococurred in the history of the universe, regardless of which types they belong to, in *Sec. 2.5.2*; the transfinite number of all the individual instances of adverse effects that have ever occurred in history, regardless of which types of situations they belong to, in *Sec. 3.2.1*; the transfinite number of all the individual instances of unintended consequences that have ever occurred in history, regardless of which types they belong to, in *Sec. 3.2.2*; the transfinite number of all the individual instances of chaotic behavior that have ever occurred in history, regardless of which main properties they have or whether some properties are "redundant" or not, as discussed earlier, in *Sec. 3.3.1*; the transfinite number of all the individual subatomic particles that have ever existed in history, regardless of whether they can be used for experiments with the quantum Zeno effect or not, in *Sec. 3.3.2*; the transfinite number of all the individuals that have ever lived in history, regardless of whether their countries are "free," "communist," or something else, in *Sec. 3.4.1*; the transfinite number of all the individuals that have ever existed in history and have used different logics, regardless of whether they are "effectual," "causal," or something else, in *Sec. 3.4.2*; the transfinite number of all the particular events that have ever occurred in history, regardless of whether they can fit in any of the different forms of determinism as discussed earlier, in *Sec. 3.5.1*; and the transfinite number of all the individual bits, joules, and objects, in respect to info, energy, and matter, that have ever existed in history, regardless of whether they will recur or not in future returns, in *Sec. 3.5.2*).

And the reverse direction also holds true.

Once more, it should be stressed, however, that there are different shades of gray (or different degrees of truth) in the two opposites, and the classification is not necessarily mutually exclusive either. In fact, even when some combinations of the two occur, they only end up sharing the same dialectic relationship, but in a different degree.

Also, there are some other relationships (as a kind of family resemblance) which have something in common with the principle, but they are not exactly the same but only more or less comparable, which varies from case to case.

Good examples of family resemblance in relation to the principle are boundedness-quasiunboundedness, smallness-largeness, microness-macroness, boundedness-unboundedness, and the like.

9th Thesis: The Preciseness-Vagueness Principle

The ninth thesis is called the preciseness-vagueness principle (on the refinement of things) in the category of "structure" in existential dialectics (which was first out worked out in *FIA* and later, *FPHMORP*), in that both preciseness and vagueness are important, not that one is better than the other, but that both are used, in different degrees of preference, in accordance to the contextual application from the perspectives of nature, the mind, culture, and society. There is no preciseness without vagueness—and vice versa.

For illustration, in relation to taxonomy, preciseness has its taxonomic clarity, just as vagueness has its classificatory flexibility. And in relation to network, vagueness has its explorative liberty, just as preciseness has its conceptual definitiveness.

For instance, on the one hand, there is preciseness (e.g., the precise identification of 4 versions of attribution theory in the article aforecited, in *Sec. 2.2.1*; the precise identification of 6 examples of works on "self-fulfilling prophecy" in the article aforecited, in *Sec. 2.2.2*; the precise identification of 4 succinct ways to describe the 2nd law in the article aforecited, in *Sec. 2.3.1*; the precise identification of 3 fields where "retrocausality" has been proposed in the article, in *Sec. 2.3.2*; the precise identification of 6 ways to address the second stage of the "two-stage" inquiry about "legal causation" in the article aforecited, in *Sec. 2.4,1*; the precise identification of 8 principles of RCA in the article aforecited, in *Sec. 2.4,2*; the precise identification of 3 types of origin myths in the article aforecited, in *Sec. 2.5.1*; the precise identification of 4 types of causes by Aristotle, in *Sec. 2.5.2*; the precise identification of 5 reporting systems of adverse effects in the article aforecited, in *Sec. 3.2.1*; the precise identification of 5 causes of unintended consequences by Merton, in *Sec. 3.2.2*; the precise identification of 5 main properties of chaotic dynamics in the article aforecited, in *Sec. 3.3.1*; the precise identification of two experiments with the quantum Zeno effect, that is, by David J. Wineland and his group at NIST in 1989 and by Mark G. Raizen and his group at the University of Texas at Austin in 2001, in the article aforecited, in *Sec. 3.3.2*; the precise identification of two different worlds that is, "the free world" and "the communist bloc," during the Cold War, when the domino theory was popular, in *Sec. 3.4.1*; the precise identification of 3 principles of effectual logic in the article aforecited, in *Sec. 3.4.2*; the precise identification of 4 different forms of determinism with "one particular factor" in the article aforecited, in *Sec. 3.5.1*; and the precise identification of 2 types of entities in "nothing," like "info" and "energy," by the authors of "Godhead," in *Sec. 3.5.2*).

On the other hand, there is vagueness (e.g., the vagueness in the identification of the 4 versions of attribution theory in the article aforecited, since it is not clear why there must be only 4, not 3, 5, 6, 7, 8, and so on, in *Sec. 2.2.1*; the vagueness in the identification of the 6 examples of works on "self-fulfilling prophecy" in the article aforecited, since it is not clear why there must be only 6, not 7, 8, 9, 10, and so on, in *Sec. 2.2.2*; the vagueness in the identification of the 4 succinct ways to describe the 2nd law in the article aforecited, since it is not clear why there must be only 4, not 5, 6, 7, and so on, in *Sec. 2.3.1*; the vagueness in the identification of the 3 fields where "retrocausality" has been proposed in the article aforecited, since it is not clear why there must be only 3, not 4,

5, 6, 7, and so on, in *Sec. 2.3.2*; the vagueness in the identification of the 6 ways to address the second stage of the "two-stage" inquiry about "legal causation" in the article aforecited, since it is not clear why there must be only 6, not 7, 8, 9, 10, and so on, in *Sec. 2.4.1*; the vagueness in the identification of the 8 principles of RCA in the article aforecited, since it is not clear why there must be only 8, not 6, 7, 9, 10, 11, 12, and so on, in *Sec. 2.4,2*; the vagueness in the identification of the 3 types of origin myths in the article aforecited, since it is not clear why there must be only 3, not 4, 5, 6, 7, and so on, in *Sec. 2.5.1*; the vagueness in the identification of the 4 types of causes by Aristotle, since it is not clear why there must be only 4, not 1, 2, 3, 5, 7, and so on, in *Sec. 2.5.2*; the vagueness in the identification of the 5 reporting systems of adverse effects in the article aforecited, since it is not clear why there must be only these 5, not 6, 7, 8, 9, and so on, in *Sec. 3.2.1*; the vagueness in the identification of the 5 causes of unintended consequences by Merton, since it is not clear why there must be only 5, not 6, 7, 8, 9, and so on, in *Sec. 3.2.2*; the vagueness in the identification of the 5 main properties of chaotic dynamics in the article aforecited, since it is not clear why there must be only 5, not 2, 3, 4, 6, 7, and so on, since some critics pointed out that the property of "sensitivity to initial conditions" in the list can be redundant, in *Sec. 3.3.1*; the vagueness in the identification of the two experiments with the quantum Zeno effect, that is, by David J. Wineland and his group at NIST in 1989 and by Mark G. Raizen and his group at the University of Texas at Austin in 2001, in the article aforecited, since it is not clear why there must be only 2, not 3, 4, 5, 6, and so on, in *Sec. 3.3.2*; the vagueness in the identification of the two different worlds that is, "the free world" and "the communist bloc," during the Cold War, when the domino theory was popular, since it is not clear why there must be only 2, not 3, 4, and so on, as some countries regarded themselves as "the Third World," especially those in the "non-aligned movement," in *Sec. 3.4.1*; the vagueness in the identification of the 3 principles of effectual logic by Sarasvathy in the article aforecited, since it is not clear why there must be only 3, not 4, 5, 6, 7 ,8, 9, and so on, since there are 5 principles in a Wikipedia article on effectuation, in *Sec. 3.4.2*; the vagueness in the identification of the 4 different forms of determinism with "one particular factor" in the article aforecited, since it is not clear why there must be only 4, not 5, 6, 7, and so on, in *Sec. 3.5.1*; and the vagueness in the identification of the 2 types of entities in "nothing," like "info" and "energy," by the authors of "Godhead," since it is not clear why there must be only 2, not 3, 4, 5, 6, and so on, in *Sec. 3.5.2*).

And the reverse direction also holds true.

Once more, it should be stressed, however, that there are different shades of gray (or different degrees of truth) in the two opposites, and the classification is not necessarily mutually exclusive either. In fact, even when some combinations of the two occur, they only end up sharing the same dialectic relationship, but in a different degree.

Also, there are some other relationships (as a kind of family resemblance) which have something in common with the principle, but they are not exactly the same but only more or less comparable, which varies from case to case.

Good examples of family resemblance in relation to the principle are clarity-ambiguity, directness-indirectness, quantitativeness-qualitativeness, specificity-obscurity, describability-nondescribability, concretness-abstractness, translatability-untranslatability, specificity-generality, clearcutness-transitionalness, sharpness-roughness, discreteness-mixedness, discreteness-vagueness, detailedness-broadness, definition-nondefinition, and the like.

10th Thesis: The Simpleness-Complicatedness Principle

The tenth thesis refers to the simpleness-complicatedness principle (on the interconnection among things) in the category of "structure" in existential dialectics (which was first out worked out in *FIA*, *FPHPROB*, nd other books), in that both simpleness and complicatedness are vital, without favoring one over the other, and each is utilized, depending on the basis of the perspectives of nature, the mind, culture, and society. There is no simpleness without complicatedness—and vice versa.

As an illustration, in relation to taxonomy, simpleness has its heuristic usefulness, just as complicatedness has its realistic representation. In relation to network, simpleness has its economical attractiveness, just as complicatedness has its practical reliability. And in relation to logic, there is the simple zeroth-order logic, just as there is the complicated higher-order logic.

For instance, on the one hand, there is simpleness (e.g., the relatively simple analysis of attribution theory by the advocates, in *Sec. 2.2.1*; the relatively simple analysis of self-fulfilling prophecy" by the advocates, in *Sec. 2.2.2*; the relatively simple analysis of the 2nd law by the advocates, in *Sec. 2.3.1*; the relatively simple analysis of "retrocausality" by the advocates, in *Sec. 2.3.2*; the relatively simple analysis of the "two-stage" inquiry about "legal causation" by the advocates, in *Sec. 2.4.1*; the relatively simple analysis of RCA by the advocates, in *Sec. 2.4.2*; the relatively simple analysis of origin myths by the advocates, in *Sec. 2.5.1*;

the relatively simple analysis of 4 types of causes by Aristotle, in *Sec. 2.5.2*; the relatively simple analysis of "adverse effects" by the advocates, in *Sec. 3.2.1*; the relatively simple analysis of unintended consequences by Merton, in *Sec. 3.2.2*; the relatively simple analysis of the butterfly effect by the advocates, in *Sec. 3.3.1*; the relatively simple analysis of the quantum Zeno effect by the advocates, in *Sec. 3.3.2*; the relatively simple analysis of the domino theory by the advocates, in *Sec. 3.4.1*; the relatively simple analysis of effectuation by the advocates, in *Sec. 3.4.2*; the relatively simple analysis of causal determinism by the advocates, in *Sec. 3.5.1*; and the relatively simple analysis of "eternal return" by the advocates, in *Sec. 3.5.2*).

On the other hand, there is complicatedness (e.g., the relatively more complicated analysis of attribution theory, by challenging the claims and assumptions, as shown in the problems pointed out by the critics as cited, in *Sec. 2.2.1*; the relatively more complicated analysis of self-fulfilling prophecy," by challenging the claims and assumptions, as shown in the problems pointed out by the critics as cited, in *Sec. 2.2.2*; the relatively more complicated analysis of the 2nd law, by challenging the claims and assumptions, as shown in the problems pointed out by the critics as cited, in *Sec. 2.3.1*; the relatively more complicated analysis of "retrocausality," by challenging the claims and assumptions, as shown in the problems pointed out by the critics as cited, in *Sec. 2.3.2*; the relatively more complicated analysis of the "two-stage" inquiry about "legal causation," by challenging the claims and assumptions, as shown in the problems pointed out by the critics as cited, in *Sec. 2.4.1*; the relatively more complicated analysis of RCA, by challenging the claims and assumptions, as shown in the problems pointed out by the critics as cited, in *Sec. 2.4.2*; the relatively more complicated analysis of origin myths, by challenging the claims and assumptions, as shown in the problems pointed out by the critics as cited, in *Sec. 2.5.1*; the relatively more complicated analysis of 4 types of causes aforecited, by challenging the claims and assumptions, as shown in the problems pointed out by the critics as cited, in *Sec. 2.5.2*; the relatively more complicated analysis of "adverse effects," by challenging the claims and assumptions, as shown in the problems pointed out by the critics as cited, in *Sec. 3.2.1*; the relatively more complicated analysis of unintended consequences, by challenging the claims and assumptions, as shown in the problems pointed out by the critics as cited, in *Sec. 3.2.2*; the relatively more complicated analysis of the butterfly effect, by challenging the claims and assumptions, as shown in the problems pointed out by the critics as cited, in *Sec. 3.3.1*; the relatively more complicated analysis of the quantum Zeno effect, by challenging the claims and assumptions, as shown in the problems pointed out by the critics as cited, in *Sec. 3.3.2*; the relatively more complicated analysis of the domino theory, by challenging the claims and assumptions, as shown in the problems pointed out by the critics as cited, in *Sec. 3.4.1*; the relatively more complicated analysis of effectuation, by challenging the claims and assumptions, as shown in the problems pointed out by the critics as cited, in *Sec. 3.4.2*; the relatively more complicated analysis of causal determinism, by challenging the claims and assumptions, as shown in the problems pointed out by the critics as cited, in *Sec. 3.5.1*; and the relatively more complicated analysis of "eternal return," by challenging the claims and assumptions, as shown in the problems pointed out by the critics as cited, in *Sec. 3.5.2*).

And the reverse direction also holds true.

Again, it should be stressed, however, that there are different shades of gray (or different degrees of truth) in the two opposites, and the classification is not necessarily mutually exclusive either. In fact, even when some combinations of the two occur, they only end up sharing the same dialectic relationship, but in a different degree.

Also, there are some other relationships (as a kind of family resemblance) which have something in common with the principle, but they are not exactly the same but only more or less comparable, which varies from case to case.

Good examples of family resemblance in relation to the principle are inflexibility-flexibility, standardization-specialization, imperfectness-perfectness, superficiality-depth, shallowness-deepness, economicalness-elaboratedness, plainness-circumspection, onesidedness-multisidedness, succinctness-duplicatedness, simpleness-sophisticatedness, crudeness-subtleness, straightness-bendedness, and the like.

11th Thesis: The Openness-Hiddenness Principle

The eleventh thesis refers to the openness-hiddenenss principle (on the detection of things) in the category of "structure" in existential dialectics (which was already worked out in my previous books, especially in *FPHU*), in that reality has its hidden face, just as it is open to outside view in some other ways. There is no openness without hiddenness—and vice versa.

For instance, on the one hand, there is openness (e.g., the open exploration of explaining "the causes of behavior and events" by individuals, in *Sec. 2.2.1*; the open exploration of the belief in "self-fulfilling prophecy" by some people, in *Sec. 2.2.2*; the open exploration of entropy in the universe by the 2nd law, in *Sec. 2.3.1*; the open exploration of "retrocausality" in para-science, in *Sec. 2.3.2*; the open exploration of using "common sense" in the first stage of establishing "factual" causation, in *Sec. 2.4.1*; the open exploration of the usefulness of incident management in problem solving, in *Sec. 2.4.2*; the open exploration of origin myths to understand "the origin of some feature of the natural or social world," in *Sec. 2.5.1*; the open exploration of different types of causes by Aristotle, in *Sec. 2.5.2*; the open exploration of the adverse effects of "the MMR vaccine," in *Sec. 3.2.1*; the open exploration of the need to make "the War on Drugs" so as to "suppress the illegal drug trade," in *Sec. 3.2.2*; the open exploration of the existence of the "butterfly effect," in *Sec. 3.3.1*; the open exploration of "the quantum Zeno effect" on the basis of "the reductionist postulate for reconciling the measurement problem," in *Sec. 3.3.2*; the open exploration of the domino effect in Southeast Asia, by U.S. President Eisenhower and others later on, in Sec. *3.4.1*; the open exploration of effectual logic as an alternative to causal logic by Sarasvathy, in *Sec. 3.4.2*; the open exploration of a "materialistic" interpretation of the universe by those for causal determinism, in *Sec. 3.5.1*; and the open exploration of "eternal return" by cosmological theories like "the oscillating universe theory" and "the Steinhardt–Turok model," in *Sec. 3.5.2*)/

On the other hand, there is hiddenness (e.g., the hidden bias in the open exploration of explaining "the causes of behavior and events" by individuals, due to different "cognitive biases," in *Sec. 2.2.1*; the hidden bias in the belief in "self-fulfilling prophecy" by some people, since what they believe in may actually be false, in *Sec. 2.2.2*; the hidden bias in the open exploration of entropy in the universe by the 2nd law, due to the problems aforecited, in *Sec. 2.3.1*; the hidden bias in the open exploration of "retrocausality" in para-science, since "mainstream scientists generally regarded these explanations as pseudoscientific," in *Sec. 2.3.2*; the hidden bias in the appeal to "common sense" in the first stage of establishing "factual" causation, since it has been criticized as unsatisfactory by some legal scholars aforecited, in *Sec. 2.4.1*; the hidden bias in the open exploration of the usefulness of incident management in problem solving, since the critics pointed out its various problems, in that it focuses too much on gradual [not radical] corrective action, that it is too reactive [not proactive enough], and so on, in *Sec. 2.4.2*; the hidden bias in the open exploration of origin myths to understand "the origin of some feature of the natural or social world," because of the different problems aforediscussed, in *Sec. 2.5.1*; the hidden bias in the open exploration of different types of causes by Aristotle, since to the critics, "Aristotle's metaphysics, his account of nature and causality, was for the most part rejected by the early modern philosophers," in *Sec. 2.5.2*; the hidden bias in the "public outcry" and "lawsuits against drug manufacturers" in regard to the claim about "autism…linked to the MMR vaccine," because "no link has been found in several large studies, and despite removal of thimerosal from vaccines a decade ago the rate of autism has not decreased as would be expected if it had been the causative agent," in *Sec. 3.2.1*; the hidden bias in the exploration of the need to make "the War on Drugs," because "the War on Drugs, intended to suppress the illegal drug trade, instead consolidates the profitability of drug cartels," in *Sec. 3.2.2*; the hidden bias in the open exploration of the existence of the "butterfly effect," since the critics pointed out that the so-called "butterfly effect" is much exaggerated, that the so-called "butterfly effect" misleadingly exclude some other effects in its analysis, that the butterfly effect can be countered by more complicated forecasting systems, that the butterfly effect does not apply in some situations, etc., in *Sec. 3.3.1*; the hidden bias in the open exploration of "the quantum Zeno effect" on the basis of "the reductionist postulate for reconciling the measurement problem," since the critics point out that "the quantum Zeno effect does not apply to all interpretations of quantum theory, in particular, the many-worlds interpretation…and the Quantum Logic Interpretation," in *Sec. 3.3.2*; the hidden bias in the open exploration of the domino effect in Southeast Asia, by U.S. President Eisenhower and others later on, since the critics pointed out that the domino theory rests on some false assumptions, that the domino theory neglects "nationalist" causes, that domino theory also ignores the cancerous problem of domesic corruption, that the domino theory had failed in its predictions, and that whether the domino effect is bad or not is relative, in *Sec. 3.4.1*; the hidden bias in the open exploration of effectual logic as an alternative to causal logic by Sarasvathy, because of the biased problems as discussed earlier, in *Sec. 3.4.2*; the hidden bias in the open exploration of a "materialistic" interpretation of the universe by those for causal determinism, because, to the critics, "it ignores the minds or souls of conscious beings," in *Sec. 3.5.1*; and the hidden bias in the open exploration of "eternal return" by cosmological theories like "the oscillating universe theory" and "the Steinhardt–Turok model," since these theories have been critcized as highly speculative without any proof, in *Sec. 3.5.2*).

And the reverse direction also holds true.

Again, it should be stressed, however, that there are different shades of gray (or different degrees of truth) in the two opposites, and the classification is not necessarily mutually exclusive either. In fact, even when some combinations of the two occur, they only end up sharing the same dialectic relationship, but in a different degree.

Also, there are some other relationships (as a kind of family resemblance) which have something in common with the principle, but they are not exactly the same but only more or less comparable, which varies from case to case.

Good examples of family resemblance in relation to the principle are overtness-covertness, participation-obstruction, publicness-privateness, openness-closedness, surface-depth, transparency-secrecy, openness-biasedness, , exposition-illusion, and so on.

12th Thesis: The Denseness-Emptiness Principle

The twelfth thesis concerns the denseness-emptiness principle (on the distribution of entities in space) in the category of "structure" in existential dialectics, which is first proposed in *FPHUP*, in that both density and void are needed, in relation to the mind, nature, culture, and society, albeit in different ways. There is no denseness without emptiness—and vice versa.

Lest any misunderstanding occurs, the term "void" is used here only as an approximation of emptiness (depending on the degree of the lack of density), since, in physics, it is well known that "empty" space is not really empty all the way, because it can be full of energy (e.g., random quantum fluctuations at the sub-atomic level, and, for that matter, dark energy in the universe) and matter (e.g., different versions of sub-atomic particles, and, for that matter, dark matter in the universe). (F. Wilczek 2008)

For instance, on the one hand, there is denseness (e.g., the relatively denser concentration of concerns with "dispositional and internal factors for success and external, uncontrollable factors for failure" by those committing "self-serving bias," in *Sec. 2.2.1*; the relatively denser concentration of concerns with "self-fulfilling prophecy" by those like Merton, in *Sec. 2.2.2*; the relatively denser concentration of concerns with "conservation of energy" in the 1st law of thermodynamics, in *Sec. 2.3.1*; the relatively denser concentration of concerns with "retrocausality" by those in para-science, in *Sec. 2.3.2*; the relatively denser concentration of concerns with "common sense" in establishing "factual causation" by the advocates of the "two-stage" inquiry, in *Sec. 2.4.1*; the relatively denser concentration of concerns with "small changes" by those in continuous improvement, in *Sec. 2.4.2*; the relatively denser concentration of concerns with "nothing" by those believers in "creation ex nihilo" myths," in *Sec. 2.5.1*; the relatively denser concentration of concerns with the metaphysics of "telos" by Aristotle, in *Sec. 2.5.2*; the relatively denser concentration of concerns with harmful side-effects by those in the "public outcry" and "lawsuits against drug manufacturers" in regard to the claim about "autism…linked to the MMR vaccine," in *Sec. 3.2.1*; the relatively denser concentration of concerns with "unintentionality" by Merton in the context of "unintended consequences, in *Sec. 3.2.2*; the relatively denser concentration of concerns with the property of "sensitivity to initial conditions" by the advocates of the butterfly effect, in *Sec. 3.3.1*; the relatively denser concentration of concerns with "the reductionist postulate" by those advocates of "the quantum Zeno effect," in *Sec. 3.3.2*; the relatively denser concentration of concerns with the spread of "world communism" by the U.S. during the Cold War, in *Sec. 3.4.1*; the relatively denser concentration of concerns with "affordable loss" by the advocates of effectuation, in *Sec. 3.4.2*; the relatively denser concentration of concerns with "materialism" by those for causal determinism, in *Sec. 3.5.1*; and the relatively denser concentration of concerns with "eternal return" by Nietzsche, in *Sec. 3.5.2*).

On the other hand, there is emptiness (e.g., the relatively less dense, or more empty, concentration of concerns with "cultural factors" by those committing "self-serving bias," in *Sec. 2.2.1*; the relatively less dense, or more empty, concentration of concerns with "self-defeating prophecy" by those like Merton, in *Sec. 2.2.2*; the relatively less dense, or more empty, concentration of concerns with "entropy" in the 1st law of thermodynamics, in *Sec. 2.3.1*; relatively less dense, or more empty, concentration of concerns with "retrocausality" by those in mainstream science, in *Sec. 2.3.2*; the relatively less dense, or more empty, concentration of concerns with "common sense" in establishing "factual causation" by the critics like Hart, Honoré, and Wright, who criticized the appeal to "common sense" in establishing "factual causation" as "unsatisfactory" and "proposed a test of sufficiency instead," in *Sec. 2.4.1*; the relatively less dense, or more empty, concentration of concerns with "radical changes" by those in continuous improvement, in *Sec. 2.4.2*; the relatively less dense, or more empty, concentration of concerns with "disorder" and "order" by those believers in"creation ex nihilo" myths, in *Sec. 2.5.1*; the relatively less dense, or more empty, concentration of concerns with the metaphysics of "telos" by contemporary scientists, in *Sec. 2.5.2*; the relatively less dense, or more empty, concentration of concerns with beneficial side-effects by those in the "public outcry" and "lawsuits against drug manufacturers" in regard to the claim about "autism…linked to the MMR vaccine," in *Sec. 3.2.1*; the relatively less dense, or more empty, concentration of concerns with "intentionality" and "nonintentionality" by Merton in the context of "unintended consequences," in *Sec. 3.2.2*; the relatively less dense, or more empty, concentration of concerns with the property of "sensitivity to initial conditions" by the critics of the butterfly effect, who argued instead that "sensitivity to initial conditions...is actually redundant in the definition, being implied by two [or for intervals, one] purely topological conditions, in *Sec. 3.3.1*; the relatively less dense, or more empty, concentration of concerns with "the many-worlds interpretation...and the Quantum Logic Interpretation" by those advocates of "the quantum Zeno effect," in *Sec. 3.3.2*; the relatively less dense, or more empty, concentration of concerns with the spread of "world communism" by Switzerland during the Cold War, as it was "neutral," in *Sec. 3.4.1*; the relatively less dense, or more empty, concentration of concerns with "optimality" by the advocates of effectuation, in *Sec. 3.4.2*; the relatively less dense, or more empty, concentration of concerns with "minds or souls" by those for causal determinism, in *Sec. 3.5.1*; and the relatively less dense, or more empty, concentration of concerns with the second law of thermodynamics for increasing entropy in the universe by Nietzsche, in *Sec. 3.5.2*).

And the reverse direction also holds true.

Again, it should be stressed, however, that there are different shades of gray (or different degrees of truth) in the two opposites, and the classification is not necessarily mutually exclusive either. In fact, even when some combinations of the two occur, they only end up sharing the same dialectic relationship, but in a different degree.

Also, there are some other relationships (as a kind of family resemblance) which have something in common with the principle, but they are not exactly the same but only more or less comparable, which varies from case to case.

Good examples of family resemblance in relation to the principle are fullness-voidness, nearness-farness, concentration-dispersion, denseness-nothingness, something-nothing, heaviness-lightness, composition-emptiness, solidity-void, presence-absence, focus-unfocus, emphasis-disemphasis, and the like.

13th Thesis: The Rule-Exception Principle

The thirteenth thesis concerns the rule-exception principle (on the extent of typicality) in the category of "structure" in existential dialectics, which is first proposed in *FPHTHAN*, in that both rules and their exceptions exist—in relation to the mind, nature, culture, and society, albeit in different ways. There is no rule without exception—and vice versa.

As the old saying goes, "There is an exception to the rule"; however, to avoid misuse, there are the following four important aspects of the relationship between rules and exceptions to be clarified:

- If there is an exception to the rule, there can be an exception to the.rule itself that there is an exception to the rule, as shown in some cases where no exception is allowed—but this regression can continue further (e.g., there is an exception to the rule that there can be an exception to the rule itself that there is an exception to the rule).
- To be an exception to the rule does not mean that one can say something nonsensual, either jokingly or seriously, and then expects others to allow an exception.
- To be an exception to the rule does not mean that one can appeal to an invalid generalization, either literally or figuratively, and then expects others to allow an exception.
- An exception to a rule means that the exception implies the existence of a rule, which does not apply in the special case under consideration—but the exception does not automatically justify that the rule is desirable, good, right, etc.

In any event, on the one hand, there are rules (e.g., the usual generalization, procedure, habit, or tendency that normal individuals tend to commit "biases and errors" in attributions, in *Sec. 2.2.1*; the usual generalization, procedure, habit, or tendency that, as stated by the Thomas theorem, "If men define situations as real, they are real in their consequences," in *Sec. 2.2.2*; the usual generalization, procedure, habit, or tendency that "the entropy of the universe tends to a maximum," in *Sec. 2.3.1*; the usual generalization, procedure, habit, or tendency that, in general, mainstream physics "does not generally employ retrocausality," in *Sec. 2.3.2*; the usual generalization, procedure, habit, or tendency that the examination of causation follows the "two-stage" approach in the U.S., in *Sec. 2.4.1*; the usual generalization, procedure, habit, or tendency that incident management is "reactive" to incidents, in *Sec. 2.4.2*; the usual generalization, procedure, habit, or tendency that "cultures take their creation-myths stories as true to varying degrees," in *Sec. 2.5.1*; the usual generalization, procedure, habit, or tendency that, to Aristotle, final causes are teleological, in *Sec. 2.5.2*; the usual generalization, procedure, habit, or tendency that "the harmful outcome" of adverse effects is not death but "is usually indicated by some result such as morbidity, mortality, alteration in body weight, levels of enzymes, loss of function, or as a pathological change detected at the microscopic, macroscopic or physiological level," in *Sec. 3.2.1*; the usual generalization, procedure, habit, or tendency that Merton's work is to focus more on "unintended consequences" as those which are "not intentional," in *Sec. 3.2.2*; the usual generalization, procedure, habit, or tendency that the "butterfly effect" exists in nature, in *Sec. 3.3.1*; the usual generalization, procedure, habit, or tendency that "an unstable [excited] particle, if observed continuously, will never decay," also known as "the quantum Zeno effect," in *Sec. 3.3.2*; the usual generalization, procedure, habit, or tendency that the domino theory refers to the spread of "world communism," in *Sec. 3.4.1*; the usual generalization, procedure, habit, or tendency that "the best entrepreneurs...prefer effectual reasoning over causal reasoning in the early stages of a new venture," in *Sec. 3.4.2*; the usual generalization, procedure, habit, or tendency that "the probabilities discovered in quantum mechanics," as Stephen Hawking explains, are not those of "traditional determinism, but rather determined probabilities" in *Sec. 3.5.1*; and the usual generalization, procedure, habit, or tendency that, in general, "with the decline of antiquity and the spread of Christianity, the concept [of eternal return] fell into disuse in the Western world," in *Sec. 3.5.2*).

On the other hand, there are exceptions (e.g., a case to which a rule does not apply, such as the exceptional case, as told by Aristotle, that "the most intelligent minds are those that can entertain an idea without necessarily believing it," so as to be able to deal with "biases and errors" better than the normal individuals, in *Sec. 2.2.1*; a case to which a rule does not apply, such as the exceptional case of "self-defeating prophecy," which counters the "Thomas theorem," in *Sec. 2.2.2*; a case to which a rule does not apply, such as the exceptional case that "in thermodynamic systems that are not closed, entropy can decrease with time," in *Sec. 2.3.1*; a case to which a rule does not apply, such as the exceptional case when "a number of theories allowing particles or information to travel backward in time have been proposed by prominent scientists" in mainstream physics, even though, as a rule, "mainstream scientists generally regarded these explanations as pseudoscientific," in *Sec. 2.3.2*; a case to which a rule does not apply, such as the exceptional cases, in which the judge can exercise some discretion [such that a defendant can still be liable even if he successfully passes the "two-stage inquiry" about legal liability] and, in addition, causation in the "two-stage inquiry" may not be relevant at all in some other legal cases, as discussed earlier, in *Sec. 2.4.1*; a case to which a rule does not apply, such as the exceptional case when incident management can become "proactive," if "insights in RCA may make it useful as a preemptive method" under cetain circumstances, in *Sec. 2.4.2*; a case to which a rule does not apply, such as the exceptional case that, even in those cultures with "creation myths," to some scientists, "the term 'myth' often refers to false or fanciful stories," in *Sec. 2.5.1*; a case to which a rule does not apply, such as the exceptional cases of "chance events," such that "not all phenomena have a final cause, e.g., chance events," in *Sec. 2.5.2*; a case to which a rule does not apply, such as the exceptional case involving "serious adverse events" or SAE, which can "cause…death," in *Sec. 3.2.1*; a case to which a rule does not apply, such as the exceptional case that what is "not intentional" does not necessarily mean "unintentional," because Merton does not distinguish between something ["non-intentional"] and something ['unintentional," in *Sec. 3.2.2*; a case to which a rule does not apply, such as the exceptional case in regard to the "butterfly effect," in that "extreme [exponential] dependence on initial conditions is not expected in pure quantum treatments," in *Sec. 3.3.1*; a case to which a rule does not apply, such as the exceptional case that "an enhancement of decay due to frequent measurements could be observed under somewhat more general conditions, leading to the so-called anti-Zeno effect," in *Sec. 3.3.2*; a case to which a rule does not apply, such as the exceptional case of the use of the domino theory to refer to the spread of "liberal democracy," because "in the 2003 invasion of Iraq, some neoconservatives argued that when a democratic government is implemented, it would then help spread democracy and liberalism across the Middle East, and a war can install a democratic government. This has often been referred to as a 'reverse domino theory,'" in *Sec. 3.4.1*; a case to which a rule does not apply, such as the exceptional case that a small number of entrepreneurs "transition well into latter stages requiring more causal reasoning," in *Sec. 3.4.2*; a case to which a rule does not apply, such as the exceptional situation, in which "in some cases, a quantum particle may indeed trace an exact path, and the probability of finding the particles in that path is one [certain]," in *Sec. 3.5.1*; and a case to which a rule does not apply, such as "the exception of Friedrich Nietzsche, who connected the thought to many of his other concepts, including *amor fati*," even though at the time, "with the decline of antiquity and the spread of Christianity, the concept [of eternal return] fell into disuse in the Western world," in *Sec. 3.5.2*).

And the reverse direction also holds true.

Again, it should be stressed, however, that there are different shades of gray (or different degrees of truth) in the two opposites, and the classification is not necessarily mutually exclusive either. In fact, even when some combinations of the two occur, they only end up sharing the same dialectic relationship, but in a different degree.

Also, there are some other relationships (as a kind of family resemblance) which have something in common with the principle, but they are not exactly the same but only more or less comparable, which varies from case to case.

Good examples of family resemblance in relation to the principle are generalization-exception, custom-deviance, procedure-exception, pattern-deviance, typicality-exception, normalcy-extremity, and the like.

14th Thesis: The Indispensability-Dispensability Principle

The fourteenth thesis concerns the indispensability-dispensability principle (on the nature of superfluity) in the category of "structure" in existential dialectics, which is first proposed in *FPHETIO*, in that both indispensability and dispensability exist—in relation to the mind, nature, culture, and society, albeit in different ways. There is no indispensability without dispensability—and vice versa.

There are the following four important aspects of the relationship between indispensability and dispensability to be clarified:

- There can be slightly different meanings in relation to an attribute; for instance, "dispensability" can mean "redundancy" (e.g., something which is superfluous and thus not really needed), or "replaceability" (e.g, something which can be replaced and thus not strictly needed).
- The indispensability-dispensability principle should not be confused with the functionality-nonfunctionality principle, since "dispensability" (like "redundancy") is not necessarily non-functional, since something can be functional but not needed.
- There can be different degrees of indispensability and dispensability, since something can be more necessary than something else on a particular occasion.

In any event, on the one hand, there is indispensability (e.g., the need for something or someone, like the selective choice of information to "explain the causes of behavior and events" in "attribution," in *Sec. 2.2.1*; the need for something or someone, like the necessary inclusion of the examples of works around the world on self-fulfilling prophecy in the article aforecited, in *Sec. 2.2.2*; the need for something or someone, like the necessary inclusion of the formulations of the second law by Clausius and Kelvin in the article aforecited, as they are two of the most important pioneers, in *Sec. 2.3.1*; the need for something or someone, like the necessary inclusion of "retrocausality" in "the Wheeler–Feynman absorber theory, proposed by John Archibald Wheeler [1945] and Richard Feynman," in *Sec. 2.3.2*; the need for something or someone, like the necessary inclusion of the examination of "causation" in the case Yorkshire Dale Steamship Co v Minister of War Transport [1942], in *Sec. 2.4.1*; the need for something or someone, like the necessary inclusion of incident management to be used in situations which require "a reactive method of identifying event[s] causes, revealing problems and solving them," in *Sec. 2.4.2*; the need for something or someone, like the necessary inclusion of origin myths in "traditional cultures," where "the entities and forces described in origin myths are…considered sacred," in *Sec. 2.5.1*; the need for something or someone, like the necessary inclusion of "efficient cause," insofar as "in the case of a statue, it is the person chiseling away which transforms a block of marble into a statue," in *Sec. 2.5.2*; the need for something or someone, like the requirement of reporting systems "in many countries," where "adverse effects are required by law to be reported, researched in clinical trials and included into the patient information accompanying medical devices and drugs for sale to the public," in the article aforecited, in *Sec. 3.2.1*; the need for something or someone, like the necessary inclusion of "unexpected benefits" and "unexpected drawbacks" as types of "unintended consequences" by Merton, in *Sec. 3.2.2*; the need for something or someone, like the necessary inclusion of the second property in the definition of "chaos" as discussed earlier, in *Sec. 3.3.1*; the need for something or someone, like the necessary inclusion of "the reductionist postulate" by the advocates of "the quantum Zeno effect," in *Sec. 3.3.2*; the need for something or someone, like the necessary inclusion of President Eisenhower in the history of the domino theory, since he "was the first to refer to countries in danger of Communist takeover as dominoes" in 1954, in *Sec. 3.4.1*; the need for something or someone, like the necessary classification of the principles of effectual logic in terms of 3 by Sarasvathy in the article aforecited, in *Sec. 3.4.2*; the need for something or someone, like the necessary inclusion of the idea that "for every event…exist conditions that could cause no other event" in the definition of "causal determinism," in *Sec. 3.5.1*; and the need for something or someone, like the necessary inclusion of "*amor fati*, 'love of fate'" to deal with "eternal return," according to Nietzsche, in *Sec. 3.5.2*).

On the other hand, there is dispensability (e.g., the superfluity of something or someone, like "information overload" in some situations, when an individual relies instead on "cognitive biases" which can "enable faster decisions when timeliness is more valuable..., as illustrated in heuristics" by discarding much of other information not needed, in *Sec. 2.2.1;* the superfluity of something or someone, like the dispensable inclusion of a variant of the Arabic story "The Ruined Man Who Became Rich Again Through a Dream" in English folklore as the "Pedlar of Swaffham," since this later citation does not add anything new to the concept of "self-fulfilling prophecy" in the article aforecited, other than just a minor digression, in *Sec. 2.2.2;* the superfluity of something or someone, like the dispensable inclusion of many other possible formulations to the second law, as the philosopher/physicist P.W. Bridgman once said that "there have been nearly as many formulations of the second law as there have been discussions of it," such that many of them are rather unnecessary and redundant, since they do not really add anything essentially new to the second law, in *Sec. 2.3.1;* the superfluity of something or someone, like the dispensable inclusion of "retrocausality" in the example about "quantum entanglement," because "the description of such nonlocal quantum entanglements can be described in a way that is manifestly free of retrocausality if the states of the observers are included in the quantum treatment, which is often but not exclusively associated with the many worlds interpretation," in *Sec. 2.3.2;* the superfluity of something or someone, like the non-necessity of the examination of "causation" in the case "under a contract of indemnity insurance," in which case the inquiry about "causation" is not relevant, in *Sec. 2.4.1;* the superfluity of something or someone, like the dispensable inclusion of "safety-based RCA" in a problem-solving situation, since there can be other alternatives to choose from, like "production-based RCA, "process-based RCA," "failure-based RCA," and so on, in *Sec. 2.4.2;* the superfluity of something or someone, like the dispensable "distinction between cosmogonic myths and origin myths," which "is not clear-cut," because "a myth about the origin of some part of the world necessarily presupposes the existence of the world—which, for many cultures, presupposes a cosmogonic myth," but this distinction is not universal in all cultures, in *Sec. 2.5.1;* the superfluity of something or someone, like the dispensable inclusion of "final causes," insofar as there are "chance events," and "Aristotle's metaphysics, his account of nature and causality, was for the most part rejected by the early modern philosophers," in *Sec. 2.5.2;* the superfluity of something or someone, like the dispensable suggestion of reporting adverse effects in Australia, where "reporting is voluntary," not required, in *Sec. 3.2.1*; the superfluity of something or someone, like the dispensable inclusion of "perverse results," since "perverse results" can be part of "unexpected benefits" and/or part of "unexpected drawbacks," so in either case it is redundant, because it can be classified as a sub-set of the first type, of the second type, or of both types, contrary to Merton's classification, in *Sec. 3.2.2*; the superfluity of something or someone, like the dispensable inclusion of the property of "sensitivity to initial conditions," since to the critics, "sensitivity to initial conditions…is actually redundant in the definition, being implied by two [or for intervals, one] purely topological conditions," in *Sec. 3.3.1*; the superfluity of something or someone, like the dispensable inclusion of "the many-worlds interpretation…and the Quantum Logic Interpretation" by those advocates of "the quantum Zeno effect," because "quantum Zeno effect does not apply to all interpretations of quantum theory," in *Sec. 3.3.2*; the superfluity of something or someone, like the dispensable inclusion of the "neocons" in the history of the domino theory, since they were more concerned with the "reverse domino theory" in the Middle East during the 2000s, in *Sec. 3.4.1*; the superfluity of something or someone, like the dispensable classification of the principles of effectual logic in terms of 5 in the Wikipedia article on effectuation, but it is not accepted in the article by Sarasvathy as discussed earlier, in *Sec. 3.4.2*; the superfluity of something or someone, like the dispensable inclusion of "linguistic determinism" in an analysis of "causal determinism," since there are other forms of determinism, like "economic determinism," "technological determinism," etc., which can be used instead, in *Sec. 3.5.1*; and the superfluity of something or someone, like the dispensable inclusion of the proof for "eternal return," since, "according to Heidegger, it is the burden imposed by the question of eternal recurrence," but not "whether or not such a thing could possibly be true," that is so important for Nietzsche, in *Sec. 3.5.2*).

And the reverse direction also holds true.

Again, it should be stressed, however, that there are different shades of gray (or different degrees of truth) in the two opposites, and the classification is not necessarily mutually exclusive either. In fact, even when some combinations of the two occur, they only end up sharing the same dialectic relationship, but in a different degree.

Also, there are some other relationships (as a kind of family resemblance) which have something in common with the principle, but they are not exactly the same but only more or less comparable, which varies from case to case.

Good examples of family resemblance in relation to the principle are necessity-duplication, essentialness-excessiveness, necessity-repetition, requiredness-prolixity, necessity-superfluity, necessity-verbosity, need-circumlocution, importance-triviality, necessity-replaceability, and the like.

In Relation to Process

The next six theses are in relation to process in existential dialectics, as shown below.

15th Thesis: The Prototypicality-Variation Principle

The fifteenth thesis concerns the prototypicality-variation principle (on the nature of duplication) in the category of "process" in existential dialectics, which was first proposed in *FPHMORPH*, in that, if there are prototypes, there are also variants of the copies. There is no prototypicality without variation—and vice versa.

There are the following four important aspects of the relationship between prototypess and their copies, as shown in the fields of morphology (e.g., "proto-languages" in *FPHMORP*), information architecture (e.g., "taxonomies" in *FIA*), and evolutionry biology (e.g., "mutation" and "variation" in *BNN*), just to cite three well-documented sources:

- Prototypes and their copies are not static and may change or die out over time, but new ones may emerge.
- Some copies may have multiple prototypes, not just one.
- It can be very challenging to trace some copies back to their prototypes, under certain difficult historical conditions.
- Copies are not solely identical duplications of prototypes but have their own variations (mutations).

In any event, on the one hand, there are prototypes (e.g., the prototype, like the example about the original work on "attribution" by Fritz Heider in the 1920s, in *Sec. 2.2.1*; the prototype, like the example about the original work on "self-fulfilling prophecy" by 'The Ruined Man Who Became Rich Again Through a Dream" in the Arabian Nights, in Sec. *2.2.2*; the prototype, like the example about the original work on the 2nd law by Sadi Carnot in 1824, in *Sec. 2.3.1*; the prototype, like the example about the original work on "retrocausality" by Michael Dummett in the 1950s, in *Sec. 2.3.2*; the prototype, like the example about the original case on "the but for test" understood as "'the man in the street' would" in Yorkshire Dale Steamship Co v Minister of War Transport [1942], in *Sec. 2.4.1*; the prototype, like the example about the original work on "continuous improvement" by W. Edwards Deming, in *Sec. 2.4.2*; the prototype, like the example about the original Greek mythology about "Antenor," in *Sec. 2.5.1*; the prototype, like the example about the original work on teleology in "final cause" by Aristotle, in *Sec. 2.5.2*; the prototype, like the example about the original act known as "National Childhood Vaccine Injury Act [NCVIA]" in 1986, requiring reporting systems of adverse effects in the U.S., in *Sec. 3.2.1*; the prototype, like the example about the original work on unintended consequences by Adam Smith in the 18th century, in *Sec. 3.2.2*; the prototype, like the example about the original work on chaos theory by Henri Poincaré in the 1880s, in *Sec. 3.3.1*; the prototype, like the example about the original description of the quantum Zeno effect by Alan Turing in 1954, in *Sec. 3.3.2*; the prototype, like the example about the original formation of the domino theory by U.S. President Dwight D. Eisenhower in 1954, in *Sec. 3.4.1*; the prototype, like the example about the original work on effectuation by Sarasvathy in 2001, in *Sec. 3.4.2*; the prototype, like the example about the original work on "causal determinism" by the Stoics in the history of the Western philosophical tradition, in *Sec. 3.5.1*; and the prototype, like the example about the original work on eternal return by Nietzsche, in *Sec. 3.5.2*).

On the other hand, there are variants (e.g., different variants of the protoptye, as shown in many studies since the original work on "attribution" by Fritz Heider in the 1920s —like the later ones by Edward E. Jones and Keith Davis on Correspondent Inference Theory, Harold Kelley on Covariation Model of Attribution, Bernard Weiner on Three-dimensional Model of Attribution, etc., though each with its own variation, contribution, and disagreement, in *Sec. 2.2.1*; different variants of the protoptye, as shown in many studies since the original work on "self-fulfilling prophecy" by 'The Ruined Man Who Became Rich Again Through a Dream" in the Arabian Nights—like the later ones such as "a variant…in English folklore" known as the "Pedlar of Swaffham," though with its own variation, contribution, and disagreement, in *Sec. 2.2.2*; different variants of the protoptye, as shown in many studies since the original work on the 2nd law by Sadi Carnot in 1824—like the later ones by Clausius, Kelvin, etc., though each with its own variation, contribution, and disagreement, in *Sec. 2.3.1*; different variants of the protoptye, as shown in many studies since the original work on "retrocausality" by Michael Dummett in the 1950s—like the later ones by Helmut Schmidt in 1978, Jan Faye in 1994, etc., though each with its own variation, contribution, and disagreement, in *Sec. 2.3.2*; different variants of the protoptye, as shown in many studies since the original case on "the but for test" understood as "'the man in the street' would" in Yorkshire Dale Steamship Co v Minister of War Transport [1942]—like the later ones such as March v Stramare (1991) in terms of "common sense," though with its own variation, contribution, and disagreement, in *Sec. 2.4.1*; different variants of the protoptye, as shown in many studies since the original work on "continous management" by W. Edwards Deming—like the later ones on RCA as a tool of "continuous improvement," "Kaizen" by Masaaki Imai, etc., though each with its own variation, contribution, and disagreement, in *Sec. 2.4.2*; different variants of the protoptye, as shown in many studies since the original Greek mythology about "Antenor"—like the later ones about the 13th-century Italian city Padua, where "each commune looked for a Roman founder and if one was not available, it invented one" and "a legend had been current in the city, attributing its foundation to the Trojan Antenor," though with its own variation, contribution, and disagreement, in *Sec. 2.5.1*; different variants of the protoptye, as shown in many studies since the original work on teleology in "final cause" by Aristotle—like the later ones by Asa Gray and T. H. Huxley in the 19th century, though each with its own variation, contribution, and disagreement, in *Sec. 2.5.2*; different variants of the protoptye, as shown in many studies since the original act known as "National Childhood Vaccine Injury Act [NCVIA]" in 1986, requiring reporting systems of adverse effects in the U.S.—like the later one known as "the Vaccine Adverse Event Reporting System" in 1990, though with its own variation, contribution, and disagreement, in *Sec. 3.2.1*; different variants of the protoptye, as shown in many studies since the original work on unintended consequences by Adam Smith in the 18th century —like the later ones by Merton in 1936, though with its own variation, contribution, and disagreement, in *Sec. 3.2.2*; different variants of the protoptye, as shown in many studies since the original work on chaos theory by Henri Poincaré in the 1880s—like the later ones by G. D. Birkhoff, A. N. Kolmogorov, M.L. Cartwright, J.E. Littlewood, Stephen Smale, and so on in the 20th century, though each with its own variation, contribution, and disagreement, in *Sec. 3.3.1*; different variants of the protoptye, as shown in many studies since the original description of the quantum Zeno effect by Alan Turing in 1954—like the later ones by Degasperis et al. in 1974, George Sudarshan and Baidyanath Misra in 1977, etc., though each with its own variation, contribution, and disagreement, in *Sec. 3.3.2*; different variants of the protoptye, as shown in many works since the original formation of the domino theory by U.S. President Dwight D. Eisenhower in 1954—like the later ones by John F. Kennedy, Richard Nixon, etc., though each with its own variation, contribution, and disagreement, in *Sec. 3.4.1*; different variants of the protoptye, as shown in many studies since the original work on effectuation by Sarasvathy in 2001—like the later one with 5 principles by The Society for Effectual Action, though with its own variation, contribution, and disagreement, in *Sec. 3.4.2*; different variants of the protoptye, as shown in many studies since the original work on "causal determinism" by the Stoics in the history of the Western philosophical tradition—like the later ones by Thomas Hobbes, Baruch Spinoza, Gottfried Leibniz, David Hume, Arthur Schopenhauer, William James, Friedrich Nietzsche, etc., though each with its own variation, contribution, and disagreement, in *Sec. 3.5.1*; and different variants of the protoptye, as shown in many studies since the original work on eternal return by Nietzsche—like the later ones by Martin Heidegger, Rudolf Steiner, Walter Kaufmann, etc., commenting on Nietzsche's work, though each with its own variation, contribution, and disagreement, in *Sec. 3.5.2*).

And the reverse direction also holds true.

Again, it should be stressed, however, that there are different shades of gray (or different degrees of truth) in the two opposites, and the classification is not necessarily mutually exclusive either. In fact, even when some combinations of the two occur, they only end up sharing the same dialectic relationship, but in a different degree.

Also, there are some other relationships (as a kind of family resemblance) which have something in common with the principle, but they are not exactly the same but only more or less comparable, which varies from case to case.

Good examples of family resemblance in relation to the principle are archetypicality-descendedness, origin-descendedness, prototypicality-duplication, archetypicality-mutation, prototypicality-copyness, ancestry-descendedness, origin-reenactment, prototypicality-recreation, and the like.

16th Thesis: The Change-Constancy Principle

The sixteenth thesis concerns the change-constancy principle (on the alteration of things) in the category of "process" in existential dialectics, which is first named in *BCPC* (and were worked out in my books like

FHC, FCD, and *FPHC),* in that change occurs over time, although constancy is also allowed.

Old players fade away, and new ones emerges, with ever new causes and ever new forms—and asymmetry undergoes changes over time too, so does symmetry. There is no change without constancy—and vice versa.

For instance, on the one hand, there is change (e.g., the ever new ways to study causation, as shown in attribution theory, in *Sec. 2.2.1*; the ever new ways to study causation, as shown in "self-fulfilling prophecy," in *Sec. 2.2.2*; the ever new ways to study causality, as shown in the work on the 2nd law of thermodynamics, in *Sec. 2.3.1*; the ever new ways to study causality, as shown in the work on "retrocausality," in *Sec. 2.3.2*; the ever new ways to study causation, as shown in the works on "factual causation" and "legal causation," in *Sec. 2.4.1*; the ever new ways to study causation, as shown in the work on RCA, in *Sec. 2.4.2*; the ever new ways to study causation, as shown in the research on "origin myths," in *Sec. 2.5.1*; the ever new ways to study causation, as shown in "telos" by Aristotle, in *Sec. 2.5.2*; the ever new ways to study causation, as shown in the work on "adverse effects," in *Sec. 3.2.1*; the ever new ways to study causation, as shown in the work on "unintended consequences," in *Sec. 3.2.2*; the ever new ways to study effect, as shown in the work on "the butterfly effect," in *Sec. 3.3.1*; the ever new ways to study effect, as shown in the work on the quantum Zeno effect, in *Sec. 3.3.2*; the ever new ways to study effect, as shown in the work on domino theory, in *Sec. 3.4.1*; the ever new ways to study causation, as shown in the research on effectuation, in *Sec. 3.4.2*; the ever new ways to study cause and effect, as shown in the research on "causal determinism," in *Sec. 3.5.1*; and the ever new ways to study cause and effect, as shown in the research on eternal return, in *Sec. 3.4.2*).

On the other hand, there is constancy (e.g., the ever constant existence of different problems with the ever new ways to study causation, as shown in the problems with attribution theory pointed out by the critics, in *Sec. 2.2.1*; the ever constant existence of different problems with the ever new ways to study causation, as shown in the problems with the study on "self-fulfilling prophecy" pointed out by the critics, in *Sec. 2.2.2*; the ever constant existence of different problems with the ever new ways to study causality, as shown in the problems with the work on the 2nd law of thermodynamics pointed out by the critics, in *Sec. 2.3.1*; the ever constant existence of different problems with the ever new ways to study causality, as shown in the problems with the work on "retrocausality" pointed out by the critics, in *Sec. 2.3.2*; the ever constant existence of different problems with the ever new ways to causation, as shown in the problems with the works on "factual causation" and "legal causation" pointed out by the critics, in *Sec. 2.4.1*; the ever constant existence of different problems with the ever new ways to study causation, as shown in the problems with the work on RCA pointed out by the critics, in *Sec. 2.4.2*; the ever constant existence of different problems with the ever new ways to study causation, as shown in the problems with the research on "origin myths" pointed out by the critics, in *Sec. 2.5.1*; the ever constant existence of different problems with the ever new ways to study causation, as shown in the problems with "telos" by Aristotle aforediscussed, in *Sec. 2.5.2*; the ever constant existence of different problems with the ever new ways to study causation, as shown in the problems with the work on "adverse effects" pointed out by the critics, in *Sec. 3.2.1*; the ever constant existence of different problems with the ever new ways to study causation, as shown in the problems with the work on "unintended consequences" pointed out by the critics, in *Sec. 3.2.2*; the ever constant existence of different problems with the ever new ways to study effect, as shown in the problems with the work on "the butterfly effect" pointed out by the critics, in *Sec. 3.3.1*; the ever constant existence of different problems with the ever new ways to study effect, as shown in the different problems with the work on quantum Zeno effect pointed out by the critics, in Sec. 3.3.2; the ever constant existence of different problems with the ever new ways to study effect, as shown in the problems with the work on domino theory pointed out by the critics, in *Sec. 3.4.1*; the ever constant existence of different problems with the ever new ways to study causation, as shown in the problems with the research on effectuation pointed out by the critics, in *Sec. 3.4.2*; the ever constant existence of different problems with the ever new ways to study cause and effect, as shown in the problems with the research on "causal determinism" pointed out by the critics, in *Sec. 3.5.2*; and the ever constant existence of different problems with the ever new ways to study cause and effect, as shown in the problems with the research on eternal return pointed out by the critics, in *Sec. 3.5.2*).

And the reverse direction also holds true.

Again, it should be stressed, however, that there are different shades of gray (or different degrees of truth) in the two opposites, and the classification is not necessarily mutually exclusive either. In fact, even when some combinations of the two occur, they only end up sharing the same dialectic relationship, but in a different degree.

Also, there are some other relationships (as a kind of family resemblance) which have something in common with the principle, but they are not exactly the same but only more or less comparable, which varies from case to case.

Good examples of family resemblance in relation to the principle are dynamicness-staticness, instability-stability, and the like.

17th Thesis: The Order-Chaos Principle

The seventeenth thesis is called the the order-chaos principle (on the pattern of things) in the category of "process" in existential dialectics (as first worked out in *FC*), in that both order and chaos are vital in the process of change in the world.

The preference for order is biased, since it does not give sufficient attention to the vital role of chaos in the transformation of the world (without somehow reducing it for the understanding of order). There is no order without chaos—and vice versa.

The scientific search for order in the world is often a hidden bias in its ontological obsession with order, since chaos is often treated as the "bad" guy, with order as the "good" guy (for the end goal of science).

Neither order nor chaos is the final end of the world, and one is not to be treated as the means for the other in the transformation of things. Both are fundamental in their recurrent dialectical interactions with each other over time, without reducing one for the other.

Order has its different forms (e.g., ascending vs. descending order in mathematics, and feeding vs. bleeding order in morphology), just as chaos has its own versions (e.g., as understood differently in chaos theory vs. complexity theory).

For instance, on the one hand, there is order (e.g., the more or less orderly view on causal explanation, if looked from the sole vantage point of those who commit "self-serving bias," in *Sec. 2.2.1*; the more or less orderly view on "self-fulfilling prophecy," if looked from the sole vantage point of the advocates, in *Sec. 2.2.2*; "in thermodynamic systems that are not closed, entropy can decrease with time, in *Sec. 2.3.1*; the more or less orderly view on causality, if looked from the sole vantage point of traditional causality, in *Sec. 2.3.2*; the more or less orderly view on establishing causation and legal liability, if looked from the sole vantage point of the "two-stage inquiry" by the advocates, in *Sec. 2.4.1*; the more or less orderly view on solving problems, if looked from the sole vantage point of RCA by the advocates. in *Sec. 2.4.2*; "order" in "creation from chaos" myths, in *Sec. 2.5.1*; the more or less orderly view on nature, if looked from the sole vantage point of "telos" by Aristotle, in *Sec. 2.5.2*; the more or less orderly view on "adverse effects," if looked from the sole vantage point of those in the "public outcry" against "hormonal contraception and hormone replacement therapy" in regard to the "adverse effects of a severe nature, such as breast cancer," in *Sec. 3.2.1*; the more or less orderly view on causation, if looked from the sole vantage point of "purposive acts" for "intended consequences," with "the hubristic belief that humans can fully control the world around them," in *Sec. 3.2.2*; "finite dimensional linear systems are never chaotic," in *Sec. 3.3.1*; the more or less orderly view on the quantum Zeno effect, if looked from the sole vantage point of the advocates, in *Sec. 3.3.2*; the more or less orderly view on the situation in Southeast Asia in the 1970s, if looked from the sole vantage point of the domino theory by the advocates, in that "Thailand, Malaysia, Indonesia, Burma, and India would be next" to fall, after South Vietnam, Laos, and Cambodia became Communist, in *Sec. 3.4.1*; the more or less orderly view on reality, if looked from the sole vantage point of the advocates of "predictive models" in causal reasoning, in *Sec. 3.4.2*; the more or less orderly view on the universe, if looked from the sole vantage point of Newtonian mechanics with its view on certainty in causal determinism, in *Sec. 3.5.1*; and the more or less orderly view on the universe, if looked from the sole vantage point of "eternal return" by the advocates, in *Sec. 3.5.2*).

On the other hand, there is chaos (e.g., the more or less chaotic view on causal explanation, if looked from the multiple, conflicting vantage points of both the advocates and the critics of attribution theory, especially in regard to the problems aforecited, such that they do not add up to much of anything coherent, in *Sec. 2.2.1*; the more or less chaotic view on "self-fulfilling prophecy," if looked from the multiple, conflicting vantage points of both the advocates, the skeptics, and the critics, especially in regard to the problems aforecited, such that they do not add up to much of anything coherent, in *Sec. 2.2.2*; the increase of entropy over time in an isolated system, according to the 2nd law, in *Sec. 2.3.1*; the more or less chaotic view on causality, if looked from the multiple, conflicting vantage points of both the advocates, the skeptics, and the critics, especially in regard to the problems with "causality," "retrocausality," etc., as discussed earlier, such that they do not add up to much of anything coherent, in *Sec. 2.3.2*; the more or less chaotic view on establishing causation and legal liability, if looked from the multiple, conflicting vantage points of both the advocates and the critics, especially in regard to the problems aforecited, such that they do not add up to much of anything coherent, in *Sec. 2.4.1*; the more or less chaotic view on solving problems, if looked from the multiple, conflicting vantage points of both the advocates and the critics about RCA, especially in regard to the different problems aforecited, such that they do not add up to much of anything which is sound, complete and coherent as a whole, in *Sec. 2.4.2*; "chaos" in "creation from chaos" myths, in *Sec. 2.5.1*; the more or less chaotic view on nature, if looked from the sole vantage point of "chance events," in *Sec. 2.5.2*; the more or less chaotic view on "hormonal contraception and hormone replacement therapy" in regard to the "adverse effects of a severe nature, such as breast cancer," if looked from the multiple, conflicting vantage points of both the advocates and the critics, especially in regard to the problems aforecited, such that they do not add up to much of anything coherent, in *Sec. 3.2.1*; the more or less chaotic view on causation, if looked from the multiple, conflicting vantage points of both the advocates and the critics in regard to "intended" and "unintended consequences," especially in relation to different problems aforecited, in *Sec. 3.2.2*; "for a dynamical system to display chaotic behaviour it has to be either nonlinear, or infinite-dimensional," in *Sec. 3.3.1*; the more or less chaotic view on the quantum Zeno effect, if looked from the multiple, conflicting vantage points of both the advocates and the critics, especially in regard to the different problems aforecited, such that they do not add up to much of anything coherent, in *Sec. 3.3.2*; the more or less chaotic view on the situation in Southeast Asia in the 1970s and afterwards, if looked from the multiple, conflicting vantage points of both the advocates and the critics of the domino theory, especially in regard to the different problems and disagreements aforecited, such that they do not add up to much of anything coherent, in *Sec. 3.4.1*; the more or less chaotic view on reality, if looked from the alternative conflicting vantage point of "contingencies" or "uncertainty" by the advocates in effectual reasoning, in *Sec. 3.4.2*; the more or less chaotic view on the universe, if looked from the alternative vantage point of chaos theory with its focus on "sensitive dependence on initial conditions" as in "the example of the butterfly effect," in *Sec. 3.5.1*; and the more or less chaotic view on the universe, if looked from the multiple conflicting vantage points of "eternal return," "increasing entropy" in the 2nd law of thermodynamics, etc., by both the advocates and the critics, especially in regard to the different problems aforecited, such that they do not add up to much of anything coherent, in *Sec. 3.5.2*).

And the reverse direction also holds true.

Once more, it should be stressed, however, that there are different shades of gray (or different degrees of truth) in the two opposites, and the classification is not necessarily mutually exclusive either. In fact, even when some combinations of the two occur, they only end up sharing the same dialectic relationship, but in a different degree.

Also, there are some other relationships (as a kind of family resemblance) which have something in common with the principle, but they are not exactly the same but only more or less comparable, which varies from case to case.

Good examples of family resemblance in relation to the principle are lawfulness-disorder, order-disorder, pattern-chaos, linearity-nonlinearity, unity-disunity, linearity-irreversalness, sequence-chaos, etc.

18th Thesis: The Slowness-Quickness Principle

The eighteenth thesis concerns the slowness-quickness principle (on the speed of change) in the category of "process" in existential dialectics (which was first worked out in *FIA*), in that both slowness and quickness co-exist, with their own internal tension, to the extent that each fights for its own relevance with the other, in accordance to the perspectives of nature, the mind, culture, and society, without one being the victor and the other being the vanquished in the long haul. There is no slowness without quickness—and vice versa.

For instance, on the one hand, there is slowness (e.g., the relatively slower speed of explaining "the causes of behavior and events," after a thorough examination of all factors, without the use of any "cognitive biases" at all, in *Sec. 2.2.1*; the relatively slower speed of a self-fulfilling prophecy to "directly or indirectly causes itself to become true," if there is no "positive feedback between belief and behavior," especially in the presence of a "self-defeating prophecy," in *Sec. 2.2.2*; the relatively slower speed of low-temperature objects, in *Sec. 2.3.1*; the relatively slower speed of "retrocausality" to be verifiable, because of the problems aforecited, in *Sec. 2.3.2*; the relatively slower speed to resolve a legal case, if "the legal concept of causation is deterministic," looking for "certainty, an absolute concept," such that "continuing scrutiny is always available and the jury can be brought back in at any time when new data becomes available," in *Sec. 2.4.1*; the relatively slower speed of "problem recurrence" with the help of RCA to "focus...correction on root causes," in *Sec. 2.4.2*; the relatively slower speed to make land, in "earth-driver" myths, when, in many cases, "these stories" describe "failed attempts to make land before the solution is found," in *Sec. 2.5.1*; the relatively slower speed to understand something, according to Aristotle, if we do not quite answer the question "why?" in *Sec. 2.5.2*; the relatively slower speed of a drug to be effective, if there are "adverse effects," in *Sec. 3.2.1*; the relatively slower speed of rabbits to spread in Australia and New Zealand, if the introduction of more rabbits in the late 19th century and the subsequent fur trade did not occur, in *Sec. 3.2.2*; the relatively slower speed of chaos theory to be accepted in the 19th century, in *Sec. 3.3.1*; the weaker the coupling is, and the longer the decoherence time, the slower it will collapse, according to the quantum Zeno effect, in *Sec. 3.3.2*; the relatively slower speed of surrounding countries to ever fall to Communism, according to the domino theory, if there is a "containment" policy to prevent the first dominoes from falling, in *Sec. 3.4.1*; the relatively slower speed to do business in accordance to effectual logic, which refuses to seek "optimality" for the "fastest, cheapest, most efficient, etc." but instead works with "contingencies" or "uncertainty," in *Sec. 3.4.2*; the relatively slower speed of "the trajectory of a bullet" as measured by Newtonian mechanics, when contrasted with the speed of light, in *Sec. 3.5.1*; and the relatively slower speed of the universe to end in a collapse or "big crunch" in our time, because there is still a long way to go before its final acceleration, according to "the oscillating universe theory," in *Sec. 3.5.2*).

On the other hand, there is quickness (e.g., the relatively quicker speed of explaining "the causes of behavior and events" with the use of "attributions," in *Sec. 2.2.1*; the relatively quicker speed of a self-fulfilling prophecy to "directly or indirectly causes itself to become true," if it is "due to positive feedback between belief and behavior" without any other inhibiting factors, in *Sec. 2.2.2*; the relatively quicker speed of high-temperature objects, in *Sec. 2.3.1;* the relatively quicker speed of traditional "causality" to be verified, as it has in "mainstream physics," in *Sec. 2.3.2*; the relatively quicker speed to resolve a scientific case, if "the scientific concept of causation is probabilistic," not looking for "certainty" but willing to live with "an expression of the uncertainty of truth, an asymptotic concept," in *Sec. 2.4.1*; "without effective incident management, an incident can rapidly disrupt business operations, information security, IT systems, employees or customers and other vital business functions," in *Sec. 2.4.2*; the relatively quicker speed to make land, in "earth-driver" myths, when, in some other cases, "these stories" describe successful "attempts to make land" with "the solution…found," in *Sec. 2.5.1*; the relatively quicker speed to understand something, according to Aristotle, if we are able to answer the question "why?" in *Sec. 2.5.2*; the relatively quicker speed of a drug to be effective, if there is no adverse effect of any kind, in *Sec. 3.2.1*; the relatively quicker speed of rabbits to spread in Australia and New Zealand, after "the introduction of rabbits in Australia and New Zealand for food was followed by an explosive growth in the rabbit population," in *Sec. 3.2.2*; the relatively quicker speed of chaos theory to be accepted in the late 20th century, in *Sec. 3.3.1*; "the stronger the coupling is, and the shorter the decoherence time, the faster it will collapse," according to the quantum Zeno effect, in

Sec. 3.3.2; the relatively quicker speed of surrounding countries to fall to Communism, according to the domino theory by U.S. President Eisenhower, when he said in 1954 that "you have a row of dominoes set up, you knock over the first one, and what will happen to the last one is the certainty that it will go over very quickly," in *Sec. 3.4.1*; the relatively quicker speed to do business in accordance to causal logic, which seeks "optimality" for the "fastest, cheapest, most efficient, etc.," in *Sec. 3.4.2*; the relatively quicker speed of light, as nothing can travel faster, according to the theory of relativity, in *Sec. 3.5.1*; and the relatively quicker speed of the universe to end in a collapse or "big crunch" in its final moments of acceleration, according to "the oscillating universe theory," in *Sec. 3.5.2*).

And the reverse direction also holds true.

Again, it should be stressed, however, that there are different shades of gray (or different degrees of truth) in the two opposites, and the classification is not necessarily mutually exclusive either. In fact, even when some combinations of the two occur, they only end up sharing the same dialectic relationship, but in a different degree.

Also, there are some other relationships (as a kind of family resemblance) which have something in common with the principle, but they are not exactly the same but only more or less comparable, which varies from case to case.

Good examples of family resemblance in relation to the principle are inconvenience-convenience, passiveness-activenessness, gradualness-abruptness, deceleration-acceleration, difficulty-ease, nonresilience-resilience, patience-impatience, deliberativeness-impulsiveness, and the like.

19th Thesis: The Expansion-Contraction Principle

The nineteenth thesis is called the expansion-contraction principle in the category of "process" in existential dialectics, in that entities in the world can both expand in some ways and contract in other ones, as part of their nature. There is no expansion without contraction—and vice versa.

This principle, although not so explicitly called, was already used in my previous works on different topics (e.g., the theory of floating consciousness in *FCD* and *FPHC*, the union of the unions in *BWT*, and the cyclical progression of system fragmentation and integration in *FCD*).

For instance, on the one hand, there is expansion (e.g., the relatively more developed ability of those with the fundamental attribution error to offer dispositional or personality-based explanations for behavior, in *Sec. 2.2.1*; the relatively more developed ability to "directly or indirectly cause" a prediction to become true among those who are vulnerable to self-fulfilling prophecy, in *Sec. 2.2.2*; the relative expansion of entropy in an isolated system over time, in *Sec. 2.3.1*; the relative increased acceptance of "retrocausality" in para-science nowadays, in *Sec. 2.3.2*; the relative spread of the "two-stage inquiry" about causation in the modern U.S. legal system, in *Sec. 2.4.1*; the relative spread of "incident management" in the U.S. nowadays, in *Sec. 2.4.2*; the relative increase of "historians of religion and other students of myth" who now see "creation myths" more as "symbolic narratives which must be understood in terms of their own cultural context," in *Sec. 2.5.1*; the relative spread of the modern view on "evolution," in that it "proceeds by…mutations arising by chance, with those that impart an advantage being retained by natural selection," in *Sec. 2.5.2*; the relative spread of required "reporting systems" of adverse effects nowadays, since "in many countries, adverse effects are required by law to be reported," in *Sec. 3.2.1*; the relative expasion of rabbits in New Zealand in the late 19th century. in *Sec. 3.2.2*; the relative expansion of the use of "electronic computer" to do "the mathematics of chaos theory" nowadays, in *Sec. 3.3.1*; according to "the time-energy indeterminacy relation" in measuring the quantum Zeno effect, "the region in which the deviations [from the exponential decay law] are appreciable" increases "when one makes the measurement process duration" longer and longer, in *Sec. 3.3.2*; the relative spread of communism in Indochina in the 1970s, *in Sec. 3.4.1*; the relatively more developed ability to deal with "optimality" among those for causal logic, in *Sec. 3.4.2*; the relative spread, nowadays, of quantum mechanics, which "casts reasonable doubt on th[e]…main thesis of determinism" in regard to "certainty," in *Sec. 3.5.1*; and the expansion of the universe after the "big bang," according to the "big bang" theory, in *Sec. 3.5.2*).

On the other hand, there is contraction (e.g., the relatively less developed ability of those with the fundamental attribution error to offer situational explanations, in *Sec. 2.2.1*; the relatively less developed ability to "directly or indirectly cause" a prediction to become true among those who are vulnerable to the opposite prophecy known as "self-defeating prophecy," in *Sec. 2.2.2*; the relative decline of entropy in an opened system over time, in *Sec. 2.3.1*; the relatively less acceptance of "retrocausality" in mainstream physics nowadays, since "established physics does not generally employ retrocausality," in *Sec. 2.3.2*; the relatively less acceptance of "strict liability" without the consideration of causation at all in the modern U.S. legal system, although there are some exceptions like "a contract of indemnity insurance," in *Sec. 2.4.1*; the relative decline of problem-solving at the level of "symptoms" in the U.S.

nowadays, after the popular implementation of "incident management," in *Sec. 2.4.2*; the relative decline of those "historians of religion and other students of myth" who now treat "creation myths" as "forms of primitive or early-stage science or religion and analyze...them in a literal or logical sense," in *Sec. 2.5.1*; the relative decline of Aristotle's idea of "telos" in contemporary mainstream science in *Sec. 2.5.2*; the relative decline of voluntary "reporting systems" of adverse effects nowadays, since, only in a few countries, reporting is voluntary by law, in *Sec. 3.2.1*; the relative decline of sheep in New Zealand in the late 19th century, because "many farmers who had overstocked their land lost many of their sheep to starvation as the rabbits spread," in *Sec. 3.2.2*; the relative decline of the work on "the mathematics of chaos theory" by "hand" nowadays, in *Sec. 3.3.1*; according to "the time-energy indeterminacy relation" in measuring the quantum Zeno effect, "the region in which the deviations [from the exponential decay law] are appreciable shrinks when one makes the measurement process duration shorter and shorter," in *Sec. 3.3.2*; the relative decline of communism in Thailand, Malaysia, Indonesia, the Philippines, etc. after the 1970s and beyond, in *Sec. 3.4.1*; the relatively less developed ability to deal with "contingencies" among those for causal logic, in *Sec. 3.4.2*; the relative decline, nowadays, of the old-fashioned view of Newtonian physics which "depicts a universe in which objects move in perfectly determined ways," although "Newtonian mechanics remain useful, and make relatively accurate predictions [e.g. calculating the trajectory of a bullet]," in *Sec. 3.5.1*; and according to the oscillating universe theory, "the universe will end in a collapse or 'big crunch,'" in *Sec. 3.5.2*).

And the reverse direction also holds true.

Again, it should be stressed, however, that there are different shades of gray (or different degrees of truth) in the two opposites, and the classification is not necessarily mutually exclusive either. In fact, even when some combinations of the two occur, they only end up sharing the same dialectic relationship, but in a different degree.

Also, there are some other relationships (as a kind of family resemblance) which have something in common with the principle, but they are not exactly the same but only more or less comparable, which varies from case to case.

Good examples of family resemblance in relation to the principle are conquest-autarky, rise-fall, spread-shrink, extendingness-shorteningness, widening-narrowing, construction-deconstruction, expansion-destruction, construction-demolition, creation-destruction, expansion-contraction, expansion-constriction, expansion-decline, growth-breakdown, formation-decay, composition-decomposition, insertion-deletion, addition-division, multiplication-division, overstatedness-understatedness, multiplication-subtraction, and so forth.

20th Thesis: The Optimality-Nonoptimality Principle

The twentieth thesis concerns the optimality-nonoptimality principle (on the nature of highly favorable options) in the category of "process" in existential dialectics, which was first proposed in *FPHMORPH*, in that both optimality and non-optimality are important, in relation to the mind, nature, culture, and society, albeit in different ways. There is no optimality without nonoptimality—and vice versa.

There are five clarifications to remember, as shown in the fields of morphology (e.g., "perfection" in *FPHMORP*), data analysis (e.g., "bounded rationality" in *FPHO*, *FFHDA* and *FPHPROP*), probability (e.g., "decision making" in *FPHO* and *FPHPROP*), economics (e.g., "negative externalities" in *FCD* and *BCPC*), and technology (e.g., "post-capitalism" in *FCD*), just to cite five well-documented sources:

- Optimality (in terms of highly favorable options) is not perfect and can be realized in different degrees.
- "Maximization" does not necessarily entail "optimization," as shown in the problem of "negative externalities" in economics.
- Non-optimality can come in all shapes and sizes, in different degrees, like "maximizing" in economics vs. "satisficing" in sociology.
- Optimality can be more feasible in the longer term of technological improvement.
- Optimality should not be confused with the beauty of simplicity, since the more optimal a process is, the more complicated (not necessarily the simpler) it can be.

In any event, on the one hand, there is optimality (e.g., the search for highly favorable options, like the quest for "rational, logical and systematic" thinking in attribution theory, in *Sec. 2.2.1*; the search for highly favorable options, like the quest for the most effective ways to apply "self-fulfilling prophecy" to the field of "public education reform" aforecited, in *Sec. 2.2.2*; the search for highly favorable options, like the quest for "the most efficient possible heat engine" using "Carnot's principle" in accordance to the 2nd law, which refers to "a cycle of a Carnot engine, fictively operated in the limiting mode of extreme slowness known as quasi-static, so that the heat and work transfers are between subsystems that are always in their own internal states of thermodynamic equilibrium," in *Sec. 2.3.1*; the search for highly favorable options, like the quest for the broadest inclusion of "cause" and "effect" to understand reality, be it by "causality" and/or "retrocausality," in those works as discussed earlier, in *Sec. 2.3.2*; the search for highly favorable options, like the quest for the best ways to establish legal liability in the debate about the "two-stage inquiry" over the decades, with different revisions and refinements aforecited, in *Sec. 2.4.1*; the search for highly favorable options, like the quest for the most effective ways to solve problems by addressing the "root causes," not the "symptoms," as in RCA in the U.S. nowadays, in *Sec. 2.4.2*; the search for highly favorable options, like the quest for the best ways to explain the origins of the world in ancient times, as shown in different "creation myths," in *Sec. 2.5.1*; the search for highly favorable options, like the quest for "teleology" by Aristotle to understand "causation," in *Sec. 2.5.2*; the search for highly favorable options, like the quest for the most "systematic reviews and meta-analyses of therapeutic interventions" so as to provide "more complete reporting of harm from clinical trials," in *Sec. 3.2.1*; the search for highly favorable options, like the quest for the complete mastery of the world, by those who have "the hubristic belief that humans can fully control the world around them," in *Sec. 3.2.2*; the search for highly favorable options, like the quest for best ways to do "the mathematics of chaos theory" nowadays by the use of "electronic computer," when "the availability of cheaper, more powerful computers broadens the applicability of chaos theory" in our time, in *Sec. 3.3.1*; the search for highly favorable options, like the quest for the possibility of the "idealized measurement" of the quantum Zeno effect in the article aforecited, in *Sec. 3.3.2*; the search for highly favorable options, like the quest for the effective way to stop "world communism" by way of the "containment policy," later reinforced by the domino theory, during the Cold War, in *Sec. 3.4.1*; the search for highly favorable options, like the quest for "optimality" for the "fastest, cheapest, most efficient, etc.," in *Sec. 3.4.2*; the search for highly favorable options, like the quest for certainty in "Newtonian physics," which "depicts a universe in which objects move in perfectly determined ways," in *Sec. 3.5.1*; and the search for highly favorable options, like the quest for the understanding of "every possible combination [of life events]" which "would at some time be attained" in "an infinite period of time," in the "eternal return" as proposed by Nietzsche, in *Sec. 3.5.2*).

On the other hand, there is non-optimality (e.g., the existence of non-optimal alternatives to optimality, like the argument for more realistic studies by the critics, who pointed out different problems with attribution theory aforedescribed, in *Sec. 2.2.1*; the existence of non-optimal alternatives to optimality, like the argument for more realistic studies by the critics, who pointed out different problems with the research on "self-fulfilling prophecy," in *Sec. 2.2.2*; the existence of non-optimal alternatives to optimality, like the argument for more realistic studies by the critics, who pointed out different problems with the 2nd law aforecited, in *Sec. 2.3.1*; the existence of non-optimal alternatives to optimality, like the argument for more realistic studies by the critics, who pointed out different problems with "causality" and "retrocausality" as discussed earlier, in *Sec. 2.3.2*; the existence of non-optimal alternatives to optimality, like the argument for more realistic studies by the critics, who pointed out different problems with the "two-stage inquiry" as discussed earlier, in *Sec. 2.4.1*; the existence of non-optimal alternatives to optimality, like the argument for more realistic studies by the critics, who pointed out different problems with RCA, including "incident management," as discussed earlier, in *Sec. 2.4.2*; the existence of non-optimal alternatives to optimality, like the argument for more realistic studies by the critics, who pointed out different problems with "creation myths" aforedescribed, in *Sec. 2.5.1*; the existence of non-optimal alternatives to optimality, like the argument for more realistic studies by the critics, who pointed out different problems with Aristotle's "teleology," in *Sec. 2.5.2*; the existence of non-optimal alternatives to optimality, like the argument for more realistic studies by the critics, who pointed out different problems with reporting systems aforecited, in *Sec. 3.2.1*; the existence of non-optimal alternatives to optimality, like the argument for more realistic studies by the critics, who pointed out different problems with the naïve belief in controlling the world, because, "akin to Murphy's law, [Merton's work] is commonly used as a wry or humorous warning against the hubristic belief that humans can fully control the world around them," in *Sec. 3.2.2*; the existence of non-optimal alternatives to optimality, like the argument for more realistic studies by the critics, who pointed out different problems with "chaos theory," as discussed earlier, regardless of the progress in the development of computers, in *Sec. 3.3.1*; the existence of non-optimal alternatives to optimality, like the argument for more realistic studies by the critics, who pointed out different problems with the work on the quantum Zeno effect aforecited, in *Sec. 3.3.2*; the existence of non-optimal alternatives to optimality, like the argument for more realistic studies by the critics, who pointed out different problems with the domino theory aforecited, in *Sec. 3.4.1*; the existence of non-optimal alternatives to optimality, like the argument for more realistic studies by the critics, who pointed out an alternative logic known as "effectual logic," in *Sec. 3.4.2*; the existence of non-optimal alternatives to optimality, like the argument for more realistic studies by the critics, who pointed out different problems with Newtonian physics, since "modern quantum mechanics casts reasonable doubt on this main thesis of determinism" in Newtonian physics, in *Sec. 3.5.1*; and the existence of non-optimal alternatives to optimality, like the argument for more realistic studies by the critics, who pointed out different probems with the "eternal return" as proposed by Nietzsche, as discussed earlier, in *Sec. 3.5.2*).

And the reverse direction also holds true.

Again, it should be stressed, however, that there are different shades of gray (or different degrees of truth) in the two opposites, and the classification is not necessarily mutually exclusive either. In fact, even when some combinations of the two occur, they only end up sharing the same dialectic relationship, but in a different degree.

Also, there are some other relationships (as a kind of family resemblance) which have something in common with the principle, but they are not exactly the same but only more or less comparable, which varies from case to case.

Good examples of family resemblance in relation to the principle are optimality-satisfaction, optimality-maximization, optimality-heuristicness, idealness-realisticness, and the like.

21st Thesis: The Simultaneity-Nonsimultaneity Principle

The twenty-first thesis concerns the simultnaneity-nonsimultaneity principle (on the sequence of time) in the category of "process" in existential dialectics, which is first proposed in *FPHPHON*, in that both simultaneity and nonsimultaneity exist—in relation to the mind, nature, culture, and society, albeit in different ways. There is no simultaneity without nonsimultaneity—and vice versa.

There are the following important aspects of the relationship between simultaneity and nonsimultaneity to be clarified:

• An event B can occur after the occurrence of another event A in a causal situation. But A and B can also occur simultaneously in a different situation, and this is important, because, in quantum mechanics (as addressed in *FPHPT*), for instance, particles move so fast that, for all practical purposes, A and B can be treated as occurring simultaneously.

- In conventional wisdom, A and its negation ~A are different and do not coexist simultaneously. But in certain circumstances, it is also important to consider A and ~A simultaneously, as shown in the interactions between two opposites in the nature vs. nature debate (as addressed in *BNN*) and in the ritual/speech coevolution debate as well as the coarticulation debate (as addressed in *FPHPHON*).
- Simultaneity does not have to be absolute, as it can be more or less so for two entities to occur simultaneously.
- On one end of the line is exteme simultaneity and on the other end is extreme nonsimultaneously, and between the two are different degrees or gradations of simultaneity or nonsimultaneity.

In any event, on the one hand, there is simultaneity (e.g., the occurrence of different things more or less at the same time, such as the simultaneous existence of "the tendency to overvalue dispositional or personality-based explanations for behavior" and also the tendency to "under-valu[e...situational explanations" among those with the fundamental attribution error, in *Sec. 2.2.1*; the occurrence of different things more or less at the same time, such as the simultaneous existence of works on "self-fulfilling prophecy" in different countries aforedescribed, in *Sec. 2.2.2*; the occurrence of different things more or less at the same time, such as the simultaneous co-existence of different "subsystems" at the beginning of an isolated non-gravitational physical system not yet in a state of thermodynamic equilibrium, in *Sec. 2.3.1*; the occurrence of different things more or less at the same time, such as the phenomenon of "synchroncity," where two or more events can occur more or less simultaneously, in *Sec. 2.3.2*; the occurrence of different things more or less at the same time, such as the simultaneous co-existence of different legal precedents for "factual causation" like Yorkshire Dale Steamship Co v Minister of War Transport and March v Stramare, in our time, in *Sec. 2.4.1*; the occurrence of different things more or less at the same time, such as the simultaneous existence of different ideas about RCA in the U.S. nowadays, like "Incident Command System," "the National Incident Management System," etc., in *Sec. 2.4.2*; the occurrence of different things more or less at the same time, such as the simultaneous existence of "two parents" in "world parent" myths, such that they "are commonly identified as Sky [usually male] and Earth [usually female]...in the primeval state" and were...tightly bound to each other," in *Sec. 2.5.1*; the occurrence of different things more or less at the same time, such as the simultaneous existence of "a block of marble" and a "sculptor," in *Sec. 2.5.2*; the occurrence of different things more or less at the same time, such as the simultaneous co-existence of "harmful" and beneficial" effects of drugs, in general, in *Sec. 3.2.1*; the occurrence of different things more or less at the same time, such as the simultaneous co-existence of "sheep" and "rabbits" in New Zealand in the later part of the 19th century, in *Sec. 3.2.2*; the occurrence of different things more or less at the same time, such as the simultaneous existence of "computers" and "the mathematics of chaos theory" nowadays, in *Sec. 3.3.1*; the occurrence of different things more or less at the same time, such as the simultaneous existence of multiple "physical possibilities" of a wave function at the quantym level prior to its collapse "into a single possibility [the superposition] as seen by an observer," in *Sec. 3.3.2*; the occurrence of different things more or less at the same time, such as the simultaneous existence of different versions of domino theory, like the older "domino theory" and the recent "reverse domino theory," in *Sec. 3.4.1*; the occurrence of different things more or less at the same time, such as the simultaneous existence of different logics, like "causal logic" and "effectual logic" nowadays, in *Sec. 3.4.2*; the occurrence of different things more or less at the same time, such as the simultaneous existence of different physical theories nowadays, like Newtonian physics, quantum mechanics, etc., in *Sec. 3.5.1*; and the occurrence of different things more or less at the same time, such as the simultaneous existence of "two parallel orbifold planes or M-branes," which "collide periodically in a higher dimensional space," according to the Steinhardt–Turok model, in *Sec. 3.5.2*).

On the other hand, there is nonsimultaneity (e.g., the occurrence of something after something else, like the occurrence of a person being "overweight" first and thereafter, making the assumption that he has "a problem with overeating" or is "lazy but "not that...[he] might have a medical reason for being heavier set," among those with the fundamental attribution error, in *Sec. 2.2.1*; the occurrence of something after something else, such as "a false definition of the situation" at the beginning of a "self-fulfilling prophecy," which afterwards evokes "a new behaviour which makes the original false conception come 'true,'" as pointed out by Merton, in *Sec. 2.2.2*; the occurrence of something after something else, such as the example that "differences in temperature, pressure, and chemical potential decrease" between different subsystems "in an isolated non-gravitational physical system" will "lead...eventually to a state of thermodynamic equilibrium" later, in *Sec. 2.3.1*; the occurrence of something after something else, such as "retrocausality," with "an effect to occur before its cause," in *Sec. 2.3.2*; the occurrence of something after something else, such as the occurrence of the legal precedent Yorkshire Dale Steamship Co v Minister of War Transport in

1942 before the legal precedent March v Stramare in 1991, in *Sec. 2.4.1*; the occurrence of something after something else, such as the historical development of the idea of "Incident Command System" before that of "the National Incident Management System" in the U.S., in *Sec. 2.4.2*; the occurrence of something after something else, such as the occurrence of the "eternal union of two parents" at the beginning "primeval state" and, afterwards, "the creation" of the world which "takes place when the two are pulled apart" afterwards, according to "world parent" myths, in *Sec. 2.5.1*; the occurrence of something after something else, such as the making of a "statue" after a sculptor chisels away "a block of marble into a statue," in *Sec. 2.5.2*; the occurrence of something after something else, as shown in the finding that beneficial effects of drugs are often known beforehand, but any "medical error" in drug dosage is often discovered afterward, in *Sec. 3.2.1*; the occurrence of something after something else, such as the "loss" of "many...sheep" due to "starvation" after "the rabbits spread" in New Zealand in the late 19th century, in *Sec. 3.2.2*; the occurrence of something after something else, such as the practice of doing "the mathematics of chaos theory" by hand in the older days before that of doing "the mathematics of chaos theory" by the use of computers nowadays, in *Sec. 3.3.1*; the occurrence of something after something else, such as the existence of a wave function with its simultaneous multiple "physical possibilities" at the quantym level first, before its collapse "into a single possibility [the superposition] as seen by an observer" thereafter, in *Sec. 3.3.2*; the occurrence of something after something else, such as the development of the older "domino theory" before the development of the recent "reverse domino theory," in *Sec. 3.4.1*; the occurrence of something after something else, such as the formal development of"causal logic" before the formal development of "effectual logic" in history, or more precisely, in 2001, in *Sec. 3.4.2*; the occurrence of something after something else, such as the develoment of Newtonian physics in history before that of quantum mechanics, in *Sec. 3.5.1*; and the occurrence of something after something else, such as "the collision" between "two parallel orbifold planes or M-branes," such that there will be "a big crunch followed immediately by a big bang," according to the Steinhardt–Turok model, in *Sec. 3.5.2*).

And the reverse direction also holds true.

Again, it should be stressed, however, that there are different shades of gray (or different degrees of truth) in the two opposites, and the classification is not necessarily mutually exclusive either. In fact, even when some combinations of the two occur, they only end up sharing the same dialectic relationship, but in a different degree.

Also, there are some other relationships (as a kind of family resemblance) which have something in common with the principle, but they are not exactly the same but only more or less comparable, which varies from case to case.

Good examples of family resemblance in relation to the principle are contemporaneity-successiveness, simultaneity-sequence, simultaneity-consecutiveness, sychronicity-sequence, and the like.

22ⁿᵈ Thesis: The Isolation-Interaction Principle

The twenty-second thesis concerns the isolation-interaction principle (on the interaction among entities) in the category of "process" in existential dialectics, which was first proposed in *FPHACCO*, in that both isolation and interaction are important, in relation to the mind, nature, culture, and society, albeit in different ways. There is no isolation without interaction—and vice versa.

There are some clarifications to remember, as shown in different case studies already addressed in my previous works (e.g., "interlanguage" in *FPHPHON,* "system integration and fragmentation" in *FCD,* "sound change" in *FPHPHON,* and "mini-systems" in *FHC*), just to cite a few well-documented sources:

- Isolation and interactions are not perfect and can be realized in different degrees.
- Isolation and interaction take time to develop.
- Interaction can have different outcomes over time (e.g., "merging," "split," "loss," etc. in sound change).
- The isolation-interaction pair should not be confused with the absoluteness-relativeness pair, although both concern the issue of autonomy, but there are different opposites in relation to autonomy (in the contexts of method, process, etc.).

In any event, on the one hand, there is isolation (e.g., the state of a situation that is separate from others, such as the isolation of thoese "people" who "feel helpless when they feel powerless to change their situation," because "this happens when people attribute negative results to their internal, stable and global factors leading them to think they have no control over their situation," in *Sec. 2.2.1*; the state of a situation that is separate from others, such as the isolation of the tale "The Ruined Man Who Became Rich Again Through a Dream" in the Arabian Nights at the beginning, before it was translated into European languages later, in *Sec.* *2.2.2*; the state of a situation that is separate from others, such as the isolation of different subsystems "in an isolated non-gravitational physical system" at the beginning, in *Sec. 2.3.1*; the state of a situation that is separate from others, such as the "correlation" between two events, where there is no causation between them, in *Sec. 2.3.2*; the state of a situation that is separate from others, such as the separation of "factual causation" from "legal causation" in the first stage of the "two-stage inquiry," in *Sec.* *2.4.1*; the state of a situation that is separate from others, such as the isolation of "root causes" from the "symptoms" in problem-solving in the older days, before the rise of RCA, in *Sec. 2.4.2*; the state of a situation that is separate from others, such as the isolation of "the previous world" as "the womb of the earth mother," according to "emergence" myths, in *Sec. 2.5.1*; the state of a situation that is separate from others, such as the prior existence of "form" before the appearance of "matter" in a particular thing, according to Aristotle, in *Sec. 2.5.2*; the state of a situation that is separate from others, such as the isolation of adverse effects from public knowledge, if they are not reported, in *Sec. 3.2.1*; the state of a situation that is separate from others, such as the isolation of Australia and New Zealand from any rabbits prior to the 19th century, in *Sec. 3.2.2*; the state of a situation that is separate from others, such as the isolation of the work on "the mathematics of chaos theory" from any use of computers in the older days, when it was done by hand, in *Sec. 3.3.1*; the state of a situation that is separate from others, such as the isolation of a subatomic particle with its simultaneous existence of multiple "physical possibilities" of a wave function at the quantym level prior to any quantum decoherence, in *Sec. 3.3.2*; the state of a situation that is separate from others, such as the isolation of Indochina from communism in the 19th century, in *Sec. 3.4.1*; the state of a situation that is separate from others, such as the isolation of "predictive models" from the focus on "situations of uncertainty" in causal logic, in *Sec. 3.4.2*; the state of a situation that is separate from others, such as the isolation of Newtonian physics in the older days before the rise of quantum mechanics, when, "taken in isolation [rather than as an approximation to quantum mechanics], Newtonian physics depicts a universe in which objects move in perfectly determined ways," in *Sec.* *3.5.1*; and the state of a situation that is separate from others, such as the isolation of "the visible four-dimensional universe" of ours prior to its collision with other "parallel orbifold planes or M-branes" in due time, according to the Steinhardt–Turok model, in *Sec. 3.5.2*).

On the other hand, there is interaction (e.g., the influence of entities on one another, such as the introduction of "cognitive bias modification" therapy to people with "learned helplessness," so that it can help "modifying cognitive biases in...people" to treat "anxiety, depression and addiction," for example, in *Sec. 2.2.1*; the influence of entities on one another, such as "a variant of this story," that is, "The Ruined Man Who Became Rich Again Through a Dream," which "later appears in English folklore as the 'Pedlar of Swaffham,'" as a literary exchange between the two cultures, in *Sec. 2.2.2*; the influence of entities on one another, such as the interaction between different subsystems "in an isolated non-gravitational physical system" as they will "lead...eventually to a state of thermodynamic equilibrium" later, after interacting with each other, in *Sec. 2.3.1*; the influence of entities on one another, such as two events in "causality" or "retrocausality," with a "cause" and an "effect," in *Sec. 2.3.2*; the influence of entities on one another, such as the interaction between "fact" and "policy" in the second stage of the "two-stage inquiry," in *Sec. 2.4.1*; the influence of entities on one another, such as the analysis of the interactions between "root causes" and "symptoms" in RCA, in *Sec. 2.4.2*; the influence of entities on one another, such as the creation of the earth mother after it is delivered from "the womb of the earth mother" in another world, according to "emergence" myths, in *Sec. 2.5.1*; the influence of entities on one another, such as the coming into existence of a particular thing as a result of the change of "matter" with "form" shaping it, in *Sec. 2.5.2*; the influence of entities on one another, such as the interaction between the law and the reporting of adverse effects, like MHRA which requires reporting adverse effects in the U.K., in *Sec. 3.2.1*; the influence of entities on one another, such as "the introduction of rabbits in Australia and New Zealand for food was followed by an explosive growth in the rabbit population," to the extent that "rabbits have become a major feral pest in these countries," in *Sec. 3.2.2*; the influence of entities on one another, such as the interaction between computers and the mathematics of chaos theory" nowadays, in *Sec. 3.3.1*; influence of entities on one another, such as the interaction between an unstable or excited particle with a measuring apparatus [by an observer] in a "wave function collapse," in *Sec. 3.3.2*; the influence of entities on one another, such as the interaction between Indochina and the communist movement in the later part of the 20th century and its fall to communism in the 1970s, in *Sec. 3.4.1*; the influence of entities on one another, such as the interaction between "people" and "contngencies" in effectual logic, in *Sec. 3.4.2*; the influence of entities on one another, such as the interaction between quantum mechanics and Newtonian physics in the 20th century, since "modern quantum mechanics casts reasonable doubt on this main thesis of determinism," in *Sec. 3.5.1*; and the influence of entities on one another, such as the interaction between "two parallel orbifold planes or M-branes" when they collide, according to the Steinhardt–Turok model, in *Sec. 3.5.2*).

And the reverse direction also holds true.

Again, it should be stressed, however, that there are different shades of gray (or different degrees of truth) in the two opposites, and the classification is not necessarily mutually exclusive either. In fact, even when some combinations of the two occur, they only end up sharing the same dialectic relationship, but in a different degree.

Also, there are some other relationships (as a kind of family resemblance) which have something in common with the principle, but they are not exactly the same but only more or less comparable, which varies from case to case.

Good examples of family resemblance in relation to the principle are isolation-exchange, isolation-intercourse, autonomy-trade, aloneness-interrelationship, autarky-commerce, insulation-interaction, secludedness-interrelationship, segregation-interaction, and the like.

In Relation to Agency

The next eight theses are in relation to agency in existential dialectics, as shown below.

23rd Thesis: The Theory-Praxis Principle

The twenty-third thesis is the theory-praxis principle (on the duality of knowledge) in the category of "agency" in existential dialectics (which was first worked out in *FPHE*), in that, if there is theoretical construction, there is likewise its practical application, both technical and normative. There is no theory without praxis—and vice versa.

For instance, on the one hand, there is theory (e.g., the theoretical construction of "attribution" in the field of psychology, in *Sec. 2.2.1*; the theoretical construction of "self-fulfilling prophecy" by Merton in the field of sociology, in *Sec. 2.2.2*; the theoretical construction of "entropy" in the field of thermodynamics, in *Sec. 2.3.1*; the theoretical construction of "retrocausality" in the field of philosophy, in *Sec. 2.3.2*; the theoretical construction of "causation" in the fields of philosophy and science, in *Sec. 2.4.1*; the theoretical construction of "incident management" in the field of business management, in *Sec. 2.4.2*; the theoretical construction of "social function" in the field of sociology, in *Sec. 2.5.1*; the theoretical construction of "teleology" by Aristotle in the field of metaphysics, in *Sec.*

2.5.2; the theoretical construction of "probabilities" in the field of statistics, in *Sec. 3.2.1*; the theoretical construction of "unintended consequences" by Merton in the field of sociology, in *Sec. 3.2.2*; the theoretical construction of "the butterfly effect" in the field of chaos theory, in *Sec. 3.3.1*; the theoretical construction of the quantum Zeno effect in the field of quantum physics, in *Sec. 3.3.2*; the theoretical construction of the "domino theory" in regard to the spread of communism in Indochina, in *Sec. 3.4.1*; the theoretical construction of "logic" in the field of philosophy in *Sec. 3.4.2*; the theoretical construction of "determined probabilities" in the field of quantum mechanics, in *Sec. 3.5.1*; and the theoretical construction of "eternal return" in the field of cosmology, in *Sec. 3.5.2*).

On the other hand, there is praxis (e.g., the practical application of "attribution theory" in the field of psychology to the area concerning "learned helplessness," when "people feel helpless when they feel powerless to change their situation," and "this happens when people attribute negative results to their internal, stable and global factors leading them to think they have no control over their situation," as applied by Martin Seligman and Steven F. Maier in 1976, in *Sec. 2.2.1*; the practical application of "self-fulfilling prophecy" by Merton in the field of sociology to the field of education, like the "public education reform" aforecited, in *Sec. 2.2.2*; the practical application of "entropy" in the field of thermodynamics to the field of cosmology, in that "taking the current view of the universe into account, it has been proposed that the universe will probably exhibit a future in which all known energy sources [such as stars] will decay," in *Sec. 2.3.1*; the practical application of "retrocausality" in the field of philosophy to the fields of science and para-science, as described earlier, in *Sec. 2.3.2*; the practical application of "causation" in the fields of philosophy and science to the field of jurisprudence, like "legal causation," in *Sec. 2.4.1*; the practical application of "incident management" in the field of business management to the field of national security, when "the National Incident Management System" was implemented by the Department of Homeland Security in the U.S., in *Sec. 2.4.2*; the practical application of "social function" in the field of sociology to the field of mythology, like "the social function of origin myths," in *Sec. 2.5.1*; the practical application of "teleology" in the field of metaphysics to the field of modern evolutionary theory by some people, like the one by Asa Gray in 1874, in *Sec. 2.5.2*; the practical application of probabilities" in the field of statistics to the field of medicine, like the calculation of "marginal probabilities of adverse effects of a severe nature, such as breast cancer" in "hormonal contraception and hormone replacement therapy," in *Sec. 3.2.1*; the practical application of "unintended consequences" by Merton in the field of sociology to the field of ecology, such as the study on "the introduction of rabbits to Australia by Europeans, which became economically and environmentally damaging," in *Sec. 3.2.2*;, the practical application of "the butterfly effect" in the field of chaos theory to the field of "quantum physics," since "the potential for sensitive dependence on initial conditions [the butterfly effect] has been studied in a number of cases in semiclassical and quantum physics including atoms in strong fields and the anisotropic Kepler problem, in *Sec. 3.3.1*; the practical application of the quantum Zeno effect in the field of quantum physics to the field of psychology, like Stapp's application of the quantum Zeno effect for his claim about "quantum mind," in *Sec. 3.3.2*; the practical application of the "domino theory" in regard to the spread of communism in Indochina to the region in Latin America, as shown by Che Guevara's call for "two, three... many Vietnams" in 1967, in *Sec. 3.4.1*; the practical application of "logic" in the field of philosophy to the field of business management, like "effectual logic," in *Sec. 3.4.2*; the practical application of "determined probabilities" in the field of quantum mechanics to the field of everyday technologies, as "these findings from quantum mechanics...allow us to build transistors and lasers,...personal computers, Blu-ray players and the internet," in *Sec. 3.5.1*; and the practical application of "eternal return" in the field of cosmology to the field of religion, like "Godhead" by Griffin and Tyrrell for a "religio-mystical representation" of the fate of the universe, in *Sec. 3.5.2*).

And the reverse direction also holds true.

Again, it should be stressed, however, that there are different shades of gray (or different degrees of truth) in the two opposites, and the classification is not necessarily mutually exclusive either. In fact, even when some combinations of the two occur, they only end up sharing the same dialectic relationship, but in a different degree.

Also, there are some other relationships (as a kind of family resemblance) which have something in common with the principle, but they are not exactly the same but only more or less comparable, which varies from case to case.

Good examples of family resemblance in relation to the principle are discovery-application, knowledge-action, invention-innovation, theory-intentionality, discourse-action, knowledge-interest, knowledge-motivation, universality-particularity, potentiality-actuality, theory-practice, and so forth.

24th Thesis: The Convention-Novelty Principle

The twenty-fourth thesis is the convention-novelty principle (on the nature of creative thinking) in the category of "agency" in existential dialectics (which was first worked out in *FPHCT*), in that, if there is conventional wisdom, there is likewise novel challenge, to the extent that both convergent and divergent thinking are part of life. There is no convention without novelty—and vice versa.

As srummarized from *FPHCT* (almost verbatim here), there are (a) "creative techniques" and (b) "creative traits," which, when satisfied—in relation to the larger context of the mind, nature, society, and culture—can be used to enhance creative works.

In addition, creative thinking has its own possibilities and limits (in relation to invention), just as it has its own promises and pitfalls (in relation to innovation)— as already analyzed in *FPHCT*).

In the end, creative thinking has its own desirability and dark sides (as also already analyzed in *FPHCT*).

With these clarifications in mind—there are good empirical examples for the convention-novelty princple.

For instance, on the one hand, there is convention (e.g., the conventional wisdom about attributions as a form of cognitive bias by Fritz Heider, in *Sec. 2.2.1*; the conventional wisdom about "self-fulfilling prophecy" in the older days, in *Sec. 2.2.2*; the conventional wisdom about "the caloric theory of heat" in the 1850s, in *Sec. 2.3.1*; the conventional wisdom about "causality" with "cause" before "effect," in *Sec. 2.3.2*; the conventional wisdom about with "common sense" in establishing "factual causation" by the advocates of the "two-stage" inquiry, in *Sec. 2.4.1*; the conventional wisdom about problem-solving at the level of "symptoms," in *Sec. 2.4.2*; the conventional wisdom about "creation myths" in the older days as "forms of primitive or early-stage science or religion" to be "analyzed...in a literal or logical sense," in *Sec. 2.5.1*; the conventional wisdom about "teleology" by Aristotle in the older days, in *Sec. 2.5.2*; the conventional wisdom about the importance of "reporting systems" for the understanding of "adverse effects," in *Sec. 3.2.1*; the conventional wisdom against "the hubristic belief that humans can fully control the world around them" in the older days, in *Sec. 3.2.2*; the conventional wisdom about the butterfly effect in modern times, in *Sec. 3.3.1*; the conventional wisdom about the quantum Zeno effect, in *Sec. 3.3.2*; the conventional wisdom about the "domino theory" in Indochina, in *Sec. 3.4.1*; conventional wisdom about "causal logic" for optimality, in *Sec. 3.4.2*; the conventional wisdom about Newtonian mechanics in the older days, in

Sec. 3.5.1; and the conventional wisdom about the big bang theory," which "in the framework of relativistic cosmology seems to be at odds with eternal return" in the older days, in *Sec. 3.5.2*).

On the other hand, there is novelty (e.g., the alternative novel challenge to the conventional wisdom about attributions as a form of cognitive bias by Fritz Heider—by the new idea of G. Gigerenzer, M. Haselton, and others that "cognitive biases can be controlled" and treated by "cognitive bias modification therapy," in *Sec. 2.2.1*; the alternative novel challenge to the conventional wisdom about "self-fulfilling prophecy" in the older days—by the new idea of "self-defeating prophecy" later, in *Sec. 2.2.2*; the alternative novel challenge to the conventional wisdom about "the caloric theory of heat" in the 1850s—by the new idea of the second law of thermodynamics, which questioned"the caloric theory of heat" popular at the time, in *Sec. 2.3.1*; the alternative novel challenge to the conventional wisdom about "causality" with "cause" before "effect" —by the new idea of "retrocausality" with "effect" before "cause," in *Sec. 2.3.2*; the alternative novel challenge to the conventional wisdom about "common sense" in establishing "factual causation" by the advocates of the "two-stage" inquiry—by the new idea of "a test of sufficiency" instead by the critics like Hart, Honoré, and Wright, in *Sec. 2.4.1*; the alternative novel challenge to the conventional wisdom about problem-solving at the level of "symptoms"—by the new idea of problem-solving at the level of "root causes," as in RCA, in *Sec. 2.4.2*; the alternative novel challenge to the conventional wisdom about "creation myths" in the older days as "forms of primitive or early-stage science or religion" to be "analyzed...in a literal or logical sense"—by the new idea nowadays that "creation myths" are "symbolic narratives which must be understood in terms of their own cultural context," in *Sec. 2.5.1*; the alternative novel challenge to the conventional wisdom about "teleology" by Aristotle in the older days—by the new idea of contemporary evolutionary theory, in that "evolution is blind," in *Sec. 3.5.2*; the alternative novel challenge to the conventional wisdom about the importance of "reporting systems" for the understanding of "adverse effects"—by the new idea about the inherent limitations of "reporting systems" as discussed earlier, in *Sec. 3.2.1*; the alternative novel challenge to the conventional wisdom against "the hubristic belief that humans can fully control the world around them" in the older days—by the new idea of Merton about "unintended consequences," in *Sec. 3.2.2*; the alternative novel challenge to the conventional wisdom about the butterfly effect in modern times—by the new ideas that the so-called "butterfly effect" is much exaggerated, that the so-called "butterfly effect" misleadingly exclude some other effects in its analysis, that the property of "sensitivity to initial conditions" can be redundant, that the butterfly effect can be countered by more complicated forecasting systems, that the butterfly effect does not apply in some situations, etc., in *Sec. 3.3.1*; the alternative novel challenge to the conventional wisdom about the quantum Zeno effect—by the new idea of Stapp in regard to his application of the quantum Zeno effect for his claim about "quantum mind," in *Sec. 3.3.2*; the alternative novel challenge to the conventional wisdom about the "domino theory" in Indochina—by the new idea of the "reverse domino theory" in the Middle East, in *Sec. 3.4.1*; the alternative novel challenge to the conventional wisdom about "causal logic" for optimality—by the new idea of "effectual logic" for "contingencies," in *Sec. 3.4.2*; the alternative novel challenge to the conventional wisdom about Newtonian mechanics in the older days —by the new idea of quantum mechanics in the 20th century, in *Sec. 3.5.1*; and the alternative novel challenge to the conventional wisdom about the big bang theory," which "in the framework of relativistic cosmology seems to be at odds with eternal return" in the older days—by the new ideas nowadays, in terms of "many different speculative big bang scenarios in quantum cosmology which actually imply eternal return," in *Sec. 3.5.2*).

And the reverse direction also holds true.

Again, it should be stressed, however, that there are different shades of gray (or different degrees of truth) in the two opposites, and the classification is not necessarily mutually exclusive either. In fact, even when some combinations of the two occur, they only end up sharing the same dialectic relationship, but in a different degree.

Also, there are some other relationships (as a kind of family resemblance) which have something in common with the principle, but they are not exactly the same but only more or less comparable, which varies from case to case.

Good examples of family resemblance in relation to the principle are convergence-divergence (or convergent thinking vs. divergent thinking), normalness-nonnormalness, conformity-nonconformity, familiarity-freshness, inertia-newness, equilibrium-disturbance, and so on.

25th Thesis: The Evolution-Transformation Principle

The twenty-fifth thesis refers to the evolution-transformation principle (on the multiple kinds of agency). in the category of "agency" in existential dialectics (which was first worked out in *FAE* and then in other books of mine).

This principle—and the symmetry-asymmetry principle, for instance—are both about agency. More precisely, the word "agency," in a formal definition, refers to "a person or thing through which power is exerted or an end is achieved." (MWD 2007) It therefore does not have to necessarily involve an intelligent lifeform.

Because of this dual meaning in agency, the evolution-transformation principle is more concerned with *the kind of agency*, that is, both about the *evolution* in the state of nature (e.g., an object of natural beauty) and the *transformation* in the world of intelligent lifeforms (e.g., a work of art). There is no evolution without transformation—and vice versa.

In classical Darwinian evolutionary theory (as more detailedly analyzed in *BNN*), evolution is "blind." But in the human world, change often takes place because of the conscious intervention of humans in transforming society and culture, just to cite two instances.

And the transformative part of the principle precisely refers to the other dimension in the dual meaning of agency, in giving technology (as invented by intelligent lifeforms like humans and, soon, post-humans) a major role to play in the change of the world, which is something that I extensively analyzed in *FHC* in the context of the technophilic lifeworld, espeically though not exclusively since modern times. The same theme is also elaborated in many other books of mine.

For instance, on the one hand, there is evolution (e.g., the natural evolution of humans to make attributions in the state of nature in a primitive way, in *Sec. 2.2.1*; the natural evolution of humans to make prediction in the state of nature in a primitive way, in *Sec. 2.2.2*; the natural evolution of humans to experience the "preferred direction of progress" in the state of nature in a primitive way, in *Sec. 2.3.1*; the natural evolution of humans to experience causality in the state of nature in a primitive way, in *Sec. 2.3.2*; the natural evolution of humans to be able to fight and harm others at times in the state of nature in a primitive way, in *Sec. 2.4.1*; the natural evolution of humans to solve problems in the state of nature in a primitive way, in *Sec. 2.4.2*; the natural evolution of humans to cope with the state of nature in a primitive way, in *Sec. 2.5.1*; the natural evolution of humans to encounter causation in the state of nature, in *Sec. 2.5.2*; the natural evolution of humans to experience diseases or injuries in the state of nature, in *Sec. 3.2.1*; the natural evolution of humans to anticipate things in the state of nature, albeit in a primitive way, in *Sec. 3.2.2*; the natural evolution of humans to encounter unpredictable outcomes in the state of nature, in *Sec. 3.3.1*; the natural evolution of humans to encounter decay of things in the state of nature, in *Sec. 3.3.2*; the natural evolution of humans to encounter chain reactions in the state of nature, like the chain reaction in an energy system to increase entropy, in *Sec. 3.4.1*; the natural evolution of humans to encoutner "uncertainty" in the state of nature, in *Sec. 3.4.2*; the natural evolution of humans to experience causation in the state of nature, in *Sec. 3.5.1*; and the natural evolution of humans to live on this planet Earth as part of the larger universe, in *Sec. 3.5.2*).

On the other hand, there is transformation (e.g., the technical transformation of human ability to deal with attributions by the invention of "cognitive bias modification therapy," or CBMT, in *Sec. 2.2.1*; the technical transformation of human ability to deal with prediction by the invention of "self-fulfilling prophecy," which, as pointed out by Merton, "is peculiar to human affairs" and "is not found in the world of nature, untouched by human hands," in *Sec. 2.2.2*; the technical transformation of human ability to understand time by the invention of the second law of thermodynamics in regard to "entropy," in *Sec. 2.3.1*; the technical transformation of human ability to understand causality by the invention of "philosophy of science" and "para-science" to study "retrocausality," in *Sec. 2.3.2*; the technical transformation of human ability to deal with fighting and harming others by the invention of "legal liability," in *Sec. 2.4.1*; the technical transformation of human ability to solve problems by the invention of RCA, in *Sec. 2.4.2*; the technical transformation of human ability to cope with the state of nature by the invention of "origin myths," in *Sec. 2.5.1*; the technical transformation of human ability to understand causation by the invention of "teleology" like the one by Aristotle, in *Sec. 2.5.2*; the technical transformation of human ability to cope with diseases or injuries by the invention of "drugs" and "surgery," with both harmful and beneficial effects, in *Sec. 3.2.1*; the technical transformation of human ability to understand the nature of anticipating things by the invention of the research on "unintended consequences" and their causes, in *Sec. 3.2.2*; the technical transformation of human ability to deal with unpredictable outcomes by the invention of chaos theory like "the butterfly effect," in *Sec. 3.3.1*; the technical transformation of human ability to understand the decay of things by the invention of quantum physics, like the study of the quantum Zeno effect, in *Sec. 3.3.2*; the technical transformation of human ability to understand chain reactions by the invention of the "domino theory" in politics and other fields, in *Sec. 3.4.1*; the technical transformation of human ability to deal with "uncertainty" by the invention of "effectual logic" for "continegencies," in *Sec. 3.4.2*; the technical transformation of human ability to understand causation by the invention of "causal determinism," in *Sec. 3.5.1*; and the technical transformation of human ability to deal with the fate of the universe by the invention of "cosmology" like different ideas of "eternal return," in *Sec. 3.5.2*).

And the reverse direction also holds true.

Again, it should be stressed, however, that there are different shades of gray (or different degrees of truth) in the two opposites, and the classification is not necessarily mutually exclusive either. In fact, even when some combinations of the two occur, they only end up sharing the same dialectic relationship, but in a different degree.

Also, there are some other relationships (as a kind of family resemblance) which have something in common with the principle, but they are not exactly the same but only more or less comparable, which varies from case to case.

Good examples of family resemblance in relation to the principle are inorganicness-volition, naturalness-technologicalness, naturalness-nonnaturalness, nonwillingness-willingness, inorganicness-motivation, evolution-creation, naturalness-artificialness, and so on.

26th Thesis: The Symmetry-Asymmetry Principle

The twenty-sixth thesis is labeled as the symmetry-asymmetry principle (on the relationships among existents) in the category of "agency" in existential dialectics (which was also already worked out in my previous books), in that there is no asymmetry without symmetry— and vice versa.

For instance, the Same can be symmetric and asymmetric towards the Others. But in case of asymmetry (as analyzed in *BDPD*), oppression and self-oppression can occur. So, when the Same is asymmetric towards the Others, the Same can also be relatively asymmetric towards itself in self-oppression, just as the Others can be likewise towards themselves. The subsequent oppressiveness is dualistic, as much by the Same against the Others and itself, as by the Others against the Same and themselves. Both oppression and self-oppression can be achieved by way of downgrading differences between the Same and the Others and of accentuating them.

This is true, even though not all forms of asymmetry have to be about oppression and self-oppression.

In addition, from Chapter Three of *FPHG*, symmetry is not perfect, to be understood in an approximate sense under many life circumstances. With this clarification in mind, hereafter are some empirical examples.

For instance, on the one hand, there is symmetry (e.g., the co-existence of different individuals to cope with attributions, be they "normal" or "the most intelligent," in *Sec. 2.2.1*; the co-existence of different entities, like animals and humans, in *Sec. 2.2.2*; the co-existence of different systems, like "closed," "open," etc., in *Sec. 2.3.1*; the co-existence of different ideas, like "causality" and "retrocausality," in Sec. *2.3.2*; the co-existence of different entities, like a judge, a defendant, etc., in *Sec. 2.4.1*; the co-existence of different approaches to RCA, like "safety-based RCA," "production-based RCA," etc., in *Sec. 2.4.2*; the co-existence of "male characters" and "female characters" in "creation myths," in *Sec. 2.5.1*; the co-existence of four causes, according to Aristotle, in *Sec. 2.5.2*; the co-existence of different reporting systems in many countries nowadays, in *Sec. 3.2.1*; the co-existence of different entities like animals and humans, in *Sec. 3.2.2*; the co-existence of different "systems" in nature, in *Sec. 3.3.1*; the co-existence of different interpretations of quantum theory, in *Sec. 3.3.2*; the co-existence of different countries in Southeast Asia, in *Sec. 3.4.1*; the co-existence of different logics, like "causal logic" and "effectual logic," in *Sec. 3.4.2*; the co-existence of different theories in physics, like classical mechanics and quantum mechanics, in *Sec. 3.5.1*; and the co-existence of different versions of "eternal return," like Jainism in India and modern scientific cosmologies in the U.S. as discussed earlier, in *Sec. 3.5.2*).

On the other hand, there is asymmetry (e.g., "normal" individuals tend to commit "biases and errors" in attributions—but, as told by Aristotle, "the most intelligent minds are those that can entertain an idea without necessarily believing it," in *Sec. 2.2.1*; "self-fulfilling prophecy," as pointed out by Merton, "is peculiar to human affairs"—but "self-fulfilling prophecy," as pointed out by Merton, "is not found in the world of nature, untouched by human hands," like animals in the wilderness, in *Sec. 2.2.2*; entropy can increase in an isolated system over time—but entropy can decrease in an opened system over time, in *Sec. 2.3.1*; "cause" before "effect" in causality, which is more accepted nowadays—but "effect" before "cause in "retrocausality," which is less accepted nowadays, in *Sec. 2.3.2*; a judge has the legal authority to decide a legal case against a defendant—but a defendant does not have the legal authority to decide a legal case against a judge, in *Sec. 2.4.1*; "safety-based RCA" is more popular in fields like "accident analysis" and "occupational safety and health"—but "production-based RCA" is more popular in fields like "quality control" and "industrial manufacturing," in *Sec. 2.4.2*; in "emergence" myths, "the role of midwife is usually played by a female deity, like the spider woman of Native American mythology"—but "male characters rarely figure into these stories," in *Sec. 2.5.1*; "Aristotle hazards a few arguments that a determination of the final cause of a phenomenon is more important than the others [the other three causes]," so "once a final cause is in place, the material, efficient and formal causes follow by necessity," in *Sec. 2.5.2*; reporting adverse effects is voluntary in Australia—but it is required in the U.S. nowadays, in *Sec. 3.2.1*; humans have "self-defeating prophecy," on average—but animals do not have "self-defeating prophecy," on average, in *Sec. 3.2.2*; "finite dimensional linear systems are never chaotic"—but "for a dynamical system to display chaotic behaviour it has to be either nonlinear, or infinite-dimensional," in *Sec. 3.3.1*; "the quantum Zeno effect" can be applied to the interpretation of quantum theory based on "the reductionist postulate for reconciling the measurement problem"—but "the quantum Zeno effect" cannot be applied to other interpretations of quantum theory like "the many-worlds interpretation...and the Quantum Logic Interpretation," because "the quantum Zeno effect does not apply to all interpretations of quantum theory," in *Sec. 3.3.2*; South Vietnam, Laos, and Cambodia in Southeast Asia fell to communism in the 1970s—but Thailand, Malaysia, Indonesia, and the Philippines did not, in *Sec. 3.4.1*; the popularity of "causal logic" is due to its being more "effect-dependent"—but the popularity of "effectual logic" is due to its being more "people-dependent," in *Sec. 3.4.2*; classical mechanics can be applied better to the macroscopic world—but quantum mechanics can be applied better to the microscopic world, in *Sec. 3.5.1*; and the Jainist version of "eternal return" is more accepted in India—but the modern scientific cosmological versions of "eternal return" as discussed earlier are more accepted in the U.S., in *Sec. 3.5.2*).

And the reverse direction also holds true.

Again, for the last time, it should be stressed, however, that there are different shades of gray (or different degrees of truth) in the two opposites, and the classification is not necessarily mutually exclusive either. In fact, even when some combinations of the two occur, they only end up sharing the same dialectic relationship, but in a different degree.

Also, there are some other relationships (as a kind of family resemblance) which have something in common with the principle, but they are not exactly the same but only more or less comparable, which varies from case to case.

Good examples of family resemblance in relation to the principle are balance-extremity, reflexiveness-unreflexiveness, equality-inequality, harmoniousness-unharrmoniousness, center-periphery, compatibility-incompatibility, proportion-disproportion, balance-unbalance, and something like that.

27th Thesis: The Softness-Hardness Principle

The twenty-seventh thesis refers to the softness-hardness principle (on the force of change) in the category of "agency" in existential dialectics (which was first worked out in *ALD*), in that any change by an agent, be it organic (like humans) or non-organic (like natural objects), can occur in a forceful (aggressive) or gentle (pacific) way, which can come in all shapes and sizes, of course. There is no softness without hardness—and vice versa.

For instance, on the one hand, there is softness (e.g., the defense of attributon theory by the advocates Fritz Heider, in *Sec. 2.2.1*; the belief in "self-fulfilling prophecy" by some people, in *Sec. 2.2.2*; the defense of the 2nd law by the advocates like Kelvin, Carnot, etc., in *Sec. 2.3.1*; the defense of "retrocausality" by the advocates like Michael Dummett, in *Sec. 2.3.2*; the defense of the "two-stage" inquiry by the advocates aforecited, in *Sec. 2.4.1*; the defense of incident management by the advocates aforecited, in *Sec. 2.4.2*; the role of "female characters" in "emergence" myths, in *Sec. 2.5.1*; the defense of "telos" by the advocates like Aristotle, in *Sec. 2.5.2*; the defense of "the MMR vaccine" by its drug manufacturers, in *Sec. 3.2.1*; the defense of the idea of "unintended consequences" by the advocates like Merton, in *Sec. 3.2.2*; the defense of the idea of "the butterfly effect" by the advocates like Lorenz, in *Sec. 3.3.1*; the defense of the quantum Zeno effect by the advocates aforecited, in *Sec. 3.3.2*; "the 'prestige' interpretation of the [domino] theory, meaning that the success of Communist revolutions in some countries, though it did not provide material support to revolutionary forces in other countries, did contribute morale and rhetorical support," in *Sec. 3.4.1*; the defense of effectual logic by the advocates aforecited, in *Sec. 3.4.2*; the defense of causal determinism by the advocates aforecited, in *Sec. 3.5.1*; and the defense of "eternal return" by the advocates like Nietzsche, in *Sec. 3.5.2*).

On the other hand, there is hardness (e.g., the critique of attributon theory, as shown in the problems pointed out by the critics aforecited, in *Sec. 2.2.1*; the rebellion against "self-fulfilling prophecy" by some people, as in "self-defeating prophecy" aforecited, in *Sec. 2.2.2*; the critique of the 2nd law, as shown in the problems pointed out by the critics aforecited, in *Sec. 2.3.1*; the critique of "retrocausality" by the critics like Antony Flew, in *Sec. 2.3.2*; the critique of the "two-stage" inquiry, as shown in the problems pointed out by the critics aforecited, in *Sec. 2.4.1*; the critique of incident management, as shown in the problems pointed out by the critics aforecited, in *Sec. 2.4.2*; the role of "male characters" in "creation ex nihilo" myths, in *Sec. 2.5.1*; the critique of "telos" by the critics like Ernst

Mayr [1992], S. H. P. Madrell [1998], etc., as shown in the problems pointed out earlier, in *Sec. 2.5.2*; the critique of "the MMR vaccine," as shown in the problems pointed out by those in lawsuits against the drug manufacturers, in *Sec. 3.2.1*; the critique of the idea of "unintended consequences" by the critics, as shown in the problems aforecited, in *Sec. 3.2.2*; the critique of the idea of "the butterfly effect" by the critics like David Orrell and Stephen Wolfram aforecited, in *Sec. 3.3.1*; the critique of the quantum Zeno effect, as shown in the problems pointed out by the critics aforecited, in *Sec. 3.3.2*; the "military" interpretation of the domino theory, in that Che Guevara called for "two, three ... many Vietnams" outside Indochina with military aid, not just morale and rhetorical support, in *Sec. 3.4.1*; the critique of effectual logic, as shown in the different problems pointed out by the critics aforecited, in *Sec. 3.4.2*; the critique of causal determinism, as shown in the problems pointed out by the critics aforecited, in *Sec. 3.5.1*; and the critique of "eternal return," as shown in the problems pointed out by the critics aforecited, in *Sec. 3.5.2*).

And the reverse direction also holds true.

Again, it should be stressed, however, that there are different shades of gray   (or different degrees of truth) in the two opposites, and the classification is not necessarily mutually exclusive either. In fact, even when some combinations of the two occur, they only end up sharing the same dialectic relationship, but in a different degree.

Also, there are some other relationships (as a kind of family resemblance) which have something in common with the principle, but they are not exactly the same but only more or less comparable, which varies from case to case.

Good examples of family resemblance in relation to the principle are peacefulness-violence, cooperation-competition, pacificity-aggression, dovishness-hawkishness, reward-punishment, peace-war, friendliness-unfriendliness, kindness-hostility, love-hatred, acceptance-discrimination, admiration-belittlement, inclusion-exclusion, cooperation-predation, like-dislike, courteousness-violence, polishedness-harshness, integration-rivalry, bribery-killing, femininity-masculinity, absorption-resistance, amicality-animosity, and the like.

28th Thesis: The Seriousness-Playfulness Principle

The twenty-eighth thesis refers to the seriousness-playfulness principle (on the extent of seriousness) in the category of "agency" in existential dialectics (which is first worked out in *FPHH*), in that, if there is seriousness, there is also playfulness, especially for any agent with some kind of intelligence life, be it about humans, animals, or, later, post-humans. There is no seriousness without playfulness—and vice versa.

Lest any misunderstanding occurs, the word "playfulness" here should not be confused with other terms like "laughter," "smile," "joke," "tickleness," and "laugh-like vocalization" (in some animals), for instance.

Being playful can come in all shapes and sizes and therefore is not necessarily tied up with any of these terms, alhough it can result from any of them, or a combination of them, or something else altogether.

This principle, together with some other principles (especially though not exclusively, like the formalness-informalness principle), have important implications for what constitutes rationality, be it about "rationality of application" at the practical level or "rationality of knowledge" at the meta-theoretical level (as summarized in *Sec. 4.20* of *FPHH*).

For instance, on the one hand, there is seriousness (e.g., the serious business of those researchers who try to understand the nature of attribution in people, in *Sec. 2.2.1*; the serious business of those who try to understand the nature of "self-fulfilling prophecy," in *Sec. 2.2.2*; the serious business of those who try to understand the nature of entropy, in *Sec. 2.3.1*; the serious business of those who try to understand the nature of "retrocausality," in *Sec. 2.3.2*; the serious business of those who try to establish "factual causation" and "legal causation," in *Sec. 2.4.1*; the serious business of those who try to understand the nature of "root causes" in problem-solving, in *Sec. 2.4.2*; the serious business of those who try to understand the origins of the world, in *Sec. 2.5.1*; the serious business of those who try to understand causation, in *Sec. 2.5.2*; the serious business of those who try to come up with effective ways of reporting adverse effects, in *Sec. 3.2.1*; the serious business of those who try to understand the causes of "unintended consequences," in *Sec. 3.2.2*; the serious business of those who try to understand the nature of "chaos," in *Sec. 3.3.1*; the serious business of those who try to understand the nature of the quantum Zeno effect, in *Sec. 3.3.2*; the serious business of those who try to understand the nature of the domino effect, in *Sec. 3.4.1*; the serious business of those who try to understand the nature of effectual logic, in *Sec. 3.4.2*; the serious business of those who try to understand the nature of causal determinism, in *Sec. 3.5.1*; and the serious business of those who try to understand the fate of the universe, in *Sec. 3.5.2*).

On the other hand, there is playfulness (e.g., the playful part of those researchers who try to understand the nature of attribution in people, when they play around with different possible versions of attribution theory over the decades, as shown in the 4 versions aforedescribed, in *Sec. 2.2.1*; the playful part of those who try to understand the nature of "self-fulfilling prophecy," when they play around with different versions around the world over the centuries, as shown in the examples aforedescribed, in Sec. 2.2.2; the playful part of those who try to understand the nature of entropy, when they play around with different formulations of the 2nd law over the centuries, as the philosopher/physicist P.W. Bridgman once said that "there have been nearly as many formulations of the second law as there have been discussions of it," in Sec. 2.3.1; the playful part of those who try to understand the nature of "retrocausality," when they play around with different possibilities over the decades, like different works on "retrocausality" as discussed earlier, in Sec. 2.3.2; the playful part of those who try to to establish "factual causation" and "legal causation," when they play around with different interpretations over the centuries, as shown in the different legal cases and disagreements among legal scholars aforecited, in Sec. 2.4.1; the playful part of those who try to understand the nature of "root causes" in problem-solving, when they play around with different approaches over the decades, like "safety-based, production-based, process-based, failure-based, and systems-based," etc., in Sec. 2.4.2; the playful part of those who try to understand the origins of the world, when they play around with different stories over the centuries, like the different types of "origin myths" aforediscussed, in Sec. 2.5.1; the playful part of those who try to understand causation, when they play around with different theories over the centuries, like "teleology" by Aristotle, "teleology in biology" by Asa Gray, etc., in Sec. 2.5.2; the playful part of those who try to come up with effective ways of reporting adverse effects, when they play around with different reporting systems over the decades, as shown in the 5 examples as discussed earlier, in Sec. 3.2.1; the playful part of those who try to understand the causes of "unintended consequences," when they play around with different possible causes over the decades, like the ones by Merton and the alternative ones by others aforecited, in Sec. 3.2.2; the playful part of those who try to understand the nature of "chaos," when they play around with different "properties" over the decades, with different views by different researchers aforecited, in Sec. 3.3.1; the playful part of those who try to understand the nature of the quantum Zeno effect, when they play around with different interpretations over the decades, like its use by Stapp for his claim about "quantum mind," in Sec. 3.3.2; the playful part of those who try to understand the nature of the domino effect, when they play around with different interpretations and versions over the decades, like the older "domino theory," the recent "reverse domino theory," etc., in Sec. 3.4.1; the playful part of those who try to understand the nature of effectual logic, when they play around with different principles over the years, like the 3 principles by Sarasvathy, the 5 principles in a Wikipedia article on effectuation, etc., in *Sec. 3.4.2*; the playful part of those who try to understand the nature of causal determinism, when they play around with different versions and possibilities over the centuries, as shown in the different examples aforediscussed, in *Sec. 3.5.1*; and the playful part of those who try to understand the fate of the universe, when they play around with different versions of "eternal return" over the centures in philosophy, religion, and cosmology, as discussed earlier, in *Sec. 3.5.2*).

And the reverse direction also holds true.

Again, it should be stressed, however, that there are different shades of gray (or different degrees of truth) in the two opposites, and the classification is not necessarily mutually exclusive either. In fact, even when some combinations of the two occur, they only end up sharing the same dialectic relationship, but in a different degree.

Also, there are some other relationships (as a kind of family resemblance) which have something in common with the principle, but they are not exactly the same but only more or less comparable, which varies from case to case.

Good examples of family resemblance in relation to the principle are seriousness-jokingness, seriousness-humorousness, seriousness-wittiness, seriousness-nonseriousness, Apollo-Dionysus, seriousness-restingness, seriousness-relaxedness, criticalness-imaginativeness, seriousness-clownishness, and so forth.

29th Thesis: The Activeness-Inactiveness Principle

The twenty-ninth thesis refers to the activeness-inactiveness principle (on the extent of activeness) in the category of "agency" in existential dialectics (which was first worked out in *FPHTRAN*), in that, if there is activeness, there is also inactiveness, especially (though not exclusively) for any agent with some kind of intelligence life, be it about humans, animals, or, later, post-humans. There is no activeness without inactiveness—and vice versa.

Being active can come in all shapes and sizes, just as a person (or an animal) can be inactive because he (or it) is tired, old, injured, sick, sleepy (or hibernating), uninterested, in a state of passive inertia (or disposition), etc.—and an object can be inactive because it is at rest, out of work (or order), etc.

This principle, together with some other principles (especially though not exclusively, like the formalness-informalness principle and seriousness-playfulness principle), have important implications for what constitutes rationality, be it about "rationality of application" at the practical level or "rationality of knowledge" at the meta-theoretical level (as summarized in *Sec. 4.20* of *FPHH*).

For instance, on the one hand, there is activeness (e.g., the relative activeness of those who can actively cope with situations after successfully receiving treatment through a "cognitive bias modification therapy," or CBMT, so as to reduce "learned helplessness," in *Sec. 2.2.1*; the relative activeness of those who "directly or indirectly cause" a prediction "to become true," as in self-fulfilling prophecy, in *Sec. 2.2.2*; the relative activeness of a closed universe when work can be done because of the availability of free energy when entropy has not yet reached its maximum, in *Sec. 2.3.1*; the relative activeness of a particle if it is not yet annihilaed by antimatter and can be understood in terms of "retrocausality" as "a change of direction of moving particles, from past to future, or from future to past," according to Yoichiro Nambu, in *Sec. 2.3.2*; relative active role of "causation" in the case Yorkshire Dale Steamship Co v Minister of War Transport [1942], in *Sec. 2.4.1*; the relatively more activeness of problem solving whem it is more "proactive," in *Sec. 2.4.2*; the relative activeness of a world with "chaos" and "order" as in "creation from chaos" myths, in *Sec. 2.5.1*; the relative activeness of "matter," when it is shaped by its "form" as the "formal cause" into something concrete, like a "table" from "wood," according to Aristotle, in *Sec. 2.5.2*; the relative activeness of those who take drugs with effective, not harmful, effects, so they can engage in nornal life activities, in *Sec. 3.2.1*; the relative activeness of rabbits in New Zealand when they were introduced and rapidly spread in the late 19th century, in *Sec. 3.2.2*; the relative activeness of those working on chaos theory nowadays, as there is so much going on in the field, in *Sec. 3.3.1*; the relative activeness of an unstable particle when its time evolution is not suppressed, in the absence of any quantum Zeno effect, in *Sec. 3.3.2*; the relative activeness of communists in Vietnam nowadays in the 2010s, as they are now in power, in *Sec. 3.4.1*; the relative active presence of "people" in effectual reasoning, since the focus in this logic is "finding and leading the right people" as "the key to creating an enduring venture," in *Sec. 3.4.2*; the relative activeness of classical mechanics when applied to the macroscopic world, in *Sec. 3.5.1*; and the relative activeness of the idea of "eternal return" in the modern Western philosopical tradition, when Friedrich Nietzsche contributed to its re-introduction by connecting "the thought to many of his other concepts, including *amor fati*," in *Sec. 3.5.2*).

On the other hand, there is inactiveness (e.g., the relative inactiveness of those with "learned helplessness," when "they feel powerless to change their situation," and "this happens when people attribute negative results to their internal, stable and global factors leading them to think they have no control over their situation," in *Sec. 2.2.1*; the relative inactiveness of those in "self-defeating prophecy" who refuse to "directly or indirectly cause" a prediction "to become true," because they do not believe in "self-fulfilling prophecy," although some of them may proceed to falsify it, but most at least refuse to cause it true, in *Sec. 2.2.2*; the relative inactiveness of a closed universe when work can no longer be done because of the non-availability of free energy when entropy already reaches its maximum, in *Sec. 2.3.1*; the relative inactiveness of a particle if it is annihilaed by antimatter and can be understood in terms of "retrocausality" as "a change of direction of moving particles, from past to future, or from future to past," according to Yoichiro Nambu, in *Sec. 2.3.2*; the relative inactive role of "causation" in the case about "a contract of indemnity insurance," in *Sec. 2.4.1*; the relative less activeness of problem solving when it is more "reactive," in *Sec. 2.4.2*; the relative inactiveness of a world where there is "nothing," as in "creation *ex nihilo*" myths, in *Sec. 2.5.1*; the relative inactiveness of "matter," when it is not yet shaped by its "form" as the "formal cause" into something particular, according to Aristotle, in *Sec. 2.5.2*; the relative inactiveness of those who take drugs with serious harmful effects, so they get very sick and cannot engage in nornal life activities, in *Sec. 3.2.1*; the relative inactiveness of many sheep in New Zealand when they were almost wiped out by the rabbits when the latter rapidly spread in the late 19th century, in *Sec. 3.2.2*; the relative inactiveness of those working on chaos theory in the 19th century, as there was not much going on in the field at that time, which was not yet developed, in *Sec. 3.3.1*; the relative inactiveness of an unstable particle when its time evolution is suppressed in the quantum Zeno effect, in *Sec. 3.3.2*; the relative inactiveness of communists in Malaysia nowadays in the 2010s, as they are now banned, in *Sec. 3.4.1*; the relative inactive presence of "predictive models" in effectual reasoning, since it is based on the motto that "To *the extent that we can control the future, we do not need to predict it,*" in *Sec. 3.4.2*; the relative inactiveness of classical mechanics when applied to the microscopic world, since quantum mechanics is more useful here, in *Sec. 3.5.1*; and the relative inactiveness of the idea of "eternal return," when, "with the decline of antiquity and the spread of Christianity, the concept [of eternal return] fell into disuse in the Western world" until the modern era," *Sec. 3.5.2*).

And the reverse direction also holds true.

Again, it should be stressed, however, that there are different shades of gray (or different degrees of truth) in the two opposites, and the classification is not necessarily mutually exclusive either. In fact, even when some combinations of the two occur, they only end up sharing the same dialectic relationship, but in a different degree.

Also, there are some other relationships (as a kind of family resemblance) which have something in common with the principle, but they are not exactly the same but only more or less comparable, which varies from case to case.

Good examples of family resemblance in relation to the principle are alertness-unalertness, activeness-decrepidness, alertness-sleepiness, activeness-tiredness, alertness-unwareness, alertness-uninterestedness, soberness-inactiveness, alertness-inactiveness, soberness-unawareness, awakenness-hibernatedness, activeness-passiveness, and so on.

30th Thesis: The Selfness-Otherness Principle

The thirtieth thesis refers to the selfness-otherness principle (on the magnitude of self-centeredness) in the category of "agency" in existential dialectics (which is first worked out in *FPHCA*), in that, if there is the tendency to be mostly centered on one's self or group, there is likewise the tendency to be mostly centered on others, especially (though not exclusively) for any agent with some kind of intelligence life, be it about humans, animals, or, later, post-humans. There is no selfness without otherness—and vice versa.

Being self-centered and being other-centered do not have to be mutually exclusive, as the two can come in all shapes and sizes, or in different degrees. And other-centeredness does not entail desirability, any more than self-centeredness implies non-desirability, as both can go either way.

In addition, whether self-centeredness constitutes a moral alternative or, conversely, an alternative to morality is of course debatable (as addressed in my other book titled *Beyond Ethics to Post-Ethics*).

For instance, on the one hand, there is selfness (e.g., the tendency to be mostly centered on one's self or group, as shown in "self serving bias," when a person "is attributing dispositional and internal factors for success and external, uncontrollable factors for failure," in *Sec. 2.2.1*; the tendency to be mostly centered on one's self or group, as shown in the Greek legend of Oedipus, in which, "warned that his child would one day kill him, Laius abandoned his newborn son Oedipus to die," in *Sec. 2.2.2*; the tendency to be mostly centered on one's self or group, as shown in the professtional self-interest to protect the "conventional" acceptance that, "by convention, for the purposes of thermodynamic analysis,…any arbitrary occasion of space-time is said to be in thermodynamic equilibrium," even though "nothing in the entire universe is or has ever been truly in exact thermodynamic equilibrium," together with other problems aforecited, in *Sec. 2.3.1*; the tendency to be mostly centered on one's self or group, as shown in the continued belief in "retrocausality" by the advocates of para-science, in spite of the fact that "these results and their underlying theory have been rejected by the mainstream scientific community," in *Sec. 2.3.2*; the tendency to be mostly centered on one's self or group, as shown in the case of R v. Blaue [1975], where "the defendant visited the home of a Jehovah's Witness and demanded sex. When she refused, he stabbed her four times," in *Sec. 2.4.1*; the tendency to be mostly centered on one's self or group, as shown in the personal preference for "small changes," not "radical changes," by those in "continuous improvement," in *Sec. 2.4.2*; the tendency to be mostly centered on one's self or group, as shown in "Greek and Hebrew founding myths," which "established the special relationship between a deity and local people who traced their origins from a hero and authenticated their ancestral rights through the founding myth," in *Sec. 2.5.1*; the tendency to be mostly centered on one's self or group, as shown in the "telos" which drives a person to do certain thing as the "final cause," so as to serve his "purpose, end, aim, or goal of something," according to Aristotle, in *Sec. 2.5.2*; the tendency to be mostly centered on one's self or group, as shown in those with "lawsuits against drug manufacturers" in regard to the claim about "autism…linked to the MMR vaccine," even though "no link has been found in several large studies, and despite removal of thimerosal from vaccines a decade ago the rate of autism has not decreased as would be expected if it had been the causative agent," in *Sec. 3.2.1*; the tendency to be mostly centered on one's self or group, as shown in the opposition by many juvenile cyclists to the introduction of a law to require the use of safety helmets, because "the youths considered wearing a bicycle helmet unfashionable," in *Sec. 3.2.2*; the tendency to be mostly centered on one's self or group, as shown in the personal prejudice of the advisor of a graduate student in Chihiro Hayashi's laboratory at Kyoto University, Yoshisuke Ueda, because, when his student "was experimenting with analog computers and noticed, on Nov. 27, 1961, what he called 'randomly transitional phenomena,'" the "advisor…did not allow him to report his findings until 1970," even though the idea was correct, in *Sec. 3.3.1*; the tendency to be mostly centered on one's self or group, as shown in the ego of Stapp in his application of the quantum Zeno effect for his claim about "quantum mind," in spite of the rejection by the critics as false, in *Sec. 3.3.2*; the tendency to be mostly centered on one's self or group, as shown in "the rivalry between the Soviet Union and China, known as the Sino-Soviet split, which began in the 1950s," which contributed to the breakup of "world communism," in *Sec. 3.4.1*; the tendency to be mostly centered on one's self or group, as shown in the focus on "competition" and "highest potential return" by those for "causal reasoning," in *Sec. 3.4.2*;, the tendency to be mostly centered on one's self or group, as shown by those who misuse causal determinism for religious purposes, as discussed earlier, in *Sec. 3.5.1*; and the tendency to be mostly centered on one's self or group, as shown in the self-interest of Nietzsche when he "dropped his plans to try to scientifically prove the theory because he realized that if he would have to eventually repeat life as it is, his presumption of infinite time means 'he' would also have to 'repeat' life differently," in *Sec. 3.5.2*).

On the other hand, there is otherness (e.g., the tendency to be mostly centered on others, as shown in "culture bias," when "people in collectivist cultures see individuals as members of groups such as families, tribes, work units, and nations, and tend to value conformity and interdependence," in *Sec. 2.2.1*; the tendency to be mostly centered on others, as shown in the academic analysis of both sides of the debate on "self-fulfilling prophecy," as an advancement in the knowledge of social psychology and micro-sociology for humanity, in *Sec. 2.2.2*; the tendency to be mostly centered on others, as shown in the academic analysis of both sides of the debate on the 2nd law, as an advancement in the knowledge of physics for humanity, in *Sec. 2.3.1*; the tendency to be mostly centered on others, as shown in the academic analysis of both sides of the debate on "retrocausality," as an advancement in the knowledge of physics for humanity, in *Sec. 2.3.2*; the tendency to be mostly centered on others, as shown in the academic analysis of both sides of the debate on the case R v. Blaue [1975], as an advancement in the knowledge of jurisprudence for humanity, in *Sec. 2.4.1*; the tendency to be mostly centered on others, as shown in the academic analysis of both sides of the debate on "small changes," as an advancement in the knowledge of management studies for humanity, in *Sec. 2.4.2*; the tendency to be mostly centered on others, as shown in the academic analysis of both sides of the debate on the social functions of "founding myths," as an advancement in the knowledge of sociology for humanity, in *Sec. 2.5.1*; the tendency to be mostly centered on others, as shown in the academic analysis of both sides of the debate on "telos," as an advancement in the knowledge of causation for humanity, in *Sec. 2.5.2*; the tendency to be mostly centered on others, as shown in the academic analysis of both sides of the debate on the claim about "autism...linked to the MMR vaccine," as an advancement in the knowledge of medicine for humanity, in *Sec. 3.2.1*; the tendency to be mostly centered on others, as shown in the introduction of a law to require the use of safety helmets so as to increase "public health" like the reduction of head injuries, in Australia in 1990, in *Sec. 3.2.2*; the tendency to be mostly centered on others, as shown in the academic analysis of both sides of the debate on the butterfly effect, as an advancement in the knowledge of physics for humanity, in *Sec. 3.3.1*; the tendency to be mostly centered on others, as shown in the academic analysis of both sides of the debate on the quantum Zeno effect, as an advancement in the knowledge of physics for humanity, in *Sec. 3.3.2*; the tendency to be mostly centered on others, as shown in the academic analysis of both sides of the debate on the validity of the domino theory, as an advancement in the knowledge of political science for humanity, in *Sec. 3.4.1*; the tendency to be mostly centered on others, as shown in the academic analysis of both sides of the debate on "causal logic" and "effectual logic," as an advancement in the knowledge of business management for humanity, in *Sec. 3.4.2*; the tendency to be mostly centered on others, as shown in the academic analysis of both sides of the debate on causal determinism, as an advancement in the knowledge of science for humanity, in *Sec. 3.5.1*; and the tendency to be mostly centered on others, as shown in the academic analysis of both sides of the debate on "eternal return," as an advancement in the knowledge of the fate of the universe for humanity in *Sec. 3.5.2*).

And the reverse direction also holds true.

Again, it should be stressed, however, that there are different shades of gray (or different degrees of truth) in the two opposites, and the classification is not necessarily mutually exclusive either. In fact, even when some combinations of the two occur, they only end up sharing the same dialectic relationship, but in a different degree.

Also, there are some other relationships (as a kind of family resemblance) which have something in common with the principle, but they are not exactly the same but only more or less comparable, which varies from case to case.

Good examples of family resemblance in relation to the principle are egoisticness-altruisticness, selfishness-unselfishness, selfness-selflessness, egocentricness-othercentricness, parasiticalness-helpfulness, take-give, and so on.

In Relation to Outcome

The next six theses are in relation to outcome in existential dialectics, as shown below.

31st Thesis: The Regression-Progression Principle

The thirty-first thesis is called the regression-progression principle (on the direction of history) in the category of "outcome" in existential dialectics (which was also already worked out in my previous books), in that neither the cyclical nor the linear views are adequate for explaining many phenomena at all levels. There is no regression without progression—and vice versa.

History progresses to more advanced forms, but with a regressive touch. Examples include no freedom without unfreedom, no equality without inequality, and no civilization without barbarity. This is not an inevitable law, but merely a highly likely empirical trend.

For instance, on the one hand, there is regression (e.g., the regression made by attribution theory, as shown in the problems pointed out by the critics, in *Sec. 2.2.1*; the regression made by the research on "self-fulfilling prophecy," as shown in the problems pointed out by the critics, in *Sec. 2.2.2*; the regression made by the 2nd law, as shown in the problems pointed out by the critics, in *Sec. 2.3.1*; the regression made by the research on "retrocausality," as shown in the problems pointed out by the critics, in *Sec. 2.3.2*; the regression made by the "two-stage" approach to jurisprudence, as shown in the problems pointed out by the critics, in *Sec. 2.4.1*; the regression made by RCA, as shown in the problems pointed out by the critics, in *Sec. 2.4.2*; the regression made by the works on origin myths, as shown in the problems pointed out by the critics, in *Sec. 2.5.1*; the regression made by Aristotle's "four causes," as shown in the problems pointed out by the critics, in *Sec. 2.5.2*; the regression made by the use of drugs, as shown in the problems of "adverse effects" pointed out by the critics, in *Sec. 3.2.1*; the regression made by the introduction of a law to require the use of safety helmets in Australia in 1990, as shown in the problem that "the decrease in exercise caused by reduced cycling as a result of helmets laws is counterproductive in terms of net health," in *Sec. 3.2.2*; the regression made by the butterfly effect, as shown in the problems pointed out by the critics, in *Sec. 3.3.1*; the regression made by the research on quantum Zeno effect, as shown in the problems pointed out by the critics, in *Sec. 3.3.2*; the regression made by the domino theory, as shown in the problems pointed out by the critics, in *Sec. 3.4.1*; the regression made by the work on effectuation, as shown in the problems pointed out by the critics, in *Sec. 3.4.2*; the regression made by the research on causal determinism, as shown in the problems pointed out by the critics, in *Sec. 3.5.1*; and the regression made by the idea of "eternal return," as shown in the problems pointed out by the critics, in *Sec. 3.5.2*).

On the other hand, there is progress (e.g., the progress made by attribution theory, as shown in the contribution to the "cognitive bias modification therapy," or CBMT, so as to reduce "learned helplessness aforecited, in *Sec. 2.2.1*; the progress made by the research on "self-fulfilling prophecy," as shown in the contribution to the "public education reform" following the "War on Poverty," in *Sec. 2.2.2*; the progress made by the 2nd law, as shown in the contribution to the understanding of "time's arrow" aforecited, in *Sec. 2.3.1*; the progress made by the research on "retrocausality," as shown in the contribution to the understanding of reality in physics, philosophy of science, and para-science aforecited, in *Sec. 2.3.2*; the progress made by the "two-stage" approach to jurisprudence, as shown in the contribution to the understanding of establishing "factual causation" and "legal causation" aforecited, in *Sec. 2.4.1*; the progress made by RCA, as shown in the contribution to the understanding of "root causes" in problem solving aforecited, in *Sec. 2.4.2*; the progress made by the works on origin myths, as shown in the contribution to the understanding of "philosophy of life," "social order," etc., as discussed earlier, in *Sec. 2.5.1*; the progress made by Aristotle's "four causes," as shown in the contribution to the understanding of causation, like "efficient cause," aforecited, in *Sec. 2.5.1*; the progress made by the use of drugs, as shown in the contribution to the beneficial uses of drugs aforecited, in *Sec. 3.2.1*; the progress made by the introduction of a law to require the use of safety helmets in Australia in 1990, as shown in the contribution to the reduction of "head or brain injury by approximately two-thirds or more," in *Sec. 3.2.2*; the progress made by the butterfly effect, as shown in the contribution to the understanding of "sensitivity to initial conditions" aforecited, in *Sec. 3.3.1*; the progress made by the research on quantum Zeno effect, as shown in the contribution to the understanding of the exponential decay law aforecited, in *Sec. 3.3.2*; the progress made by the domino theory, as shown in the contribution to the containment of communism in other Southeast Asian countries which did not fall to communism, as discussed earlier, in *Sec. 3.4.1*; the progress made by the work on effectuation, as shown in the contribution to the understanding of doing business in "situations of uncertainty" aforecited, in *Sec. 3.4.2*;, the progress made by the research on causal determinism, as shown in the contribution to the understanding of "day-to-day physics" by Newtonian physics aforecited, in *Sec. 3.5.1*; and the progress made by the idea of "eternal return," as shown in the contribution to the understanding of the fate of the universe aforecited in *Sec. 3.5.2*).

And the reverse direction also holds true.

Again, it should be stressed, however, that there are different shades of gray (or different degrees of truth) in the two opposites, and the classification is not necessarily mutually exclusive either. In fact, even when some combinations of the two occur, they only end up sharing the same dialectic relationship, but in a different degree.

Also, there are some other relationships (as a kind of family resemblance) which have something in common with the principle, but they are not exactly the same but only more or less comparable, which varies from case to case.

Good examples of family resemblance in relation to the principle are undesirability-desirability, risk-opportunity, badness-goodness, cost-benefit, dysfunctionality-functionality, cyclicity-linearity, failure-success, setback-progress, reversal-linearity, and so on.

32nd Thesis: The Same-Difference Principle

The thirty-second thesis refers to the same-difference principle (on the metamorphosis of change) in the category of "outcome" in existential dialectics (which was worked out in *ALD* and other books of mine), in that an entity, as it evolves over time, can be both different from and similar to its opposing alternatives and does not have to be solely more different from them over time. There is no similarity without difference—and vice versa.

Opposites are not absolute in a black-or-white fashion; so, an entity can become relatively more similar to (or more different from) its opposite over time.

This is further constrained by another principle, that is, the symmetry-asymmetry principle about the relationships among existents under the category about agency in existential dialectics, in that if there is symmetry (equality) between two entities, there is likewise asymmetry (inequality) emerging in a different way.

For instance, on the one hand, there is similarity in outcome (e.g., the contribution to the molding and control of beliefs, values, and behaviors, regardless of whether this be done by way of "learned helplessness," or by way of "CBMT," in *Sec. 2.2.1*; the contribution to the molding and control of beliefs, values, and behaviors, regardless of whether this be done by way of "self-fulfilling prophecy," or by way of "self-defeating prophecy," in *Sec. 2.2.2*; the contribution to the molding and control of beliefs, values, and behaviors, regardless of whether this be done by way of "time's arow," or by way of "eternal recurrence." in *Sec. 2.3.1*; the contribution to the molding and control of beliefs, values, and behaviors, regardless of whether this be done by way of the acceptance of causality, or by way of the acceptance of "retrocausality," in *Sec. 2.3.2*; the contribution to the molding and control of beliefs, values, and behaviors, regardless of whether this be done by way of "legal causation," or by way of "scientific assertions," in *Sec. 2.4.1*; the contribution to the molding and control of beliefs, values, and behaviors, regardless of whether this be done by way of "continuous improvement," or by way of "research and development," in *Sec. 2.4.2*; the contribution to the molding and control of beliefs, values, and behaviors, regardless of whether this be done by way of "emergence" myths, or by way of "creation ex nihilo" myths, in *Sec. 2.5.1*; the contribution to the molding and control of beliefs, values, and behaviors, regardless of whether this be done by way of Aristotelian metaphysics, or by way of modern evolutionary theory, in *Sec. 2.5.2*; the contribution to the molding and control of beliefs, values, and behaviors, regardless of whether this be done by way of the required reporting system of adverse effects in the U.K., or by way of the voluntary reporting system of adverse effects in Australia, in *Sec. 3.2.1*; the contribution to the molding and control of beliefs, values, and behaviors, regardless of whether this be done by way of the "mandatory" use of safety helmets, or by way of voluntary the "use of safety helmets," in *Sec. 3.2.2*; the contribution to the molding and control of beliefs, values, and behaviors, regardless of whether this be done by way of the acceptance of "chaos theory," or by way of the acceptance of "physical determinsm," in *Sec. 3.3.1*; the contribution to the molding and control of beliefs, values, and behaviors, regardless of whether this be done by way of the belief in "quantum physics," or by way of the belief in "quantum biology," in *Sec. 3.3.2*; the contribution to the molding and control of beliefs, values, and behaviors, regardless of whether this be done by way of the acceptance of the spread of "world communism" by the Soviet Union, or by way of the rejection of the spread of "world communism" by the U.S.A., in *Sec. 3.4.1*; the contribution to the molding and control of beliefs, values, and behaviors, regardless of whether this be done by way of causal reasoning, or by way of effectual reasoning, in *Sec. 3.4.2*; the contribution to the molding and control of beliefs, values, and behaviors, regardless of whether this be done by way of the belief in classical mechanics, or by way of the belief in quantum mechanics, in *Sec. 3.5.1*; and the contribution to the molding and control of beliefs, values, and behaviors, regardless of whether this be done by way of the acceptance of the "oscillating universe theory," or by way of the acceptance of the "Godhead" theory in *Sec. 3.5.2*).

On the other hand, there is difference in outcome (e.g., the contribution to the molding and control of beliefs, values, and behaviors by way of "learned helplessness" for a relatively more pessimistic worldview—but the contribution to the molding and control of beliefs, values, and behaviors by way of "CBMT" for a relatively more optimistic worldview, in *Sec. 2.2.1*; the contribution to the molding and control of beliefs, values, and behaviors by way of "self-fulfilling prophecy" for a relatively more gullible mindset—but the contribution to the molding and control of beliefs, values, and behaviors by way of "self-defeating prophecy" for a relatively more rebellious mindset, in *Sec. 2.2.2*; the contribution to the molding and control of beliefs, values, and behaviors by way of "time's arow" for a relatively more physical worldview—but the contribution to the molding and control of beliefs, values, and behaviors by way of "eternal recurrence" for a relatively more metaphysical worldview, in *Sec. 2.3.1*; the contribution to the molding and control of beliefs, values, and behaviors by way of the acceptance of causality for a relatively more mainstream worldview—but the contribution to the molding and control of beliefs, values, and behaviors by way of the acceptance of "retrocausality" for a relatively more radical worldview, in *Sec. 2.3.2*; the contribution to the molding and control of beliefs, values, and behaviors by way of "legal causation" for a relatively more deterministic worldview—but the contribution to the molding and control of beliefs, values, and behaviors by way of "scientific assertions" for a relatively more probabilistic worldview, in *Sec. 2.4.1*; the contribution to the molding and control of beliefs, values, and behaviors by way of "continuous improvement" for a relatively more gradual lifeworld—but the contribution to the molding and control of beliefs, values, and behaviors by way of "research and development" for a relatively more transformative lifeworld, in *Sec. 2.4.2*; the contribution to the molding and control of beliefs, values, and behaviors by way of "emergence" myths, for a relatively more feminine worldview—but the contribution to the molding and control of beliefs, values, and behaviors by way of "creation *ex nihilo*" myths for a relatively more masculine worldview, in *Sec. 2.5.1*; the contribution to the molding and control of beliefs, values, and behaviors by way of Aristotelian metaphysics for a relatively more teleological worldview—but the contribution to the molding and control of beliefs, values, and behaviors by way of modern evolutionary theory for a relatively more chanceful worldview, in *Sec.*

2.5.2; the contribution to the molding and control of beliefs, values, and behaviors by way of the required reporting system of adverse effects in the U.K. for a relatively more state-regulated lifeworld—but the contribution to the molding and control of beliefs, values, and behaviors by way of the voluntary reporting system of adverse effects in Australia for a relatively more market-oriented lifeworld, in *Sec. 3.2.1*; the contribution to the molding and control of beliefs, values, and behaviors by way of the "mandatory" use of safety helmets for a relatively more state-regulated lifeworld, in spite of its unintended consequences—but the contribution to the molding and control of beliefs, values, and behaviors by way of the voluntary "use of safety helmets" for a relatively more market-oriented lifeworld, in spite of its contribution to head injuries, in *Sec. 3.2.2*; the contribution to the molding and control of beliefs, values, and behaviors by way of the acceptance of "chaos theory" for a relatively more unpredictable view of nature—but the contribution to the molding and control of beliefs, values, and behaviors by way of the acceptance of "physical determinsm" for a relatively more predictable view of nature, in *Sec. 3.3.1*; the contribution to the molding and control of beliefs, values, and behaviors by way of the belief in "quantum physics" for a relatively more material worldview—but the contribution to the molding and control of beliefs, values, and behaviors by way of the belief in "quantum biology" for a relatively more spiritual   worldview, in *Sec. 3.3.2*; the contribution to the molding and control of beliefs, values, and behaviors by way of the acceptance of the spread of "world communism" by the Soviet Union for a relatively more left-wing lifeworld—but the contribution to the molding and control of beliefs, values, and behaviors by way of the rejection of the spread of "world communism" by the U.S.A. for a relatively more right-wing lifeworld, in *Sec. 3.4.1*; the contribution to the molding and control of beliefs, values, and behaviors by way of causal reasoning for a relatively more predictive worldview—but the contribution to the molding and control of beliefs, values, and behaviors by way of effectual reasoning for a relatively more unpredictive worldview, in *Sec. 3.4.2*; the contribution to the molding and control of beliefs, values, and behaviors by way of the belief in classical mechanics for a relatively more certain worldview—but the contribution to the molding and control of beliefs, values, and behaviors by way of the belief in quantum mechanics for a relatively more uncertain worldview, in *Sec. 3.5.1*; and the contribution to the molding and control of beliefs, values, and behaviors by way of the acceptance of the "oscillating universe theory" for a relatively more scientific worldview—but the contribution to the molding and control of beliefs, values, and behaviors by way of the acceptance of the "Godhead" theory for a relatively more religio-mystical worldview, in *Sec. 3.5.2*).

And the reverse direction also holds true.

Again, it should be stressed, however, that there are different shades of gray　(or different degrees of truth) in the two opposites, and the classification is not necessarily mutually exclusive either. In fact, even when some combinations of the two occur, they only end up sharing the same dialectic relationship, but in a different degree.

Also, there are some other relationships (as a kind of family resemblance) which have something in common with the principle, but they are not exactly the same but only more or less comparable, which varies from case to case.

Good examples of family resemblance in relation to the principle are homogeneity-heterogeneity, we-they, similarity-contrast, assimilation-dissimilation, and so forth.

33rd Thesis: The Stability-Reaction Principle

The thirty-third thesis is called the stability-reaction principle (on the feedback mechanism for further changes) in the category of "outcome" in existential dialectics (which was first worked out in *FPHCHEM*), in that once an outcome becomes stabilized over time (which varies from case to case), there is resistance to it, such that it undergoes further changes in its multifaceted interactions with the outside world　(e.g., with other entities, energy, space, and so on).

There is no stability without reaction (to stability for further changes)—and vice versa.

Works on chemical reactions (as in *FPHCHEM*) and feedback mechanisms for learning in adaptive management (as in *BNR*), just to name a few of them, have contributed to the understanding of stability and instability.

For instance, on the one hand, there is stability in outcome (e.g., the relatively more stable condition of attribution theory in the older days, in *Sec. 2.2.1*; the relatively more stable condition of the idea of "self-fulfilling prophecy" in the older days, in *Sec. 2.2.2*; the relatively more stable condition of the 2nd law in modern time, in *Sec. 2.3.1*; the relatively more stable condition of the acceptance of causality in the older days, in *Sec. 2.3.2*; the relatively more stable condition of the appeal to "common sense" in the first stage of the "two-stage inquiry" in the older days, in *Sec. 2.4.1*; the relatively more stable condition of problem solving at the level of "symptoms" by some in the older days, in *Sec. 2.4.2*; the relatively more stable condition of "the previous world" as "the womb of the earth mother," according to "emergence" myths, in *Sec. 2.5.1*; the relatively more stable condition of Aristotle's idea of "final cause" in the older days, in *Sec. 2.5.2*; the situation in the earlier days, when, "because of the lack of these data and uncertainty about methods for synthesising them, individuals conducting systematic reviews and meta-analyses of therapeutic interventions often unknowingly overemphasise health benefit," in *Sec. 3.2.1*; the relatively more stable condition of not wearing safety helmets in Australia prior to 1990, in *Sec. 3.2.2*; the relatively more stable condition of the popularity of the butterfly effect in modern time, in *Sec. 3.3.1*; the relatively more stable condition of the work on the quantum Zeno effect in the later half of the 20th century, in *Sec. 3.3.2*; the relatively more stable condition of the domino theory in the older days, when it focused on Indochina, in *Sec. 3.4.1*; the relatively more stable condition of the formal framework of causal reasoning in the older days, in *Sec. 3.4.2*; the relatively more stable condition of Newtonian mechanics in the older days, in *Sec. 3.5.1*; and the relatively more stable condition of "the big bang theory in the framework of relativistic cosmology" which "seems to be at odds with eternal return" in the older days, in *Sec. 3.5.2*).

On the other hand, there is reaction in outcome (e.g., attribution theory in the older days then led to further changes later on, when nowadays, there is "cognitive bias modification therapy" to treat cognitive biases, in *Sec. 2.2.1*; the idea of "self-fulfilling prophecy" in the older days then led to further changes later on, when nowadays, there is the idea of "self-defeating prophecy," in *Sec. 2.2.2*; the 2nd law in modern time then led to further changes later on, when nowadays, there are different criticisms against it, as discussed earlier, in *Sec. 2.3.1*; the acceptance of causality in the older days then led to further changes later on, when nowadays, there is the alternative idea of "retrocausality," in *Sec. 2.3.2*; the appeal to "common sense" in the first stage of the "two-stage inquiry" in the older days then led to further changes later on, when nowadays, it was challenged by Hart, Honoré, and Wright for "a test of sufficiency" instead, in *Sec. 2.4.1*; problem solving at the level of "symptoms" by some in the older days then led to further changes later on, when nowadays, there is the alternative like RCA, in *Sec. 2.4.2*; "the previous world" as "the womb of the earth mother," according to "emergence" myths, then led to further changes later on, when it eventually delivered the earth mother, in *Sec. 2.5.1*; Aristotle's idea of "final cause" in the older days then led to further changes later on, when in the modern era, Asa Gray interpreted "telos" with "modern evolutionary theory," in *Sec. 2.5.2*; the situation in the earlier days [when, "because of the lack of these data and uncertainty about methods for synthesising them, individuals conducting systematic reviews and meta-analyses of therapeutic interventions often unknowingly overemphasise health benefit] then led to further changes later on, when nowadays, "to balance the overemphasis on benefit, scholars have called for more complete reporting of harm from clinical trials," in *Sec. 3.2.1*; not wearing safety helmets in Australia prior to 1990 then led to further changes later on, when in 1990 there was a law introduced to require the use of safety helmets, in spite of its unintended consequences, in *Sec. 3.2.2*; the popularity of the butterfly effect in modern time then led to further changes later on, when nowadays, there are the criticisms that the so-called "butterfly effect" is much exaggerated, that the so-called "butterfly effect" misleadingly exclude some other effects in its analysis, that the butterfly effect can be countered by more complicated forecasting systems, that the butterfly effect does not apply in some situations, etc., in *Sec. 3.3.1*; the work on the quantum Zeno effect in the later half of the 20th century then led to further changes later on, when nowadays, there is the proposal for "quantum mind" in quantum biology, in *Sec. 3.3.2*; the domino theory in the older days, when it focused on Indochina, then led to further changes later on, when in the 2000s, the neocons proposed the "reverse domino theory" for the Middle East, in *Sec. 3.4.1*; the formal framework of causal reasoning in the older days then led to further changes later on, when nowadays, there is the alternative formal development of effectual reasoning, in *Sec. 3.4.2*; Newtonian mechanics in the older days then led to further changes later on, when it was later challenged by quantum mechanics in the 20th century, in *Sec. 3.5.1*; and "the big bang theory in the framework of relativistic cosmology" which "seems to be at odds with eternal return" in the older days then led to further changes later on, when "there are now many different speculative big bang scenarios in quantum cosmology which actually imply eternal return," in *Sec. 3.5.2*).

And the reverse direction also holds true.

Again, it should be stressed, however, that there are different shades of gray (or different degrees of truth) in the two opposites, and the classification is not necessarily mutually exclusive either. In fact, even when some combinations of the two occur, they only end up sharing the same dialectic relationship, but in a different degree.

Also, there are some other relationships (as a kind of family resemblance) which have something in common with the principle, but they are not exactly the same but only more or less comparable, which varies from case to case.

Good examples of family resemblance in relation to the principle are stability-forwardness, normalcy-feedback, balance-forwardness, balance-reaction, consolidation-modification, normalcy-feedback, stability-breakup, rest-motion, and the like.

34th Thesis: The Functionality-Nonfunctionality Principle

The thirty-fourth thesis is called the functionality-nonfunctionality principle (on the presence of function) in the category of "outcome" in existential dialectics (which is first worked out in *FPHCA*), in that, if there is the presence of action for which something or someone is fitted, there is likewise the relative lack of action for which something or someone is fitted. There is no functionality without nonfunctionallity—and vice versa.

A *function* should not be confused with an *alternative function,* which is just another kind of function, just as *nonfunction* should not be confused with *dysfunction* (which has more to do with malfunction and is thus related more to the regression-progression principle).

In addition, being functional (or useful) and being nonfunctional (or useless) do not have to be mutually exclusive, as the two can come in all shapes and sizes, or in different degrees. And what is functional at one time may become nonfunctional at another time, and vice-versa.

For instance, on the one hand, there is functionality in outcome (e.g., the presence of action for which something or someone is fitted, as shown in "attributions," which serve the function of explaining "the causes of behavior and events" for some people, as "cognitive biases may lead to more effective actions in a given context," in *Sec. 2.2.1*; the presence of action for which something or someone is fitted, as shown in "self-fulfilling prophecy," which serves the function of making prediction become true, in *Sec. 2.2.2*; the presence of action for which something or someone is fitted, as shown in the construction of the 2nd law of thermodynamics, which serves the function of explaining time's arrow, among other things, in *Sec. 2.3.1*; the presence of action for which something or someone is fitted, as shown in the research on "retrocausality," which serves the function of explaining reality from a radical, or non-mainstream viewpoint, in *Sec. 2.3.2*; the presence of action for which something or someone is fitted, as shown in the "two-stage inquiry," which serves the function of establishing "factual causation" and "legal causation" for legal cases, in *Sec. 2.4.1*; the presence of action for which something or someone is fitted, as shown in the use of incident management, which serves the function of providing reactive and gradual changes in problem solving, in *Sec. 2.4.2*; the presence of action for which something or someone is fitted, as shown in "origin myths," which serve different functions like the provision of "social order," etc., in *Sec. 2.5.1*; the presence of action for which something or someone is fitted, as shown in Aristotle's philosophy of "four causes," which serves the function of providing a teleological view of causation, in *Sec. 2.5.2*; the presence of action for which something or someone is fitted, as shown in the creation of "reporting systems," which serves the function of legally requiring the reporting of adverse effects for better understanding, in *Sec. 3.2.1*; the presence of action for which something or someone is fitted, as shown in the introduction of a law to require the use of safety helmets in Australia in 1990, which serves the function to enhance public health, like the reduciton of head injuries, in *Sec. 3.2.2*; the presence of action for which something or someone is fitted, as shown in the proposal of "the butterfly effect," which serves the function of providing an understanding of chaotic dynamics, in *Sec. 3.3.1*; the presence of action for which something or someone is fitted, as shown in the proposal of the quantum Zeno effect, which serves the function of explaining the nature of "decay" in quantum physics, in *Sec. 3.3.2*; the presence of action for which something or someone is fitted, as shown in the domino theory, which serves the function of justifying the need "for American intervention around the world" during the Cold War, in *Sec. 3.4.1*; the presence of action for which something or someone is fitted, as shown in the formal development of effectual logic, which serves the function of providing principles for decision-making in situations of uncertainty, in *Sec. 3.4.2*; the presence of action for which something or someone is fitted, as shown in the development of Newtonian physics, which serves the function of providing a deterministic worldview, in *Sec. 3.5.1*; and the presence of action for which something or someone is fitted, as shown in the idea of "eternal return," which serves the function of accounting for the future fate of the universe, in *Sec. 3.5.2*).

On the other hand, there is nonfunctionality in outcome (e.g., the relative lack of action for which something or someone is fitted, as shown in the problems with attributions as cognitive biases, such that they are not as functional as the advocates would like us to believe, in *Sec. 2.2.1*; the relative lack of action for which something or someone is fitted, as shown in the problems with "self-fulfilling prophecy," such that it is not as functional as the advocates would like us to believe, in *Sec. 2.2.2*; the relative lack of action for which something or someone is fitted, as shown in the problems with the 2nd law of thermodynamics aforecited, such that it is not as functional as the advocates would like us to believe, in *Sec. 2.3.1*; the relative lack of action for which something or someone is fitted, as shown in the problems with the research on "retrocausality," such that it is not as functional as the advocates would like us to believe, in *Sec. 2.3.2*; the relative lack of action for which something or someone is fitted, as shown in the problems with the "two-stage inquiry," such that it is not as functional as the advocates would like us to believe, in *Sec. 2.4.1*; the relative lack of action for which something or someone is fitted, as shown in the problems with incident management, such that it is not as functional as the advocates would like us to believe, in *Sec. 2.4.2*; the relative lack of action for which something or someone is fitted, as shown in different problems with "origin myths" as discussed earlier, such that is not as functional as the advocates would like us to believe, in *Sec. 2.5.1*; the relative lack of action for which something or someone is fitted, as shown in the problems with Aristotle's philosophy of "four causes," such that it is not as functional as the advocates would like us to believe, in *Sec. 2.5.2*; the relative lack of action for which something or someone is fitted, as shown in the problems with "reporting systems," such that they are not as functional as the advocates would like us to believe, in *Sec. 3.2.1*; the relative lack of action for which something or someone is fitted, as shown in the problem that "the decrease in exercise caused by reduced cycling as a result of helmets laws is counterproductive in terms of net health," such that it is not as functional as the advocates would like us to believe, in *Sec. 3.2.2*; the relative lack of action for which something or someone is fitted, as shown in the different problems with the idea of "the butterfly effect" as discussed earlier, such that it is not as functional as the advocates would like us to believe, in *Sec. 3.3.1*; the relative lack of action for which something or someone is fitted, as shown in the different problems with the quantum Zeno effect, such that it is not as functional as the advocates would like us to believe, in *Sec. 3.3.2*; the relative lack of action for which something or someone is fitted, as shown in the different problems with the domino theory, such that it is not as functional as the advocates would like us to believe, in *Sec. 3.4.1*; the relative lack of action for which something or someone is fitted, as shown in the different problems with the formal development of effectual logic, such that it is not as functional as the advocates would like us to believe, in *Sec. 3.4.2*; the relative lack of action for which something or someone is fitted, as shown in the problems with Newtonian physics challenged by quantum mechanics, such that it is not as functional as the advocates would like us to believe, in *Sec. 3.5.1*; and the relative lack of action for which something or someone is fitted, as shown in the different problems with the idea of "eternal return," such that it is not as functional as the advocates would like us to believe, in *Sec. 3.5.2*).

And the reverse direction also holds true.

Again, it should be stressed, however, that there are different shades of gray (or different degrees of truth) in the two opposites, and the classification is not necessarily mutually exclusive either. In fact, even when some combinations of the two occur, they only end up sharing the same dialectic relationship, but in a different degree.

Also, there are some other relationships (as a kind of family resemblance) which have something in common with the principle, but they are not exactly the same but only more or less comparable, which varies from case to case.

Good examples of family resemblance in relation to the principle are usefulness-nonusefulness, valueness-nonvalueness, usefulness-uselessness, and the like.

35ᵗʰ Thesis: The Intentionality-Nonintentionality Principle

The thirty-fifth thesis is called the intentionality-nonintentionality principle (on the planning for outcomes) in the category of "outcome" in existential dialectics (which is first worked out in *FPHW*), in that, if there is the planning or design of something for a certain outcome, there is likewise the relative absence of planning or design of something for a certain outcome. There is no intentionality without nonintentionallity—and vice versa.

An intention for an outcome does not have to be certain, so the outcome can even be counter-intentional in being the opposite of what was originally planned. In this sense, counter-intentionality is a special case of non-intentionality; in other words, there are unintended consequences which can be just the opposite of what was originally planned.

An intention for an outcome is mostly relevant to intelligent life, but there are non-intelligent life and non-living matter in the universe too, so nonintentionality is also important.

In addition, an intention does not have to be obvious or straightforward, as William Shakspeare once famously said: "I must be cruel only to be kind."

Especially, works on unintended consequences (like *FPHAERO*) have contributed to the understanding of nonintentionality.

In any event, on the one hand, there is intentionality in outcome (e.g., the planning or design of something for a certain outcome, as shown in the intended consequences in regard to attribution, as those who used attribution intended to explain "the causes of behavior and events" aforediscussed, in *Sec. 2.2.1*; the planning or design of something for a certain outcome, as shown in the intended consequences in regard to self-fulfilling prophecy, as those who used it intended to directly or indirectly make the prediction come true, in *Sec. 2.2.2*; the planning or design of something for a certain outcome, as shown in the intended consequences in regard to the proposal of the 2nd law, as those who used it intended to explain time's arrow on the basis of entropy, as described earlier, in *Sec. 2.3.1*; the planning or design of something for a certain outcome, as shown in the intended consequences in regard to retrocausality, as those who used it intended to explain a new view of causality in the reverse direction, in those cases as discussed earlier, in *Sec. 2.3.2*; the planning or design of something for a certain outcome, as shown in the intended consequences in regard to the "two-stage inquiry," as those who used it intended to establish "factual causation" and "legal causation" for legal liability, as discussed earlier, in *Sec. 2.4.1*; the planning or design of something for a certain outcome, as shown in the intended consequences in regard to RCA, as those who used it intended "to solve problems by attempting to identify and correct the root causes of events" aforediscussed, in *Sec. 2.4.2*; the planning or design of something for a certain outcome, as shown in the intended consequences in regard to origin myths, as those who used them intended to perform social functions, like the actual outcome of "social order" as pointed out by some scholars, in *Sec. 2.5.1*; the planning or design of something for a certain outcome, as shown in the intended consequences in regard to "final cause," as Aristotle who used it intended to provide a teleological view of the world, like the support of Asa Gray in the modern era to combine "telos" with "modern evolutionary theory," in *Sec. 2.5.2*; the planning or design of something for a certain outcome, as shown in the intended consequences in regard to reporting adverse effects now required in many countries, as these different laws were intended to do, as discussed earlier, in *Sec. 3.2.1*; the planning or design of something for a certain outcome, as shown in the intended consequences in regard to the reduction of head injuries, as those who supported a law to require the use of safety helmets in Australia in 1990 intended to have for public health, in *Sec. 3.2.2*; the planning or design of something for a certain outcome, as shown in the intended consequences in regard to "the butterfly effect," as those who used it intended to explain the nature of chaotic dynamics aforediscussed, in *Sec. 3.3.1*; the planning or design of something for a certain outcome, as shown in the intended consequences in regard to the quantum Zeno effect, as those who used it intended to explain the nature of "decay" in quantum physics, in *Sec. 3.3.2*; the planning or design of something for a certain outcome, as shown in the intended consequences in regard to the U.S. involvement in Indochina in the 1960s and 1970s so as to stop the spread of communism in South Vietnam, Laos, and Cambodia, in accordance to the domino theory, in *Sec. 3.4.1*; the planning or design of something for a certain outcome, as shown in the intended consequences in regard to the mainstream use of causal reasoning, as those who used it intended to achieve optimality, for example, in *Sec. 3.4.2*; the planning or design of something for a certain outcome, as shown in the intended consequences in regard to "accurate predictions" like "calculating the trajectory of a bullet" by Newtonian physics, as those who used it intended to explain causal determinism in day-to-day physics aforediscussed, in *Sec. 3.5.1*; and the planning or design of something for a certain outcome, as shown in the intended consequences, in regard to the big bang theory about "the singularity point" coming "out of nothing" at the beginning of the universe, as those who used it intended to explain the origin of the universe and its subsequent expansion in this way, in *Sec. 3.5.2*).

On the other hand, there is nonintentionality in outcome (e.g., the relative absence of planning or design of something for a certain outcome, such that the outcome can even be counter-intentional in being the opposite of what was originally planned, as shown in the problems of cognitive biases, which can "lead to perceptual distortion, inaccurate judgment, illogical interpretation, or what is broadly called irrationality"— contrary to the original intention of those who use attributions as a way to explain "the causes of behavior and events," in *Sec. 2.2.1*; the relative absence of planning or design of something for a certain outcome, such that the outcome can even be counter-intentional in being the opposite of what was originally planned, as shown in "self-defeating prophecy," in which "the audience of a prediction has an interest in seeing it falsified" in a rebellious way—contrary to the original intention of those who spread a "self-fulfilling prophecy," so as to directly or indirectly make the prediction come true, in *Sec. 2.2.2*; the relative absence of planning or design of something for a certain outcome, such that the outcome can even be counter-intentional in being the opposite of what was originally planned, as shown in the criticisms that the second law is not consistent with some well-established theorems, that there are uncertainties in regard to the application of the second law to the future scenarios of the universe, that it does not explain its own origin, that the second law is not quite accurate in some small systems, that the second law makes some questionable assumptions which limit its range of application, and that it exaggerates the occurrence of "equilibrium states—contrary to the original intention of those who proposed the 2nd law to explain time's arrow on the basis of entropy, in *Sec. 2.3.1*; the relative absence of planning or design of something for a certain outcome, such that the outcome can even be counter-intentional in being the opposite of what was originally planned, as shown in the use of "retrocausality" in "the Wheeler–Feynman absorber theory," but this usage does not have "anything to do with cause and effect" at all—contrary to the original intention of Michael Dummett to propose "retrocausality" so as to propose a new view of causality in the reverse direction, in *Sec. 2.3.2*; the relative absence of planning or design of something for a certain outcome, such that the outcome can even be counter-intentional in being the opposite of what was originally planned, as shown in some legal cases when the judge can exercise some discretion [such that a defendant can still be liable even if he successfully passes the "two-stage inquiry"] and, in addition, causation in the "two-stage inquiry" may not be relevant at all in some oher legal cases, as discussed earlier—contrary to the original intention of those to propose the "two-stage inquiry" as a way to establish "factual causation" and "legal causation" for legal liability, in *Sec. 2.4.1*; the relative absence of planning or design of something for a certain outcome, such that the outcome can even be counter-intentional in being the opposite of what was originally planned, as shown in the rise of incidents like hacking "faced by companies in developed nations all across the world," in spite of the implementation of RCA, such that "over half of the world's hacking attempts on Trans National Corporations [TNCs] take place in North America [57%]" and "23% of attempts take place in Europe"—contrary to the original intention of those to propose RCA as a more effective way "to solve problems by attempting to identify and correct the root causes of events," in *Sec. 2.4.2*; the relative absence of planning or design of something for a certain outcome, such that the outcome can even be counter-intentional in being the opposite of what was originally planned, as shown in the critique of "social order" by Karl Marx as a deceptive exploitative economic structure by the dominant upper class agaisnt the oppressed lower class—contrary to the original intention of those who proposed the origin myths for social functions, like the actual outcome of "social order," in *Sec. 2.5.1*; the relative absence of planning or design of something for a certain outcome, such that the outcome can even be counter-intentional in being the opposite of what was originally planned, as shown in the unintended outcome that "Aristotle's metaphysics, his account of nature and causality, was for the most part rejected by the early modern philosophers"—contrary to the original intention of Aristotle to have it accepted, in *Sec. 2.5.2*; the relative absence of planning or design of something for a certain outcome, such that the outcome can even be counter-intentional in being the opposite of what was originally planned, as shown in the limitations of reporting systems aforecited—contrary to the original intention of those to construct effective reporting systems, in *Sec. 3.2.1*; the relative absence of planning or design of something for a certain outcome, such that the outcome can even be counter-intentional in being the opposite of what was originally planned, as shown in "the decrease in exercise caused by reduced cycling as a result of helmets laws" which "is counterproductive in terms of net health"—contrary to the original intention of those who supported the law to require the use of safety helmets in Australia in 1990, as a way to enhance public health, in *Sec. 3.2.2*; the relative absence of planning or design of something for a certain outcome, such that the outcome can even be counter-intentional in being the opposite of what was originally planned, as shown in the different new criticisms against the idea of "the butterfly effect," as discussed earlier—contrary to the original intention of those who used it to explain the nature of chaotic dynamics, in *Sec. 3.3.1*; the relative absence of planning or design of something for a certain outcome, such that the outcome can even be counter-intentional in being the opposite of what was originally planned, as shown by Stapp's application of the quantum Zeno effect for his claim about "quantum mind" in quantum biology—contrary to the original intention of those who used it to explain the nature of "decay" in quantum physics, in *Sec. 3.3.2*; the relative absence of planning or design of something for a certain outcome, such that the outcome can even be counter-intentional in being the opposite of what was originally planned, as shown in the fall of South Vietnam, Laos, and Cambodia to communism in the 1970s—contrary to the original intention of the U.S. involvement in Indochina in the 1960s and 1970s to stop communism, in *Sec. 3.4.1*; the relative absence of planning or design of something for a certain outcome, such that the outcome can even be counter-intentional in being the opposite of what was originally planned, as shown in the recent proposal of effectual reasoning for decision-making in situations of uncertainty, as an alternative to causal reasoning—contrary to the original intention of those who used causal reasoning to achieve optimality, for example, in *Sec. 3.4.2*; the relative absence of planning or design of something for a certain outcome, such that the outcome can even be counter-intentional in being the opposite of what was originally planned, as shown in the re-interpretation of Newtonian mechanics on the basis of "sensitive dependence on initial conditions" known as "the butterfly effect, which is one of the subjects of chaos theory"—contrary to the original intention of those who used Newtonian physics to explain causal determinism, in *Sec. 3.5.1*; and the relative absence of planning or design of something for a certain outcome, such that the outcome can even be counter-intentional in being the opposite of what was originally planned, as shown in the re-interpretation, by Griffin and Tyrrell, of "nothing" with "all energy and all information" for a "religio-mysical view of "Godhead"—contrary to the original intention of those who proposed the big bang theory for a more secular interpretation, in *Sec. 3.5.2*).

And the reverse direction also holds true.

Again, it should be stressed, however, that there are different shades of gray (or different degrees of truth) in the two opposites, and the classification is not necessarily mutually exclusive either. In fact, even when some combinations of the two occur, they only end up sharing the same dialectic relationship, but in a different degree.

Also, there are some other relationships (as a kind of family resemblance) which have something in common with the principle, but they are not exactly the same but only more or less comparable, which varies from case to case.

Good examples of family resemblance in relation to the principle are purposiveness-nonpurposiveness, intention-accidentalness, awareness-unawareness, design-randomness, etc.

36th Thesis: The Survivability-Nonsurvivability Principle

The thirty-sixth thesis is called the survivability-nonsurvivability principle (on the survival of things) in the category of "outcome" in existential dialectics (which is first worked out in *FPHPROB*), in that, if there are some entities which survive at certain times, there are likewise other entities which do not survive. There is no survivability without nonsurvivability—and vice versa.

In nature, for illustration, there are some animals which survive in hard times, whereas others do not—and this is true, not just among different species but also among different members of the same species (and the phenomenon of "selection" in evolutionary biology has much to say on this, as already addressed in *BNN*).

Of course, the principle is not restricted solely to the animal world, since it can be used to other cases concerning non-animals too (e.g., trees, lakes, etc. in the natural world—or empires, companies, etc. in the human world).

But one should not confuse this principle with the expansion-contraction principle, since those entities which survive, say, can still expand or contract over time (e.g., those animals which survive can be more capable in some activities but not in others, for instance).

Nor should this principle be confused with the stability-reaction principle, in that the condition of both survivability and non-survivability may lead to further changes later on (as shown in the emergence of new species after the extinction of some old ones, as already explained in *BNR*).

In any event, on the one hand, there is survivability in outcome (e.g., the relative survival, nowadays, of positive thinking like "CBMT" in the U.S., on average, in *Sec. 2.2.1*; the relative survival of a "self-fulfilling prophecy," if the audience directly or indirectly makes the prediction come true, in *Sec. 2.2.2*; the relative survival, nowadays, of the 2nd law of thermodynamics to be applied to a closed system, in *Sec. 2.3.1*; the relative survival, nowadays, of the idea of "retrocausality" in "para-science," in *Sec. 2.3.2*; the relative survival, nowadays, of the "two-stage inquiry" about legal liability in the U.S. legal system, in *Sec. 2.4.1*; the relative survival, nowadays, of RCA in the U.S., in *Sec. 2.4.2*; the relative survival, nowadays, of the view about "creation myths," in that they are "symbolic narratives which must be understood in terms of their own cultural context," in *Sec. 2.5.1*; the relative survival, nowadays, of modern evolutionary theory that "evolution is blind," in *Sec. 2.5.2*; the relative survival, nowadays, of required "reporting" of adverse effects in many countries, in *Sec. 3.2.1*; the relative survival of rabbits in New Zealand in the late 19th century, as they rapidly spread after introduction, in *Sec. 3.2.2*; the relative survival, nowadays, of the practice to do the mathematics of chaos theory by computers, in *Sec. 3.3.1*; the relative survival, nowadays, of the interpretation of quantum theory which copes with "the quantum Zeno effect" on the basis of "the reductionist postulate for reconciling the measurement problem," in *Sec. 3.3.2*; the relative survival, nowadays, of the "reverse domino theory" in regard to the situation in the Middle East, in *Sec. 3.4.1*; the relative survival, nowadays, of effectual logic, in *Sec. 3.4.2*; the relative survival, nowadays, of quantum mechanics, in *Sec. 3.5.1*; and the relative survival, nowadays, of the big bang theory, as shown in "different speculative big bang scenarios in quantum cosmology which actually imply eternal return," in *Sec. 3.5.2*).

On the other hand, there is non-survivability in outcome (e.g., the relative non-survival, nowadays, of the fatalistic trend like "learned helplessness" in the U.S., on average, in *Sec. 2.2.1*; the relative non-survival of a "self-defeating prophecy," when "the audience of a prediction has an interest in seeing it falsified," as in "self-defeating prophecy," in *Sec. 2.2.2*; the relative non-survival, nowadays, of the 2nd law of thermodynamics to be applied to an open system, in *Sec. 2.3.1*; the relative non-survival, nowadays, of the idea of "retrocausality" in "mainstream physics," since "established physics does not generally employ retrocausality," in *Sec. 2.3.2*; the relative non-survival, nowadays, of the use of the mens rea in "strict liability" cases in the U.S. legal system, in *Sec. 2.4.1*; the relative non-survival, nowadays, of problem solving at the level of "symptoms," especially after the rise of RCA in the U.S., in *Sec. 2.4.2*; the relative non-survival, nowadays, of the view about "creation myths," in that there are simply "forms of primitive or early-stage science or religion" to be "analyzed…in a literal or logical sense," in *Sec. 2.5.1*; the relative non-survival, nowadays, of Aristotle's teleology in modern biology, in *Sec. 2.5.2*; the relative non-survival, nowadays, of voluntary "reporting" of adverse effects in many countries, that is, with the exception of a few countries like Australia, in *Sec. 3.2.1*; the relative non-survival of sheep in New Zealand in the late 19th century, because "many farmers who had overstocked their land lost many of their sheep to starvation as the rabbits spread," in *Sec. 3.2.2*; the relative non-survival, nowadays, of the practice to do the mathematics of chaos theory by hand, in *Sec. 3.3.1*; the relative non-survival, nowadays, of the attempt to apply "the quantum Zeno effect" to other interpretations of quantum theory, because "the quantum Zeno effect does not apply to all interpretations of quantum theory" like "the many-worlds interpretation…and the Quantum Logic Interpretation," in *Sec. 3.3.2*; the relative non-survival, nowadays, of the "domino theory" in regard to the situation in Southeast Asia, in *Sec. 3.4.1*; the relative non-survival, nowadays, of the focus on causal logic without any attention to alternative logics like effectual logic, in *Sec. 3.4.2*; the relative non-survival, nowadays, of classical mechanics to be applied to the microscopic world, although it remains "useful" and makes "relatively accurate predictions" for day-to-day physics like "calculating the trajectory of a bullet," in *Sec. 3.5.1*; and the relative non-survival, nowadays, of the faith in the "scarab [or dung beetle]," which "was viewed as a sign of eternal renewal and reemergence of life, a reminder of the life to come," in ancient Egypt, in *Sec. 3.5.2*).

And the reverse direction also holds true.

Again, it should be stressed, however, that there are different shades of gray (or different degrees of truth) in the two opposites, and the classification is not necessarily mutually exclusive either. In fact, even when some combinations of the two occur, they only end up sharing the same dialectic relationship, but in a different degree.

Also, there are some other relationships (as a kind of family resemblance) which have something in common with the principle, but they are not exactly the same but only more or less comparable, which varies from case to case.

Good examples of family resemblance in relation to the principle are survival-extinction, existence-nonexistence, life-death, etc.

37th Thesis: The Materiality-Nonmateriality Principle

The thirty-seventh thesis is called the materiality-nonmateriality principle (on the impact of spirituality) in the category of "outcome" in existential dialectics (which is first worked out in *FPHETIO*), in that, if there are material entities which evolve over time, there are likewise nonmaterial entities which become developed over time. There is no materiality without nonmateriality—and vice versa.

There are some clarifications to remember, as shown in different original visions of mine already worked out in my previous books (e.g., "free-spirited after-postmodernity" in *FCD* and the 2 volumes of *FHC*, "post-capitalism" in *FCD* and *BCPC*, "post-democracy" in *FCD* and *BDPD*, "post-civilization" in *BCIV*, "unfolding unconsciousness" in *FPHU*, "floating consciousness" in *FPHC* and *FPHR*, "hyper-spatial consciousness" in *FPHC* and *FPHST*, "post-ethics" in *BEPE*, "multiverse" in *FPHST* and *BCOS*, "the alteration of space-time" in *FPHST*, etc.), just to cite a few well-documented sources:

• Entities do not have to be of material existence only (e.g., space-time, matter-energy, Having, etc.), as there are also non-material ones (e.g., Being, Belonging, etc.).
• Non-material entities need not be narrowly understood in religious terms only (e.g., faith, praying, etc.), as there are non-religious spiritual types too (e.g., fasting, meditation, communality, etc.).
• Non-material entities do not have to be misleadingly trapped within the now debunked old-fashioned analytical framework of teleology (as they are constrained by the predictability-unpredictability principle, the functionality-nonfunctionality principle, and so on).
• Non-material entities can become more developed in outcome over time, but they can be both desirable and undesirable (as constrained by the regression-progression principle, for instance).
• Non-material entities do not just stay constant but undergo changes over time (as constrained by the change-constancy principle, the stability-reaction principle, and so on).
• Non-material entities can take different forms and contents over time (as constrained by the same-difference principle, for instance), and

good examples are the visions in relation to the mind, nature, culture, and society (as proposed in my previous books aforecited).

In any event, on the one hand, there is materiality in outcome (e.g., the material outcome in relation to space-time, matter-energy, Having, etc., like "the classically conditioned dogs that got electrical shocks" and then "made no attempt to escape the situation" of "learned helplessness," in *Sec. 2.2.1*; the material outcome in relation to space-time, matter-energy, Having, etc., like the lack of "self-fulfilling prophecy" in animals, as pointed out by Merton, who wrote that "it is not found in the world of nature, untouched by human hands," in *Sec. 2.2.2*; the material outcome in relation to space-time, matter-energy, Having, etc., like the use of the 2nd law to explain the future fate of the universe, in that "an expanding universe...is not in a thermodynamical equilibrium, and simple considerations leading to the heat death scenario are not valid," in *Sec. 2.3.1*; the material outcome in relation to space-time, matter-energy, Having, etc., like the use of "retrocausality" to understand "antimatter" in "the Wheeler–Feynman absorber theory, proposed by John Archibald Wheeler and Richard Feynman," in *Sec. 2.3.2*; the material outcome in relation to space-time, matter-energy, Having, etc., like the use of "causation" for legal liability, as in "proximate cause" to establish "legal causation," in *Sec. 2.4.1*; the material outcome in relation to space-time, matter-energy, Having, etc., like the use of RCA for problem solving in business management, in *Sec. 2.4.2*; the material outcome in relation to space-time, matter-energy, Having, etc., like the use of "earth driver" myths by some people to justify their attempt to "build...suitable lands," in *Sec. 2.5.1*; the material outcome in relation to space-time, matter-energy, Having, etc., like the use of "material cause" to understand that a "table" is made of "wood," for instance, in *Sec. 2.5.2*; the material outcome in relation to space-time, matter-energy, Having, etc., like the adverse effect of "hormonal contraception and hormone replacement therapy," such as "breast cancer," in *Sec. 3.2.1*; the material outcome in relation to space-time, matter-energy, Having, etc., like the use of the idea of "unintended consequences" to understand the "unintended consequences of environmental intervention" in the examples aforecited, in *Sec. 3.2.2*; the material outcome in relation to space-time, matter-energy, Having, etc., like the use of chaotic theory for the study of chaotic dynamics, in *Sec. 3.3.1*; the material outcome in relation to space-time, matter-energy, Having, etc., like the use of "the quantum Zeno effect" to understand quantum physics in regard to the exponential decay law, in *Sec. 3.3.2*; the material outcome in relation to space-time, matter-energy,

Having, etc., like the application of the domino effect to understand chain reactions in the state of nature, like the chain reaction in an energy system to increase entropy, in *Sec. 3.4.1*; the material outcome in relation to space-time, matter-energy, Having, etc., like the use of causal reasoning to seek "the highest potential return" or "profit," in *Sec. 3.4.2*; the material outcome in relation to space-time, matter-energy, Having, etc., like the use of causal determinism to explain a "materialistic" world, in *Sec. 3.5.1*; and the material outcome in relation to space-time, matter-energy, Having, etc., like the use of the big bang theory on the basis of the oscillating universe model by Vilenkin and Tegmark, to provide a secular interpretation of the fate of the universe, in *Sec. 3.5.2*).

On the other hand, there is non-materiality in outcome (e.g., the nonmaterial outcome in relation to the quest for Being, Belonging, etc., like the quest for "rational, logical and systematic" thinking in attribution theory for higher intellignet lifeforms, in *Sec. 2.2.1*; the nonmaterial outcome in relation to the quest for Being, Belonging, etc., like the search for "divine prophecy" among humans, as shown in the Greek legend of Zeus, in which "when it was predicted that Zeus would overthrow his father, Cronos, and usurp his throne as King of the Gods, he actively waged war against him in a direct attempt to fulfill this prophecy," in *Sec. 2.2.2*; the nonmaterial outcome in relation to the quest for Being, Belonging, etc., like the spiritual search for "eternal recurrence" in Indian philosphy, ancient Egyptian cosmology, and modern Western philosophy like the one by Friedrich Nietzsche for the "Overman," in *Sec. 2.3.1*; the nonmaterial outcome in relation to the quest for Being, Belonging, etc., like the spiritual search for "prayer healing" by "retrocausality" in para-science, in *Sec. 2.3.2*; the nonmaterial outcome in relation to the quest for Being, Belonging, etc., like the spiritual search among humans for the "first cause," also known as "the unmoved mover" or "the active intelligent," as in medieval theology by Thomas Aquinas, in *Sec. 2.4.1*; the nonmaterial outcome in relation to the quest for Being, Belonging, etc., like the spiritual search among humans for understanding the deepest root of causation, all the way to the "first cause" or the "prime mover" in metaphysics, not just "root causes" in business management, in *Sec. 2.4.2*; the nonmaterial outcome in relation to the quest for Being, Belonging, etc., like the spiritual search among humans for "origin myths" to be used as "the basis of a worldview that reaffirms and guides how people relate to the natural world, to any assumed spiritual world, and to each other," in *Sec. 2.5.1*; the nonmaterial outcome in relation to the quest for Being, Belonging, etc., like the spiritual search by Aristotle for a metaphysics of "telos" in the universe, all the way to the "unmoved mover" or "active intellect," to be used later on by Thomas Aquinas for medieval theology, in *Sec. 2.5.2*; the nonmaterial outcome in relation to the quest for Being, Belonging, etc., like the spiritual search among humans, as shown in the use of "evil eyes" to protect oneself from evil spirits in some religious cultures, even though they do not always produce the effective results, in *Sec. 3.2.1*; the nonmaterial outcome in relation to the quest for Being, Belonging, etc., like the spiritual search among humans to be God-men for the mastering of the world, which, however, is countered by the idea of "unintended consequences" as "a wry or humorous warning against the hubristic belief that humans can fully control the world around them," in *Sec. 3.2.2*; the nonmaterial outcome in relation to the quest for Being, Belonging, etc., like the spiritual search among humans for "time travel" with the use of "chaos theory," so as to change "history" for the better, in popular culture, in *Sec. 3.3.1*; the nonmaterial outcome in relation to the quest for Being, Belonging, etc., like the spiritual search among humans for the mind over matter, as shown by Stapp's application of the quantum Zeno effect for his claim about "quantum mind" in quantum biology, in *Sec. 3.3.2*, the nonmaterial outcome in relation to the quest for Being, Belonging, etc., like the spiritual search among humans for "freedom," as in the use of the domino theory to justify the U.S. involvement around the world to stop the spread of communism during the Cold War, in *Sec. 3.4.1*; the nonmaterial outcome in relation to the quest for Being, Belonging, etc., like the spiritual search among humans "to achieve their best potential" by the use of effectual logic, which helps "people" create that which "will embody their deepest passions and aspirations while enabling them to achieve their best potential," in *Sec. 3.4.2*; the nonmaterial outcome in relation to the quest for Being, Belonging, etc., like the spiritual search among humans for "God," as shown by the use of causal determinism for "theological determinism" aforecited, in *Sec. 3.5.1*; and the nonmaterial outcome in relation to the quest for Being, Belonging, etc., like the spiritual search among humans for supernatural entities, like the re-interpretation, by Griffin and Tyrrell, of the big bang theory on the basis of coming out of "nothing" with "all energy and all information" for a "religio-mysical view of "Godhead," in *Sec. 3.5.2*).

And the reverse direction also holds true.

Again, it should be stressed, however, that there are different shades of gray (or different degrees of truth) in the two opposites, and the classification is not necessarily mutually exclusive either. In fact, even when some combinations of the two occur, they only end up sharing the same dialectic relationship, but in a different degree.

Also, there are some other relationships (as a kind of family resemblance) which have something in common with the principle, but they are not exactly the same but only more or less comparable, which varies from case to case.

Good examples of family resemblance in relation to the principle are materiality-mentality, physicality-suprasensibility, materiality-spirituality, mundaneness-sacredness, etc.

38th Thesis: The Post-Human Plurality

And the thirty-eighth thesis is about the role of "post-humans," which I originally proposed in my previous books, starting with the first book titled *The Future of Human Civilization* in 2000 and all others afterwards.

As already pointed out in *Sec. 1.8*, I need to emphasize, as this is something that I used to repeat (*almost verbatim*) from my previous books, two clarifications here about the term "post-human" as a neologism in my works.

Firstly, the word "post-human" here should *not* be confused with another term which looks similar but has a totally different meaning in the literature of postmodernism, namely, "post-humanism"—which constitutes a critique of "humanism" as tradionally understood (especially, though not exclusively, in relation to the idea of progress in science and reason in the Enlightenment project). (WK 2008)

My works reject the project of "postmodernism" and propose the future world of what I orignally called "after-postmodernity" in *FHC* and *FCD*, for instance.

And secondly, the word "post-human" here should also *not* be confused with a similar term which is used to champion the ideology of technology for the future co-existence between humans and cyborgs in "trans-humanism." (WK 2008a)

Instead, my term "post-human" in relation to "posthuman-ism" also rejects "transhumanism" (especially, though not exclusively, in relation to the promises of technology) and refers to something else altogether, that is, the future extinction of humans and its post-human successors in deep space and beyond unto multiverses.

My critique of "transhumanism" was more extensively elabroated in *Sec. 2.4.1* of *BEPE*—just as my critique of different futuristic scenarios of fictional artificial intelligence in science fiction was given in *Sec. 3.5.2* of *FPHCOM*.

With these two clarifications in mind (as summarized in *Table 1.31*)—the post-human plurality in etioology can be addressed in relation to five main directions, based on my *pluralist theory of etiology*, as analysed in this book (together with my visions as already worked out in my previous books).

Firstly, the post-human plurality in etiology will learn from my *pluralist theory of etiology*, in relation to the dialectic context of no analysis of cause without that of effect (and vice versa), to be later transcended altogether, in the context of etiology.

Secondly, the post-human plurality in etiology will learn from my *pluralist theory of etiology* in relation to the four perspectives of the mind, nature, society, and culture.

Thirdly, the post-human plurality in etiology will learn from my *pluralist theory of etiology* in relation to the non-privilege of any specific theory over others in the literature and the non-integration of them all (as they are not necessarily compatible with each other).

Fourthly, the post-human plurality in etiology will have to confront the new challenges as posed by the long-term civilizational development of intelligent life in the distant future, both here on this planet Earth and elsewhere in deep space until multiverses.

As this is something that I regularly pointed out in my previous books for background information (and summarize here, *almost verbatim*, with some updates), I already worked out, in my numerous books, what these new challenges will be and provide different original visions to meet them—especially in regard to the following future evolutions:

- of the mind (e.g., "interconnected health care," "supersession computing," "metamorphic humor," "contrarian personality," "hyper-martial body," "hyper-sexual body," "floating consciousness," "hyper-spatial consciousness," "thinking machines," "unfolding unconsciousness," "thinking robots," "genetically altered superior beings," "cyborgs," and others)
- of nature (e.g., "resilient natural resources," "transdisciplinary architecture," "creational chemistry," "multilateral sound," "resettlement geology," "post-cosmology," "the alteration of space-time," "the creation of new matter-energy," "selective geometry," and the like)
- of society (e.g., "post-capitalism," "post-democracy," "authoritarian liberal democracy," "double-sided accounting," "transfigurative waste," "panoramic transportation," "cyclical-progressive migration," "reflective criminology," "interventive-reshaping geography," "detached gambling," "heterodox education," "multifaceted war and peace," "virtual organizations," the movement of "cyclical

progression" at both structural and systemic levels, "ambivalent technology," and so forth)
- of culture   (e.g., "fusional morphology," "modificative sports," "inquisitive culinary art," "interactive semantics," "transdisciplinary performing arts," "comparative-impartial literature," "post-human mind games," "comparative-substitutive religion," "post-ethics," "post-civilization,"   "transformative   aesthetic   experience," "contrastive mathematical-logic," and the whatnot)
- in history (e.g., "multifold history," the age of "after-postmodernity," etc.)
- in methodology (e.g., "sophisticated methodolgial holism," "critical-dialectic formal science," "complex data analysis," "interpretivist probability," etc.)
- in ontology   (e.g., "existential dialectics," "contrastive rationality," etc.)

Of course, the examples (as listed above) are not exhaustive but illustrative, since my numerous books have worked out many other visions (as already roughly summarized in *Sec.1.8* and *Sec. 1.9*). Many, though not all, of my visions on the mind, nature, society, culture, history, methodology, and ontology (as cited above) are summarized in the tables as shown in Chapter One and Chapter Four (especially in *Table 4.43* about my original theories on numerous topics).

And finally, or fifthly, the post-human plurality in etiology will learn from my *pluralist theory of etiology* in regard to the need to go beyond both cause and effect altogether—to be further elaborated in the next section.

Towards the Post-Human Plurality

This "post-human" plurality in etiology to go beyond both cause and effect altogether can be understood in terms of nine great future transformations of etiology, in relation to the mind, nature, society, and culture—as explained below (and summarized in *Table 1.2*).

Nine Great Future Transformations of Etiology

The nine great future transformations of etiology (in relation to the mind, nature, society, and culture) can be explained hereafter, with the caveat, however, that the classification in terms of nine is solely illustrative, as there is no objective basis that it must be classified in term of nine (as this is something that I often stressed and repeated in my previous books, albeit in the context of different topics).

The First Great Future Transformation of Etiology

The first great future transformation of etiology in the post-human era concerns what I originally call *new goals,* in relation to the mind.

This search for "new goals" will give future advanced humans and later their successors, namely, the post-humans, the capacity to be motivated to study etiology in a way that current humans cannot.

There are already some indications that the future of etiology is moving toward this direction.

Consider, for illustration, the different "goals" as already seen in the history of etiology, such as the quest for the reduction of cognitive bias (*Sec. 2.2.1*), the quest for better public education on self-fulfilling prophecy (*Sec. 2.2.2*), the quest for the understanding of space-time (*Sec. 2.3.1*), the quest for the possibility of retrocausality (*Sec. 2.3.2*), the aim to determine legal liability (*Sec. 2.4.1*), the aim to better understand the root causes of business problems (*Sec. 2.4.2*), the quest for understanding the origin of the world (*Sec. 2.5.1*), the aim to find out the typology of causes (*Sec. 2.5.2*), the search for the prevention of adverse effects (*Sec. 3.2.1*), the quest for the understanding of unintended consequences (*Sec. 3.2.2*), the aim to cope with chaos (*Sec. 3.3.1*), the quest for the control of the time evolution of particles (*Sec. 3.3.2*), the Cold War against world communism (*Sec. 3.4.1*), the aim to start businesses in situations of uncertainty (*Sec. 3.4.2*), the quest for the understanding of causal determinism (*Sec. 3.5.1*), and the aim to resolve the chicken-and-egg problem (*Sec. 3.5.2*), for instance.

More importantly, this future quest for new goals should also be understood in relation to my previous works on the future "post-human" supersession of the human mind from the combined perspectives of the mind, nature, society, and culture—with good examples like "supersession computing," "metamorphic humor," "contrarian personality," "hyper-martial body," "hyper-sexual body," "floating consciousness," "hyper-spatial consciousness," "unfolding unconsciousness," "thinking robots," "thinking machines," "genetically altered superior beings," "cyborgs," and others.

In any event, all these are just some illustrative (relatively primitive) examples in our time, of course, but the important point to remember here is that the search for different new goals will further transform etiology at the more advanced level in the post-human future that the human world has never known.

The Second Great Future Transformation of Etiology

The second great future transformation of etiology in the post-human era concerns what I originally call *new means,* in relation to the mind.

This quest for "new means" will give future advanced humans and later their successors, namely, the post-humans, the capacity to find novel options to achieve the goals in regard to etiology in a way that current humans cannot.

There are already some indications that the future of etiology is moving toward this direction.

Consider, for illustration, the different "means" as already seen in the history of etiology, such as common sense psychology as a way to study attribution (*Sec. 2.2.1*), the Thomas theorem as a way to understand self-fulfilling prophecy (*Sec. 2.2.2*), the 2nd law of thermodynamics as a way to understand time's arrow (*Sec. 2.3.1*), para-science as a way to study retrocausality (*Sec. 2.3.2*), the examination of factual causation as a way to determine legal liability (*Sec. 2.4.1*), RCA as a way to solve business problems (*Sec. 2.4.2*), creation myths as a way to understand origin myths (*Sec. 2.5.1*), Aristotle's four causes as a way to classify causation (*Sec. 2.5.2*), reporting systems as a way to discover adverse effects (*Sec. 3.2.1*), Merton's work as a way to understand unintended consequences (*Sec. 3.2.2*), the butterfly effect as a way to understand chaos theory (*Sec. 3.3.1*), the study of quantum Zeno effect as a way to understand how to control time evolution (*Sec. 3.3.2*), domino theory as a way to justify American intervention in the world (*Sec. 3.4.1*), effectuation as a way to do business in situations of uncertainty (*Sec. 3.4.2*), karma as a way to understand determinism (*Sec. 3.5.1*), and the idea of eternal return as a way to solve the chicken-and-egg problem (*Sec. 3.5.2*), for instance.

All these are just some illustrative (relatively primitive) examples in our time, of course, but the important point to remember here is that the search for different new means will further transform etiology at the more advanced level in the post-human future that the human world has never known.

The Third Great Future Transformation of Etiology

The third great future transformation of etiology in the post-human era concerns what I originally call *new comparisons*, in relation to nature.

This search for "new comparisons" will give future advanced humans and later their successors, namely, the post-humans, the ability to learn from animals, plants, and the universe, through comparison and contrast, about etiology in a way that current humans cannot.

There are already some indications that the future of etiology is moving toward this direction.

Consider, for illustration, the different forms of comparison and contrast as already seen in the history of etiology, such as the comparison and contrast between time's arrow in nature and time's arrow in society (*Sec. 2.3.1*), the comparison and contrast between retrocausality in nature and prayer healing in the mind, as in para-science (*Sec. 2.3.2*), the comparison and contrast between male/female characters in the universe as portrayed in creation myths and male/female characters as actually existing in human society (*Sec. 2.5.1*), the comparison and contrast between humans and nature in regard to different causes (*Sec. 2.5.2*), the comparison and contrast between unintended consequences in society and unintended consequences in the environment (*Sec. 3.2.2*), the comparison and contrast between chaos in nature and chaos in society, like the work on weather (*Sec. 3.3.1*), the comparison and contrast between particles in nature and human measurement of them (*Sec. 3.3.2*), the comparison and contrast between chemical chain reactions and political chain reactions (*Sec. 3.4.1*), the comparison and contrast between causal determinism in day-to-day physics and causal determinism in ethics (*Sec. 3.5.1*), and the comparison and contrast between eternal return in nature like cosmology and eternal return in culture like religion (*Sec. 3.5.2*), for instance.

All these are just some illustrative (relatively primitive) examples in our time, of course, but the important point to remember here is that the search for different new comparisons will further transform etiology at the more advanced level in the post-human future that the human world has never known.

The Fourth Great Future Transformation of Etiology

The fourth great future transformation of etiology in the post-human era concerns what I originally call *new integrations*, in relation to nature.

This search for "new integrations" will give future advanced humans and later their successors, namely, the post-humans, the ability to live and interact with nature for etiology in a way that current humans cannot.

There are already some indications that the future of etiology is moving toward this direction.

Consider, for illustration, the different integrations for etiology as already seen in the history of etiology, such as the integration of time's arrow in nature with society (*Sec. 2.3.1*), the integration of the study of radioactive decay in nature with the study of retrocausal psychokinesis in psychology (*Sec. 2.3.2*), the integration of nature with humans in regard to "a sense of place in the world" in creation myths (*Sec. 2.5.1*), the integration of nature with humans for a general typology of causes (*Sec. 2.5.2*), the integration of nature with society in the study of the unintended consequences of enviromental intervention (*Sec. 3.2.2*), the integration of nature with society in the study of the impact of weather on society (*Sec. 3.3.1*), the integration of nature with society in the study of how to control the time evolution of particles (*Sec. 3.3.2*), the integration of nature with nurture in the debate on the interactions between nature and nurture (*Sec. 3.5.1*), and the integration of nature with culture for a comprehensive idea of eternal return for all things, like the one by Nietzsche (*Sec. 3.5.2*), for instance.

More importantly, this future quest for new integrations should also be understood in relation to my previous works on the future "post-human" adventures into different dimensions of space-time unto multiverses from the combined perspectives of the mind, nature, society, and culture—with good examples like "the alteration of space-time" (*Table 1.3* and *Table 1.4*), "multiverses" (*Table 1.7* and *Table 1.8*), "hyperspace" (*Table 1.9* and *Table 1.25*), "time travel" (*Table 1.10* and *Table 1.11*), and others.

In addition, in my previous book titled *The Future of Post-Human Geology* (2010), I already envisioned the three great future transformations of geology, namely, "solar geology," "galactic geology," and "cosmic geology," in the context of my "resettlement theory of geology," in that humans and later post-humans will explore and migrate to other planets, solar systems, galaxies, and cosmos in the long haul.

Then, in another book of mine titled *The Future of Post-Human Geography* (2011), I linked the two books together, since geography has much to learn from geology (as in "physical geography," which, as already introduced in *Sec. 1.3* of *FPHGEOG*, relies heavily on the earth sciences) and discussed the search for "new explorations" in the context of the three forms of environments outside the planet Earth, namely, what I originally called "solar geography," "galactic geography," and "cosmic geography"—as a further elaboration of the three great future transformations of geology (in *FPHGEOL*).

Later, in still another book of mine titled *The Future of Post-Human Migration* (2012), I envisioned the future integrations in different forms, namely, what I originally called "solar migration," "galactic migration," "clustery migration," "cosmic migration," and "multiversal migration."

And then, in an additional book of mine titled *The Future of Post-Human Transportation* (2012), I envisioned the future integrations in different forms, namely, what I originally called "solar transportation," "galactic transportation," "clustery transportation," "cosmic transportation," and "multiversal transportation."

This extension is consistent with my other theory, namely, "the theory of the cyclical progression of system integration and fragmentation" in *FCD* (2002)—at the social-systemic level (as already clarified in *Sec. 1.8* and shown below):

$$\text{Local} \rightarrow \text{Regional} \rightarrow \text{Global} \rightarrow \text{Solar} \rightarrow$$
$$\text{Galactic} \rightarrow \text{Clustery}... \rightarrow \text{Multiversal}$$

All these are just some illustrative (relatively primitive) examples in our time, of course, but the important point to remember here is that the search for different new integrations will further transform etiology at the more advanced level in the post-human future that the human world has never known.

The Fifth Great Future Transformation of Etiology

The fifth great future transformation of etiology in the post-human era concerns what I originally call *new praxes*, in relation to society.

This search for "new praxes" will give future advanced humans and later their successors, namely, the post-humans, the ability to engage in practice (like activism, politics, personal experience, etc.) for the future of etiology in a way that current humans cannot.

There are already some indications that the future of etiology is moving toward this direction.

Consider, for illustration, the different praxes as already seen in history of etiology like the practical application of "attribution theory" in the field of psychology to the area concerning "learned helplessness" (*Sec. 2.2.1*), the practical application of "self-fulfilling prophecy" by Merton in the field of sociology to the field of education, like the "public education reform" (*Sec. 2.2.2*), the practical application of "entropy" in the field of thermodynamics to the field of cosmology (*Sec. 2.3.1*), the practical application of "retrocausality" in the field of philosophy to the fields of science and para-science (*Sec. 2.3.2*), the practical application of "causation" in the fields of philosophy and science to the field of jurisprudence (*Sec. 2.4.1*), the practical application of "incident management" in the field of business management to the field of national security (*Sec. 2.4.2*), the practical application of "social function" in the field of sociology to the field of mythology (*Sec. 2.5.1*), the practical application of "teleology" in the field of metaphysics to the field of modern evolutionary theory (*Sec. 2.5.2*), the practical application of probabilities" in the field of statistics to the field of medicine (*Sec. 3.2.1*), the practical application of "unintended consequences" by Merton in the field of sociology to the field of ecology (*Sec. 3.2.2*), the practical application of "the butterfly effect" in the field of chaos theory to the field of "quantum physics" (*Sec. 3.3.1*), the practical application of the quantum Zeno effect in the field of quantum physics to the field of psychology (*Sec. 3.3.2*), the practical application of the "domino theory" in regard to the spread of communism in Indochina to the region in Latin America (*Sec. 3.4.1*), the practical application of "logic" in the field of philosophy to the field of business management (*Sec. 3.4.2*), the practical application of "determined probabilities" in the field of quantum mechanics to the field of everyday technologies (*Sec. 3.5.1*), and the practical application of "eternal return" in the field of cosmology to the field of religion (*Sec. 3.5.2*), for instance.

All these are just some illustrative (relatively primitive) examples in our time, of course, but the important point to remember here is that the search for different new praxes will further transform etiology at the more advanced level in the post-human future that the human world has never known.

The Sixth Great Future Transformation of Etiology

The sixth great future transformation of etiology in the post-human era concerns what I originally call *new technologies*, in relation to society.

This search for "new technologies" will give future advanced humans and later their successors, namely, the post-humans, the ability to come up with different techniques, materials, and experiments for etiology in a way that current humans cannot.

There are already some indications that the future of etiology is moving toward this direction.

Consider, for illustration, the use of different technologies as already seen in the history of etiology, such as the technique of cognitive bias modification therapy (*Sec. 2.2.1*), the technique of writing stories and tales on "self-fulfilling prophecy" (*Sec. 2.2.2*), the technique of using mathematics to study entropy (*Sec. 2.3.1*), the technique of thought experiments to study retrocausality (*Sec. 2.3.2*), the technique of establishing legal causation (*Sec. 2.4.1*), the technique of doing incident management (*Sec. 2.4.2*), the technique of interpreting creation myths (*Sec. 2.5.1*), the technique of interpreting Aristotle's understanding of "teleology" (*Sec. 2.5.2*), the technique of medical procedures (*Sec. 3.2.1*), the technology to make drugs with unintended consequences (*Sec. 3.2.2*), computer technology to study chaos theory (*Sec. 3.3.1*), the technology to do periodic measurements of quantum Zeno effect (*Sec. 3.3.2*), the technique of doing propaganda by way of domino theory (*Sec. 3.4.1*), the technique of doing strategic partnership (*Sec. 3.4.2*), the technique of doing mathematical models to study determinism (*Sec. 3.5.1*), and the technique of creating the Steinhardt–Turok Model (*Sec. 3.5.2*), for instance.

All these are just some illustrative (relatively primitive) examples in our time, of course, but the important point to remember here is that the search for new technologies will further transform etiology at the more advanced level in the post-human future that the human world has never known.

The Seventh Great Future Transformation of Etiology

The seventh great future transformation of etiology in the post-human era concerns what I originally call *new stratifications*, in relation to society.

This emergence of "new stratifications" will lead future advanced humans and later their successors, namely, the post-humans, to face new inequalities in etiology in a way that current humans cannot.

There are already some indications that the future of etiology is moving toward this direction.

Consider, for illustration, the different inequalities as already seen in the history of etiology, such as "normal" individuals vs. the "most intelligent minds" on cogntiive biases (*Sec. 2.2.1*), humans vs. animals on "self-fulfilling prophecy" (*Sec. 2.2.2*), entropy in an isolated system vs. entropy in an opened system (*Sec. 2.3.1*), the popularity of causality vs. the popularity of retrocausality (*Sec. 2.3.2*), a judge vs. a defendant (*Sec. 2.4.1*), the acceptance of "safety-based RCA" vs. the acceptance of "production-based RCA" (*Sec. 2.4.2*), female characters vs. "male characters" in creation myths (*Sec. 2.5.1*), "final cause" vs. other three causes (*Sec. 2.5.2*), voluntary reporting of adverse effects vs. mandatory reporting of adverse effects (*Sec. 3.2.1*), humans vs. animals in regard to "self-defeating prophecy" (*Sec. 3.2.2*), finite dimensional linear systems vs. nonlinear or infinite-dimensional" systems in regard to chaotic dynamics (*Sec. 3.3.1*), the application of the "the quantum Zeno effect" to quantum theory on the basis of "the reductionist postulate vs. the application of "the quantum Zeno effect" on the basis of other interpretations of quantum theory (*Sec. 3.3.2*), Indochina vs. the rest of ASEAN in regard to the domino effect (*Sec. 3.4.1*), the popularity of "causal logic" vs. the popularity of "effectual logic" (*Sec. 3.4.2*), classical mechanics vs. quantum mechanics (*Sec. 3.5.1*), and the religious Jainist version of "eternal return" vs. the secular scientific cosmological versions of "eternal return" (*Sec. 3.5.2*), for instance.

All these are just some illustrative (relatively primitive) examples in our time, of course, but the important point to remember here is that the emergence of new stratifications will further transform etiology at the more advanced level in the post-human future that the human world has never known.

The Eighth Great Future Transformation of Etiology

The eighth great future transformation of etiology in the post-human era concerns what I originally call *new sub-fields*, in relation to culture.

This search for "new sub-fields" will give future advanced humans and later their successors, namely, the post-humans, the ability to explore new specialties (or new games) for etiology in a way that current humans cannot.

There are already some indications that the future of etiology is moving toward this direction.

Consider, for illustration, the different sub-fields as already seen in the history of etiology, such as the subfield of cognitive psychology (*Sec. 2.2.1*), the subfield of social psychology (*Sec. 2.2.2*), the subfield of thermodynamics (*Sec. 2.3.1*), the subfield of philosophy of science (*Sec. 2.3.2*), the subfield of jurisprudence (*Sec. 2.4.1*), the subfield of business management (*Sec. 2.4.2*), the subfield of mythology (*Sec. 2.5.1*), the subfield of Aristotelian philosophy (*Sec. 2.5.2*), the subfield of medicine (*Sec. 3.2.1*), the subfield of micro-sociology (*Sec. 3.2.2*), the subfield of chaos theory (*Sec. 3.3.1*), the subfield of quantum physics (*Sec. 3.3.2*), the subfield of international politics (*Sec. 3.4.1*), the subfield of entrepreneurship (*Sec. 3.4.2*), the subfield of metaphysics (*Sec. 3.5.1*), and the subfield of cosmology (*Sec. 3.5.2*), for instance.

All these are just some illustrative (relatively primitive) examples in our time, of course, but the important point to remember here is that the search for new sub-fields will further transform etiology at the more advanced level in the post-human future that the human world has never known.

The Ninth Great Future Transformation of Etiology

And the ninth great future transformation of etiology in the post-human era concerns what I originally call *new interpretations*, in relation to culture.

This search for "new interpretations" will give future advanced humans and later their successors, namely, the post-humans, the ability to come up with different evaluations and views about etiology in a way that current humans cannot.

There are already some indications that the future of etiology is moving toward this direction.

Consider, for illustration, the different interpretations as already seen in the history of etiology, such as the argument for cognitive bias modification (*Sec. 2.2.1*), the positive interpretation of "self-fulfilling prophecy" by William James (*Sec. 2.2.2*), the argument for increasing entropy over time (*Sec. 2.3.1*), the argument for retrocausality (*Sec. 2.3.2*), the argument for the two-stage enquiry (*Sec. 2.4.1*), the argument for RCA (*Sec. 2.4.2*), the argument for the social functions of origin myths (*Sec. 2.5.1*), the argument for teleology in causation (*Sec. 2.5.2*), the argument for reporting systems of adverse effects (*Sec. 3.2.1*), the argument against adverse effects of unintended consequences (*Sec. 3.2.2*), the argument for the butterfly effect (*Sec. 3.3.1*), the argument for quantum Zeno effect (*Sec. 3.3.2*), the argument for the U.S. intervention in world affairs (*Sec. 3.4.1*), the argument for effectual logic   (*Sec. 3.4.2*), the argument for causal determinism (*Sec. 3.5.1*), and the argument for eternal return (*Sec. 3.5.2*), for instance.

All these are just some illustrative (relatively primitive) examples in our time, of course, but the important point to remember here is that the search for new interpretations will further transform etiology at the more advanced level in the post-human future that the human world has never known.

Enormous Implications

These nine great future transformations of etiology have enormous implications for some soul-searching questions which have challenged some of the best minds in the history of etiology (in relation to cause and effect).

For illustration, consider the following questions in the history of etiology:

• Ex: can effect come before cause, or is retrocausality possible?
• Ex: which comes first, the chicken or the egg?
• Ex: to which extent is indeterminism true?
• Ex: is there the first cause of everything?
• Ex: does causal determmism negate free will?

• Ex: is eternal return really true?
• Ex: to what extent do chaos and chance affect the universe?
• Ex: what causes this universe into existence?
• Ex: can causation be frozen, as in quantum Zeno effect?

Questions and disagreements like this will receive new answers in the future history of etiology in the advanced human and later post-human eras, at least in two fundamental ways.

The first fundamental way is to examine the relationships between cause and effect—such that their possibility (or impossibility) and desirability (or undesirability) are not to the extent that the respective defenders would like us to believe.

The different views about etiology, as already addressed in *Sec. 1.1*, *Sec. 1.5*, and the rest of the book, are just different ways to understand etiology and its future, with each from its own vantage point.

Each view has its own merits and defects and is preferred over others by different proponents with their own different interests, but none of them is possible (or impossible) and desirable (or undesirable) to the extent that its respective advocates would like us to believe.

And the second fundamental way is to inquire about, and then transcend, in the long haul, the debate about cause and effect, such that it will be shifted to different directions, as shown in the nine great future transformations that I have envisioned and outlined above. To transcend them all is to move into these different directions, in conjunction with the various visions of my previous books (as already summarized in *Sec. 1.8* and also earlier in this chapter, with the further help of the tables at this end of Chapter One and this chapter).

Some good examples can be summarized below:

• Ex: to explore new versions of free will
• Ex: to inquire about the causation of different universes
• Ex: to make retrocausality possible
• Ex: to offer new answers to the chicken-and-egg problem
• Ex: to seek the interactions between determinism and indeterminism
• Ex: to search for the possible first cause(s) of everything
• Ex: to make eternal return come true (or close to it)
• Ex: to aim for the better use of chaos and chance
• Ex: to look for the potential of stopping causation
• Ex: to alter space-time in the post-human direction (with different visions of mine as indicated earlier)

Of course, these examples are illustrative, not exhaustive.

Lest any misunderstanding occurs, one must remember that these great future transformations of etiology will bring neither utopia nor dystopia, regardless of some questionable religio-mystical speculations about "Godhead" in our time, just to cite an obvious example (in *Sec. 3.5.2*)—as this is something that I have warned time and again in all of my previous books, *almost verbatim*.

In any event, as I so often stressed in my previous books, it is not up to us current humans to decide whether or not, or to what extent, the post-human future of etiology will be for better and for worse, because it will be judged by the values and beliefs of future post-humans on earth and in deep space unto multiverses—in a way that the entire history of the human world has never known.

Thus is the future of etiology—and of its post-human fate.

**Table 4.1. Sophisticated Methodological Holism
(Part I)**

• "My methodological holism implies the partiality-totality principle in the ontology of existential dialectics (see the table on the partiality-totality principle for summary), which is against the varieties of (a) reductionism and (b) reverse-reductionism, in relation to (i) concept, (ii) theory, (iii) methodology, and (iv) ontology." (*FC*)

• "[M]y methodological holism here is not opposed to methodological individualism but includes it (and, for that matter, other methodologies too)...." (*FPHC*) For this reason (and others too, as summarized hereafter), my version of methodological holism is sophisticated—not vulgar as sometimes used by inapt scholars using the same term. (*FC*)

• "[M]y methodological holism does not democratically presume that all levels are equally valid, as all levels are not created equal. In other words, in relation to issue X, level A may be more relevant than level B, but in relation to Y, level B can be more relevant than level A instead." (*FPHC*) One excellent example of this vulgar democratic presumption is what I called in *BNN* "the compromise fallacy." (*FC*)

• My methodological holism does not presume that a lower level of analysis is more important than a higher level, solely because the former serves as the foundation for the latter—and vice versa, for that matter. One excellent example of this reductionistic presumption is what I called in *FPHST* "the foundation fallacy." (*FPHST, FC*)

(continued on next page)

Table 4.1. Sophisticated Methodological Holism
(Part II)

• "[M]y methodological holism does not make any a-priori postulation that there must be a definite (and, for that matter, indefinite) number of levels" in any analysis. (*FPHC*) Nor does it dogmatically require that there must be a certain combination of levels of analysis in a given inquiry. (*FC*)

• "[M]ethodological holism, in my usage, does not assume that all levels...can necessarily be integrated, since methodological holism is not aimed to search for the holy grail of 'an integral theory...' (as is the case for Wilber). In other words, it allows that sometimes some levels may experience irreducible gaps between them, to be understood, at best, as empirical correlations, not as causal relations...." (*FPHC*)

• "[D]ifferent levels may overlap and even interact with each other in a given context (but sometimes may not), and the fact that I even proposed different ways of re-classifying the levels (whenever needed) in *FDC* reinforces this point....The dual danger here is either forcefully making different levels interact when they are just different (or, metaphorically speaking, apples and oranges) or inappropriately ignoring their interactions when some situations instead require them." (*FPHC*)

• "[T]o understand different levels from their own (unique) perspectives (as required by my methodological holism) is not the same as trying to reduce them to a preferred level in the process of learning from other levels. This second kind of multidisciplinary work is not genuine and does no justice to the unique complexities and merits inherent at each level." (*FPHC*)

(continued on next page)

**Table 4.1. Sophisticated Methodological Holism
(Part III)**

• "[My] methodological holism walks a fine line between the artificial classification (separation) of levels and the simultaneous incorporation of them, if only for the sake of human scholarly endeavor. It should be reminded that nature does not impose upon itself the academic classification of the levels of analysis as humans have. The enterprise of classification is therefore anthropocentric." (*FPHC*)

• "[M]y methodological holism advocates neither epistemic subjectivism nor epistemic non-subjectivism (e.g., realism, idealism, and historicism), neither epistemic relativism (e.g., subjectivism, historicism) nor epistemic absolutism (e.g., realism, positivism), neither epistemic reductionism nor epistemic emergencism, and neither epistemic objectivism (e.g., realism, idealism) nor epistemic historicism....Neither does methodological holism, in my usage, accept the false meta-conceptual dichotomy between nominalism and realism....These false dichotomies...are to be transcended. In other words, methodological holism does not fully accept epistemic realism, positivism (a form of epistemic idealism), historicism, subjectivism, and reductionism in epistemology and philosophy of science but learns from the strengths and weaknesses of all of the opposing approaches without siding with any of them...." (*FPHC*)

• "Sophisticated methodological holism is subject to the constraints as imposed by the syntax of existential dialectics (e.g., the partiality-totality principle and the predictability-unpredictability principle). Even in predictability, outcomes are subject to uncertainty, the degree of which varies from case to case." (*FC*)

(continued on next page)

Table 4.1. Sophisticated Methodological Holism
(Part IV)

• "Sophisticated methodological holism—when applied, especially though not exclusively, as illustrated in my numerous works—can enrich the understanding of reality in some distinctive ways. Here are three examples (as revealed in each of my books)." (*FPHCT; FPHL*)

—"Firstly, it provides a comprehensive analysis of a subject matter, from which much can be learned about reality," "both in relation to the perspectives of the mind, nature, society, and culture and also in relation to a new classification of the subject matter."

—"Secondly, it suggests some visions of the future in relation to the subject matter in question."

—"And thirdly, it proposes some insights on meta-theory (e.g., methodology and ontology) in general—with the clear understanding, however, of the dilemma of specific vs. general ontology (as shown in the table on the syntax of existential dialectics in the context of the dilemma of ontology). For this very reason, all of these ways are important, without reducing one into the analysis of another."

• "In the end, my meta-theory (both sophisticated methodological holism and existential dialectics) serves as a foundation to unify all domains of knowledge into *an unified theory of everything* (by way of some ontological principles and the comprehensive perspectives of the mind, nature, society, and culture). This is so, without commiting the sins of reductionism and reverse-reductionism (as often seen in many holistic approaches, with the fad of sysems approach—be it about systems theory, chaos theory, complexity theory, or else—as a most recent notorious example, which I debunked in *The Future of Complexity* and also in *The Future of Post-Human Formal Science*). My distinctive approach makes good use of different schools of thought without favoring any of them nor trying to integrate them (as they are not necessarily compatible with each other), so as to adjust for subjectivity, diversity, conflict, and complexity, for example. In this sense, the word "unified" does not have to mean integrative approach, in a narrow sense, nor systems approach, in a broad one, both of which I reject while learning from them." (*FPHFS; FPHS*)

Sources: A summary of *Sec.1.2* in *FPHC*—and also from *BNN, FPHST, ALD, FC, FPHCT*, and the rest of all other books of mine. See the books for more detail.

Table 4.2. On Reductionism and Reverse-Reductionism
(Part I)

• **The Partiality-Totality Principle**
—The partiality-totality principle in the ontology of existential dialectics targets against the varieties of reductionism and reverse-reductionism (as already worked out in my previous books).

• **Against the Varieties of Reductionism**
—*Conceptual Reductionism*
  • Some illustrative instances involve myriad dualities like mind vs. body, self vs. world, democracy vs. non-democracy, and the like (as already addressed in *FHC*, *FPHC*, and *BDPD*, for instance).
—*Theoretical Reductionism*
  • A fascinating case study concerns what I originally called "the foundation fallacy" in *FPHST*, in any attempt to naively understand space-time from the physical perspective as the foundation and, consequently, to dangerously dismiss other perspectives.
  • In *FAE*, I elaborated further these versions of reductionism in the literature on aesthetics (e.g., form vs. content, representation vs. expression, critics vs. artists, and externalism vs. internalism).
  • In *FIA*, I revealed other forms of reductionism in the literature on information architecture (e.g., the constructivist argument).
  • In *FPHU*, I showed the persistent legacy of reductionism, this time, in the literature on anomalous experience (e.g., the obsession with physics, chemistry, and biology for explaining anomalous experience).
  • In *FPHE*, I examined another case of reductionism in action, in the context of engineering (e.g., technical constraints vs. normative constraints).
  • In *FPHMM*, I elaborated one more version of reductionism, in relation to the three domains of communication (e.g., the competing views on sending, connecting, and receiving).
  • In *FPHCT*, I explored another version of reductionism, in relation to invention and innovation (e.g., the bio-psychological argument vs. the socio-cultural arguments).

(continued on next page)

Table 4.2. On Reductionism and Reverse-Reductionism (Part II)

• **Against the Varieties of Reductionism** *(cont'd)*
—*Theoretical Reductionism (cont'd)*
  • In *FPHG*, I identify another version of reductionism, in relation to infinity, symmetry, and dimensionality (e.g., the Euclidean argument vs. the non-Euclidean arguments).
  • In *FPHUP*, I analyzed another version of reductionism, in relation to density and void (e.g., the engineering argument and the ecology argument).
  • In *FPHL*, I examined another version of reductionism, in relation to structure and context (e.g., the structuralist argument and the contextualist argument).
  • In *PFHO*, I explored another version of reductionism, in relation to communcation, decision-making, and leadership (e.g., the rational-system argument vs. the natural-system argument).
  • In *PFHMA*, I revealed another version of reductionism, in relation to the martial body and spirit (e.g., the spiritual argument vs. the materialist argument vs. the defensive argument).
  • In *PFHS*, I analyzed another version of reductionism, in relation to the sexual body and spirit (e.g., the naturalist argument vs. the constructivist argument).
  • In *PFHLAW*, I examined another version of reductionism, in relation to law (e.g., the necessity argument vs. the contengency argument).
  • In *FPHWP*, I showed another version of reductionism, in relation to war and peace (e.g., the aggressivist argument vs. the pacifist argument).
  • In *BEPE*, I analyzed another version of reductionism, in relation to morality and immorality (e.g., the objectivist argument vs. the non-objectivist argument vs. the skeptical argument).
  • In *BCOS*, I examined another version of reductionism, in relation to the contested beginnings and speculative ends of the universe (e.g., the scientific argument vs. the religious argument vs. the esoteric argument vs. the metaphysical argument).
  • In *FPHP*, I show another version of reductionism, in relation to normality and abnormality (e.g., the natural argument vs. the social argument vs. the cultural argument vs. the mental argument).

(continued on next page)

Table 4.2. On Reductionism and Reverse-Reductionism
(Part III)

* **Against the Varieties of Reductionism** *(cont'd)*
  —*Theoretical Reductionism (cont'd)*
  * In *FPHGEOL*, I scrutinized another version of reductionism, in relation to statics and dynamics (e.g., the catastrophe argument vs. the uniformity argument vs. the revision argument).
  * In *FPHCHESS*, I showed another version of reductionism, in relation to tactics and strategy (e.g., the natural argument vs. the social argument vs. the cultural argument vs. the mental argument).
  * In *FPHR*, I revealed another version of reductionism, in relation to secularness and sacredness (e.g., the critical argument vs. the skeptical argument vs. the theist argument).
  * In *FPHEDU*, I examined another version of reductionism, in relation to teaching and learning (e.g., the teacher-centered argument vs. the student-centered argument vs. the balanced argument).
  * In *FPHH*, I explored another version of reductionism, in relation to joking and laughing (e.g., the natural argument vs. the social argument vs. the cultural argument vs. the mental argument).
  * In *FPHA*, I proposed another version of reductionism, in relation to sound and silence (e.g., the natural argument vs. the social argument vs. the cultural argument vs. the mental argument).
  * In *FPHGAM*, I proposed another version of reductionism, in relation to risk and caution (e.g., the natural argument vs. the social argument vs. the cultural argument vs. the mental argument).
  * In *FPHCOM*, I worked out another version of reductionism, in relation to hardware and software (e.g., the natural argument vs. the social argument vs. the cultural argument vs. the mental argument).
  * In *FPHLIT*, I proposed another version of reductionism, in relation to fiction and non-fiction (e.g., the natural argument vs. the social argument vs. the cultural argument vs. the mental argument).
  * In *FPHCHEM*, I proposed another version of reductionism, in relation to substances and their changes (e.g., the natural argument vs. the social argument vs. the cultural argument vs. the mental argument).

(continued on next page)

**Table 4.2. On Reductionism and Reverse-Reductionism
(Part IV)**

• **Against the Varieties of Reductionism** *(cont'd)*
—*Theoretical Reductionism (cont'd)*
   • In *FPHDA*, I proposed another version of reductionism, in relation to quantitative and qualitative research (e.g., the natural argument vs. the social argument vs. the cultural argument vs. the mental argument).
   • In *FPHGEOG*, I proposed another version of reductionism, in relation to environments and their interactions (e.g., the natural argument vs. the social argument vs. the cultural argument vs. the mental argument).
   • In *FPHPA*, I proposed another version of reductionism, in relation to the body and its presence (e.g., the natural argument vs. the social argument vs. the cultural argument vs. the mental argument).
   • In *FPHSEM*, I proposed another version of reductionism, in relation to internality and externality (e.g., the natural argument vs. the social argument vs. the cultural argument vs. the mental argument).
   • In *FPHARCH*, I proposed another version of reductionism, in relation to form and function (e.g., the natural argument vs. the social argument vs. the cultural argument vs. the mental argument).
   • In *FPHCRIM*, I proposed another version of reductionism, in relation to heroes and villains (e.g., the natural argument vs. the social argument vs. the cultural argument vs. the mental argument).
   • In *FPHHIST*, I proposed another version of reductionism, in relation to universality and relativity (e.g., the natural argument vs. the social argument vs. the cultural argument vs. the mental argument).
   • In *FPHMIG*, I proposed another version of reductionism, in relation to Sameness, Otherness, and identity (e.g., the natural argument vs. the social argument vs. the cultural argument vs. the mental argument).

(continued on next page)

Table 4.2. On Reductionism and Reverse-Reductionism
(Part V)

• **Against the Varieties of Reductionism** *(cont'd)*
—*Theoretical Reductionism (cont'd)*
  • In *FPHTRAN*, I proposed another version of reductionism, in relation to networks and operations (e.g., the natural argument vs. the social argument vs. the cultural argument vs. the mental argument).
  • In *FPHCA*, I proposed another version of reductionism, in relation to ingredients and techniques (e.g., the natural argument vs. the social argument vs. the cultural argument vs. the mental argument).
  • In *FPHW*, I proposed another version of reductionism, in relation to uselessness and usefulness (e.g., the natural argument vs. the social argument vs. the cultural argument vs. the mental argument).
  • In *BNR*, I proposed another version of reductionism, in relation to diversity and discontinuity (e.g., the natural argument vs. the social argument vs. the cultural argument vs. the mental argument).
  • In *FPHSPORT*, I proposed another version of reductionism, in relation to training and winning (e.g., the natural argument vs. the social argument vs. the cultural argument vs. the mental argument).
  • In *FPHPROB*, I proposed another version of reductionism, in relation to objectivity and subjectivity (e.g., the natural argument vs. the social argument vs. the cultural argument vs. the mental argument).
  • In *FPHMORP*, I proposed another version of reductionism, in relation to typologies and rules (e.g., the natural argument vs. the social argument vs. the cultural argument vs. the mental argument).
  • In *FPHHC*, I proposed another version of reductionism, in relation to mind and body (e.g., the natural argument vs. the social argument vs. the cultural argument vs. the mental argument).

(continued on next page)

Table 4.2. On Reductionism and Reverse-Reductionism
(Part VI)

• **Against the Varieties of Reductionism** *(cont'd)*
—*Theoretical Reductionism (cont'd)*
   • In *FPHTHAN*, I proposed another version of reductionism, in relation to death and after-death (e.g., the natural argument vs. the social argument vs. the cultural argument vs. the mental argument).
   • In *FPHVA*, I proposed another version of reductionism, in relation to techniques and spirits (e.g., the natural argument vs. the social argument vs. the cultural argument vs. the mental argument).
   • In *FPHAERO*, I proposed another version of reductionism, in relation to predictability and nonpredictability (e.g., the natural argument vs. the social argument vs. the cultural argument vs. the mental argument).
   • In *FPHPHON*, I proposed another version of reductionism, in relation to generality and specificity (e.g., the natural argument vs. the social argument vs. the cultural argument vs. the mental argument).
   • In *FPHACCO*, I proposed another version of reductionism, in relation to addiction and subtraction (e.g., the natural argument vs. the social argument vs. the cultural argument vs. the mental argument).
   • And in *FPHETIO*, I propose another version of reductionism, in relation to cause and effect (e.g., the natural argument vs. the social argument vs. the cultural argument vs. the mental argument).

(continued on next page)

Table 4.2. On Reductionism and Reverse-Reductionism
(Part VII)

• **Against the Varieties of Reductionism** *(cont'd)*
—*Methodological Reductionism*
  • A good instance concerns the debate between different versions of qualitative and quantitative methods (as already analyzed in *FC* and also *FHC*). In *FPHML*, I examined similar reductionism, this time, in the literature on mathematical logic (e.g., the obsession with consistency, soundness, and completeness). And in *FPHFS*, I also explored the problems of reductionism in the context of formal science (e.g., the analytical argument).
—*Ontological Reductionism*
  • An excellent example is the debate between emergentism and reductionism in complexity theory and also in psychology (as elaborated in *FPHC*, in the context of Being and Becoming).

• **Against the Varieties of Reverse-Reductionism**
—*Conceptual Reverse-Reductionism*
  • Any concept of "art" (e.g., fine art, cave art, outsider art, junk art) is deemed acceptable in postmodernism (as already addressed in Ch.4 of *FHC*).
—*Theoretical Reverse-Reductionism*
  • There are numerous art and literary theories co-exist. Take the case of literary studies, as there are now Literary Structuralism, Marxist Literary Criticism, New Criticism, Phenomenology, Hermeneutics, Language-Game Literary Criticism, Feminist Literary Criticism, Reception Theory, Reader Response Criticism, Poststructuralism, Semiotics, Pyschoanalytic Literary Criticism, just to cite some well-known ones, with no one being said to be better than any others (as detailedly analyzed in Ch.4 of *FHC*). (S. Raman 1997) In *BNN*, I even introduced "the compromise fallacy" as another good illustration of theoretical reverse-reductionism, in misleadingly treating both genetic and environmental approaches as equally valid.

(continued on next page)

**Table 4.2. On Reductionism and Reverse-Reductionism
(Part VIII)**

• **Against the Varieties of Reverse-Reductionism** *(cont'd)*
—*Methodological Reverse-Reductionism*
  • There is the "anything-goes" mentality in postmodernism (e.g., doing art without praxis, doing art with praxis, and doing art by sublation), as analyzed in Ch.4 of *FHC*. And in *FPHFS*, I also exposed the problems of reverse-reductionism in the context of formal science in relation to systems theory.
—*Ontological Reverse-Reductionism*
  • There are likewise no privileged ontology, and the door is open for anything in postmodernism (e.g., the equal status of the ontology of Being vs. that of Becoming, as already addressed in Ch.4 of *FHC*—and also in *FPHC*). In *FAE*, I also introduced another version of reverse-reductionism, that is, "the pluralist fallacy," in the context of understanding aesthetic experience, for instance— although this fallacy has been committed not exclusively in relation to the ontological level (but also at the conceptual, theoretical, and methodological ones).

Sources: From my previous books.

Table 4.3. The Concepton of Existential Dialectics
(Part I)

• **Sets and Elements**
—Sets
  • Ex: the Same
  • Ex: the Others
—Elements
  • Ex: whites in 20th century America (in the set of "the Same")
  • Ex: Iraq during the U.S. invasion in 2003 (in the set of "the Others")

• **Relations, Operations, Functions**
—Relations (e.g., "belongs," "equals to," "is greater than")
  • Ex: symmetric interactions within the Same (or the Others)
  • Ex: asymmetric interactions between the Same and the Others
—Operations (e.g., "and," "or," "not," "if...then")
  • Ex: if the Same oppresses the Others, it will also oppress itself.
  • Ex: the Same is not the Others.
—Functions (e.g., goals)
  • Ex: the Same is hegemonic in relation to the Others.

• **Truth Values**
—"1" if True (in Symbolic Logic)
  • Ex: the proposition that imperial Japan was hegemonic to China during WWII
—"0" if False (in Symbolic Logic)
  • Ex: the proposition that Grenada invaded France in 2003
—"1" & "0" if Both True and False (in Dialectic Logic)
  • Ex: the proposition that the rabbit-duck picture refers to a duck
—"~1" & "~0" if Neither True Nor False (or N/A, in Dialectic Logic)
  • Ex: the proposition that God really exists

(continued on next page)

Table 4.3. The Conception of Existential Dialectics
(Part II)

• **Axioms and Postulates**
—Axioms
  • Ex: the reflexive axiom—"any quantity is equal to itself"
—Postulates
  • Ex: the SSS postulate—"if the three sides of a triangle are congruent to their corresponding parts, then the triangles are congruent"

• **Theorems and Principles**
—Theorems (and Principles) in Existential Dialectics
  • *In Relation to Agency*
    —#37: The formalness-informalness principle
    —#36: The absoluteness-relativeness principle
    —#35: The partiality-totality principle
    —#34: The predictability-unpredictability principle
    —#33: The explicability-inexplicability principle
    —#32: The fiction-reality principle
    —#31: The cognitiveness-noncognitiveness principle
  • *In Relation to Structure*
    —#30: The finiteness-transfiniteness principle
    —#29: The preciseness-vagueness principle
    —#28: The simpleness-complicatedness principle
    —#27: The openness-hiddenness principle
    —#26: The denseness-emptiness principle
    —#25: The rule-exception principle
    —#24: The indispensability-dispensability principle
  • *In Relation to Process*
    —#23: The prototypicality-variation principle
    —#22: The change-constancy principle
    —#21: The order-chaos principle
    —#20: The slowness-quickness principle
    —#19: The expansion-contraction principle
    —#18: The optimality-nonoptimality principle
    —#17: The simultaneity-nonsimultaneity principle
    —#16: The isolation-interaction principle

(continued on next page)

Table 4.3. The Conception of Existential Dialectics
(Part III)

• **Theorems and Principles (*cont'd*)**
—Theorems (and Principles) in Existential Dialectics
  • *In Relation to Agency*
    —#15: The theory-praxis principle
    —#14: The convention-novelty principle
    —#13: The evolution-transformation principle
    —#12: The symmetry-asymmetry principle
    —#11: The softness-hardness principle
    —#10: The seriousness-playfulness principle
    —#09: The activeness-inactiveness principle
    —#08: The selfness-otherness principle
  • *In Relation to Outcome*
    —#07: The regression-progression principle
    —#06: The same-difference principle
    —#05: The stability-reaction principle
    —#04: The functionality-nonfunctionality principle
    —#03: The intentionality-nonintentionality principle
    —#02: The survivability-nonsurvivability principle
    —#01: The materiality-nonmateriality principle

Notes: The categories and examples in each are solely illustrative (not exhaustive). The comparison is also relative (not absolute), nor are they mutually exclusive. As generalities, they allow exceptions.
Sources: Starting from Ch.6 of *BCPC* and also from other books of mine

Table 4.4. The Syntax of Existential Dialectics I:
The Principles
(Part I)

• **In Relation to Method**
—*The Formalness-Informalness Principle*
(On the Formal Requirements of Logical Systems)
  • The formal requirements of a logical system (e.g., consistency, soundness, and completeness) have both usefulness and non-usefulness, to the extent that, if there are formal systems requiring them, there are alternative ones which do not. Thus, it does *not* exclude classical logics but simply goes beyond both classical and non-classical logics, while learning something from each. There is no formalness without informalness—and vice versa.
  • For instance, existential dialectics can make use of both classical logics under certain conditions (e.g., especially, though not exclusively, when they are clear-cut, etc.) and non-classical logics under alternative conditions (especially, though not exclusively, when they are "unknown," "irrelevant," "ambiguous," "possible," with "different degrees of truth," empirically inconsistent in a desirable way, etc.). (WK 2008u)
  • Family resemblance: e.g., logicalness-nonlogicalness, rationality-nonrationality, etc.
  • Sources: From *FPHML, FPHH, FPHGAM, FPHSEM,* and my later books.

(continued on next page)

Table 4.4. The Syntax of Existential Dialectics I:
The Principles
(Part II)

• **In Relation to Method** *(cont'd)*
—*The Absoluteness-Relativeness Principle*
(On the Multiplicity of Things)
  • There is the multiplicity of things in reality, be they about entities, qualities (or properties), and relationships, such that what is acceptable from one standpoint may not be so from another. For instance, if there is something absolute, there is likewise something relative. There is no absoluteness without relativeness—and vice versa.
  • Both absoluteness and relativeness here are also relevant to different modalities often cited in the literature on ontology, such as possibility (e.g., something "can" happen) and its opposite (e.g., impossibility) in alethic modalities, probability (e.g., something "will" happen) and its opposite (e.g., improbability) in temporal modalities, and necessity (e.g., something "should" happen) and its opposite (e.g., contingency) in alethic modalities.
  • Family resemblance: e.g., independence-dependence, universalness-relativeness, immanence-transcendence, autonomy-dependency, internalness-externalness, etc.
  • Sources: From *FPHK*. See also my later books.

(continued on next page)

Table 4.4. The Syntax of Existential Dialectics I:
The Principles
(Part III)

• **In Relation to Method** *(cont'd)*
—*The Partiality-Totality Principle*
  (On the Relationships between Whole and Parts)
  • The whole is not the sum of the parts. There is no partiality without totality—and vice versa.
  • Any inquiry about a phenomenon in the work is to guard against the varieties of (a) reductionism and (b) reverse-reductionism.
  • Reductionism and reverse-reductionism can be (i) conceptual, (ii) theoretical, (iii) methodological, and (iv) ontological.
  • Works on emergence (as in *FC*), gestalt psychology (as in *FPHGEOL*), the hermeneutic circle (as in *FPHDA*), and mental language (as in *FPHSEM*), to name just a few of them, have contributed to the understanding of whole and parts.
  • Family resemblance: e.g., individualisticness-holisticness, partness-wholeness, analysis-synthesis, etc.
  • Sources: Especially from *FC* & *FPHGEOL*. See also my later books.

(continued on next page)

Table 4.4. The Syntax of Existential Dialectics I:
The Principles
(Part IV)

• **In Relation to Method** *(cont'd)*
—*The Predictability-Unpredictability Principle*
(On the Occurrence of Events)
  • Both predictability and unpredictability have a major role to play in the occurrence of things, so that neither determinism nor indeterminism wins the centuries-old fight. There is no predictability without unpredictability—and vice versa.
  • There are events which are predictable, just as there are those which are not. Or what is regarded as unpredictable at one point in time may turn out to be predictable later, and, conversely, what is deemed as predictable may turn out to not be so predictable. Even in predictability, outcomes are subject to uncertainty, the degree of which varies from case to case.
  • Works on complexity theory (as in *FC*), quantum mechanics (as in *FPHST* and *FPHG*), subjective (or Bayesian) probability (as in *FPHPROB*), "special causes" (as in *FPHGAM*), measurement uncertainty (as in *FPHPROB*), the butterfly effect (as in *FPHAERO*), and unintended consequences (as in *FPHAERO*), just to name a few of them, have contributed to the understanding of uncertainity.
  • The predictability-unpredictability principle is not to be confused with the absoluteness-relativeness principle; although both can address the issue of probability, the former is concerned with the extent of certainty in prediction, whereas the latter focuses on the relativity of viewpoints.
  • Family resemblance: e.g., sureness-arbitrariness, certainty-uncertainty, deterministicness-indeterministicness, sureness-doubtfulness, likeliness-riskiness, deterministicness-randomness, reliability-unreliability, etc.
  • Sources: Especially from *FC* & *FPHGAM.* See also my later books.

(continued on next page)

Table 4.4. The Syntax of Existential Dialectics I:
The Principles
(Part V)

• **In Relation to Method** *(cont'd)*
—*The Explicability-Inexplicability Principle*
(On the Underlying Mechanisms of Things)
• Both explicability and inexplicability are part of the understanding of things. There is no explicability without inexplicability—and vice versa.
• This principle tells us the duality of the research dilemma, in that, if reality can be explained in some ways, it also has its other ways which are not quite explainable, at a given point in time.
• Family resemblance: e.g., underlyingness-regularness, causation-regularness, causation-correlation, relation-nonrelation, explanation-description, explanation-narration, explanation-interpretation, etc.
• Sources: Especially from *FPHU*—and also *FPHC*. See also my later books.

—*The Fiction-Reality Principle*
(On the different faces of Reality)
• If there is reality, there is also fiction, especially for any agent with some kind of intelligence life, be it about humans, animals, or, later, post-humans. There is no reality without fiction—and vice versa.
• The distinction between reality and fiction is not absolute, since there can be a mixture of both. Fiction can have non-fictional elements, just as non-fiction can have fictional ones. So, the distinction is in degree, not in kind.
• Family resemblance: e.g., fiction-nonfiction, fiction-fact, imagination-fact, subjectivity-objectivity, imagination-nonfiction, inaccuracy-accuracy, error-reality, misunderstanding-correctness, arbitrariness-reality, speculation-reality, etc.
• Sources: First from *FPHLIT*.

(continued on next page)

Table 4.4. The Syntax of Existential Dialectics I:
The Principles
(Part VI)

• **In Relation to Method** *(cont'd)*
 —*The Cognitiveness-Noncognitiveness Principle*
 (On the Understanding of Meaning)
   • If a view of things is based on reason and evidences, it is also
     affected by non-cognitive factors (such that it is neither true nor
     false in the latter case)—and vice versa. In other words, there is no
     cognitiveness without noncognitiveness—and vice versa.
   • Noncognitive factors can come in all shapes and sizes, and good
     examples include envy, jealousy, power, nationality, race, gender,
     age, class, greed, lust, status, faith, anger, sadness, joy, fear, wish,
     etc.
   • Communication, even in its ideal type, is seldom solely based reason
     and evidences, as falsely assumed during the Age of the
     Enlightenment and its continued supporters nowadays. What is
     understood about something is often twisted on the basis of
     something else too. In these cases, what is at stake is often neither
     true nor false (which is something that classical logic has sidelined
     and ignored).
   • Family resemblance: e.g., proposition-attitude, cognition-emotion,
     cognition-prescription, justification-nonjustification, recognition-
     nonrecogntion, reason-perception, theory-extratheory, reason-
     emotion, etc.
   • Sources: First from *BNR*.

(continued on next page)

Table 4.4. The Syntax of Existential Dialectics I:
The Principles
(Part VII)

• In Relation to Structure
—*The Finiteness-Transfiniteness Principle*
(On the Nature of Numbers)
- If there are finite things, there are likewise transfinite ones. There is no finiteness without transfiniteness—and vice versa.
- To avoid confusion, my usage of the word "transfinite" here differs radically from the one used by Cantor (and other mathematicians) for "relative" infinity—and is more limited, in light of the problems confronting any attempt to understand the idea of infinity, be it by intuition, imagination, and conception (as detailedly analyzed in *Sec. 2.2.3* of *FPHG*).
- Instead, by "transfinity," I allow numbers which can be many times larger—or smaller, for that matter—than the finite things that we encounter in daily life, but they do not have to be related to the idea of infinity at all (which may not exist).
- Of course, there may be some *borderline* cases, in which it is not clear whether the number in question is transfinite (in my usage) or simply a mathematical convenience. A good example of a borderline case is the Planck unit of length for "the smallest space possibly measured in nature," which is "less than billionths of trillionths of trillionths of an inch" (or something like 1.6×10^{-35} meters).
- That said—my usage of "transfinity" can also resolve (or better, dissolve) an age-old problem in philosophy known as "Zeno's paradoxes" (as already explained in *Sec. 2.2.3* of *FPHG*).
- Family resemblance: e.g., boundedness-quasiunboundedness, smallness-largeness, boundedness-unboundedness, etc.
- Source: From *FPHG*. See also my later books.

(continued on next page)

**Table 4.4. The Syntax of Existential Dialectics I:
The Principles
(Part VIII)**

* **In Relation to Structure** *(cont'd)*
 —*The Preciseness-Vagueness Principle*
 (On the Refinement of Things)
 * Both preciseness and vagueness are important, not that one is better than the other, but that both are used, in different degrees of preference, in accordance to the contextual application from the perspectives of nature, the mind, culture, and society. Even when both are used in a combination, the dilemma is shifted instead to one of combinational concern. There is no preciseness without vagueness—and vice versa.
 * In relation to taxonomy, preciseness has its taxonomic clarity, just as vagueness has its classificatory flexibility, for instance. And in relation to network, vagueness has its explorative liberty, just as preciseness has its conceptual definitiveness, for instance.
 * Family resemblance: e.g., clarity-ambiguity, directness-indirectness, quantitativeness-qualitativeness, describability-nondescribability, sharpness-roughness, specificity-generality, concreteness-abstractness, specificity-obscurity, translatability-untranslatability, clearcutness-transitionalness, discreteness-mixedness, discreteness-vagueness, detailedness-broadness, definition-nondefinition, etc.
 * Sources: Especially from *FIA* and *FPHMORP*. See also my later books.

(continued on next page)

Table 4.4. The Syntax of Existential Dialectics I:
The Principles
(Part IX)

• **In Relation to Structure** *(cont'd)*
—*The Simpleness-Complicatedness Principle*
(On the Interconnection among Things)
  • Both simpleness and complicatedness are vital, without favoring one over the other, in that each is utilized, depending on the basis of the perspectives of nature, the mind, culture, and society. And even when a combination of them is preferred, the dilemma is only shifted to a combinational degree of concern. There is no simpleness without complicatedness—and vice versa.
  • For illustration, in relation to taxonomy, simpleness has its heuristic usefulness, just as complicatedness has its realistic representation, for instance. In relation to network, simpleness has its economical attractiveness, just as complicatedness has its practical reliability, for instance. And in relation to logic, there is the simple zeroth-order logic, just as there is the complicated higher-order logic.
  • Family resemblance: e.g., inflexibility-flexibility, standardization-specialization, imperfectness-perfectness, superficiality-depth, shallowness-deepness, economicalness-elaboratedness, plainness-circumspection, onesidedness-multisidedness, succinctness-duplicatedness, simpleness-sophisticatedness, crudeness-subtleness, straightness-bendedness, etc.
  • Sources: Especially from *FIA* and *FPHPROB*. See also my later books.

(continued on next page)

Table 4.4. The Syntax of Existential Dialectics I:
The Principles
(Part X)

• **In Relation to Structure** *(cont'd)*
—*The Openness-Hiddenness Principle*
(On the Detection of Things)
  • Reality has its hidden face, just as it is open to outside view in some other ways. There is no openness without hiddenness—and vice versa.
  • For instance, in the context of anomalous experience, certain aspects of reality can be open for examination (e.g., the experiment with SPECT images, the transmission of telepathemic bit, and the use of metonymies and metaphors). Other aspects, however, remain hidden, and examples include the elusive deeper nature of spiritual reality in the intangible realm, the undetectability of different branched universes, the underlying mechanisms of signals traveling between different folds of physical space-time, and the dependence on language and the bias for science and logic).
  • Family resemblance: e.g., overtness-covertness, publicness-privateness, openness-closedness, transparency-secrecy, openness-biasedness, participation-obstruction, exposition-illusion, surface-depth, etc.
  • Sources: Especially from *FPHU*. See also my later books.

(continued on next page)

**Table 4.4. The Syntax of Existential Dialectics I:
The Principles
(Part XI)**

• **In Relation to Structure** *(cont'd)*
—*The Denseness-Emptiness Principle*
(On the Distribution of Entities in Space)
  • Both density and void are needed, in relation to the mind, nature, culture, and society, albeit in different ways. There is no denseness without emptiness—and vice versa.
  • For clarity, the term "void" is used here only as an approximation of emptiness (depending on the degree of the lack of density), since, in physics, it is well known that "empty" space is not really empty all the way, because it can be full of energy (e.g., random quantum fluctuations at the sub-atomic level, and, for that matter, dark energy in the universe) and matter (e.g., different versions of sub-atomic particles, and, for that matter, dark matter in the universe).
  • Family resemblance: e.g., fullness-voidness, nearness-farness, concentration-dispersion, denseness-nothingness, presence-absence, focus-unfocus, solidness-void, something-nothing, heaviness-lightness, composition-emptiness, emphasis-disemphasis, etc.
• Sources: First worked out in *FPHUP*. See also my later books.

(continued on next page)

Table 4.4. The Syntax of Existential Dialectics I:
The Principles
(Part XII)

* **In Relation to Structure** *(cont'd)*
—*The Rule-Exception Principle*
(On the Extent of Typicality)
* Both rules and their exceptions exist, in relation to the mind, nature, culture, and society, albeit in different ways. There is no rule without exception—and vice versa.
* As the old saying goes, "There is an exception to the rule"; however, to avoid misuse, there are the following four important aspects of the relationship between rules and exceptions to be clarified.
* If there is an exception to the rule, there can be an exception to the.rule itself that there is an exception to the rule, as shown in some cases where no exception is allowed—but this regression can continue further (e.g., there is an exception to the rule that there can be an exception to the rule itself that there is an exception to the rule).
* To be an exception to the rule does not mean that one can say something nonsensical, either jokingly or seriously, and then expects others to allow an exception.
* To be an exception to the rule does not mean that one can appeal to an invalid generalization, either literally or figuratively, and then expects others to allow an exception.
* An exception to a rule means that the exception implies the existence of a rule, which does not apply in the special case under consideration—but the exception does not automatically justify that the rule is desirable, good, right, etc.
* Family resemblance: e.g., generalization-exception, custom-deviance, procedure-exception, typicality-exception, normalcy-extremity, pattern-deviance, and the like.
* Sources: First worked out in *FPHTHAN*. See also my later books.

(continued on next page)

Table 4.4. The Syntax of Existential Dialectics I:
The Principles
(Part XIII)

• **In Relation to Structure** *(cont'd)*
—*The Indispensability-Dispensability Principle*
(On the Nature of Superfluity)
  • Both indispensability and dispensability exist—in relation to the mind, nature, culture, and society, albeit in different ways. There is no indispensability without dispensability—and vice versa.
  • There can be slightly different meanings in relation to an attribute; for instance, "dispensability" can mean "redundancy" (e.g., something which is superfluous and thus not really needed), or "replaceability" (e.g, something which can be replaced and thus not strictly needed).
  • The indispensability-dispensability principle should not be confused with the functionality-nonfunctionality principle, since "dispensability" (like "redundancy") is not necessarily non-functional, since something can be functional but not needed.
  • There can be different degrees of indispensability and dispensability, since something can be more necessary than something else on a particular occasion.
  • Family resemblance: e.g., need-circumlocution, requiredness-prolixity, necessity-verbosity, necessity-superfluity, necessity-duplication, essentialness-excessiveness, necessity-repetition, importance-triviality, necessity-replaceability, and the like.
  • Sources: First worked out in *FPHETIO*. See also my later books.

(continued on next page)

Table 4.4. The Syntax of Existential Dialectics I:
The Principles
(Part XIV)

• **In Relation to Process**
—*The Prototypicality-Variation Principle*
  (On the Nature of Duplication)
  • If there are prototypes, there are also variants of the copies. There is no prototypicality without variation—and vice versa.
  • Prototypes and their copies are not static and may change or die out over time, but new ones may emerge.
  • Some copies may have multiple prototypes, not just one.
  • It can be very challenging to trace some copies back to their prototypes, under certain difficult historical conditions.
  • Copies are not solely identical duplications of prototypes but have their own variations (mutations).
  • Family resemblance: e.g., archetypicality-descendedness, origin-descendedness, ancestry-descendedness, prototypicality-duplication, archetypicality-mutation, origin-reenactment, prototypicality-recreation, prototypicality-copyness, and the like.
  • Sources: First worked out in *FPHMORP*. See also my later books.

—*The Change-Constancy Principle*
  (On the Alteration of Things)
  • Change occurs over time, although constancy is also allowed. There is no change without constancy—and vice versa.
  • Asymmetry undergoes changes over time, so does symmetry.
  • Old players fade away, and new ones emerges, with ever new causes and ever new forms.
  • Family resemblance: e.g., dynamicness-staticness, instability-stability, etc.
  • Sources: First named in *BCPC*. Especially from *FHC*, *FCD*, and *FPHC*. See also other books of mine (from that point on).

(continued on next page)

Table 4.4. The Syntax of Existential Dialectics I:
The Principles
(Part XV)

- **In Relation to Process** *(cont'd)*
  —*The Order-Chaos Principle*
  (On the Pattern of Things)
  - Both order and chaos are vital in the process of change in the world. The preference for order is biased, since it does not give sufficient attention to the vital role of chaos in the transformation of the world (without somehow reducing it for the understanding of order). There is no order without chaos—and vice versa.
  - The scientific search for order in the world is often a hidden bias in its ontological obsession with order, since chaos is often treated as the "bad" guy, with order as the "good" guy (for the end goal of science).
  - Neither order nor chaos is the final end of the world, and one is not to be treated as the means for the other in the transformation of things. Both are fundamental in their recurrent dialectical interactions with each other over time, without reducing one for the other.
  - Order has its different forms (e.g., ascending vs. descending order in mathematics, and feeding vs. bleeding order in morphology), just as chaos has its own versions (e.g., as understood differently in chaos theory vs. complexity theory).
  - Family resemblance: e.g., lawfulness-disorder, order-disorder, linearity-nonlinearity, linearity-irreversalness, pattern-chaos, unity-disunity, sequence-chaos, etc.
  - Sources: Especially from *FC*. See also my later books.

(continued on next page)

Table 4.4. The Syntax of Existential Dialectics I:
The Principles
(Part XVI)

• **In Relation to Process** *(cont'd)*
—*The Slowness-Quickness Principle*
(On the Speed of Change)
• Both slowness and quickness co-exist, with their own internal tension, to the extent that each fights for its own relevance with the other, in accordance to the perspectives of nature, the mind, culture, and society, without one being the victor and the other being the vanquished in the long haul. Even when both are chosen in other cases, this dilemma is only transferred into something else with a combinational character. There is no slowness without quickness—and vice versa.
• In relation to taxonomy, quickness has its efficient usability, just as slowness has its aesthetic appeal, for instance. And in relation to network, quickness has its adventurous readiness, just as slowness has its risk-adverse convenience, for instance.
• Family resemblance: e.g., inconvenience-convenience, passiveness-activenessness, gradualness-abruptness, deceleration-acceleration, difficulty-ease, nonresilience-resilience, patience-impatience, deliberativeness-impulsiveness, etc.
• Sources: Especially from *FIA*. See also my later books.

(continued on next page)

Table 4.4. The Syntax of Existential Dialectics I:
The Principles
(Part XVII)

• **In Relation to Process** *(cont'd)*
—*The Expansion-Contraction Principle*
  (On the Growth of Things)
  • Entities in the world can both expand in some ways and contract in other ones, as part of their nature. There is no expansion without contraction—and vice versa.
  • For instance, in the context of anomalous experience, one of its most fascinating expressions is none other than the analysis of different causes of the slow but steady expansion (and, furthermore, if put in a different way, unfolding) of unconsciousness.
  • Family resemblance: e.g., conquest-autarky, rise-fall, spread-shrink, extendingness-shorteningness, widening-narrowing, expansion-destruction, expansion-decline, construction-demolition, creation-destruction, construction-deconstruction, expansion-contraction, composition-decomposition, growth-breakdown, formation-decay, expansion-constriction, insertion-deletion, addition-division, multiplication-division, multiplication-subtraction, overstatedness-understatedness, etc.
  • Sources: Especially from *FPHU*. See also my later books.

(continued on next page)

Table 4.4. The Syntax of Existential Dialectics I:
The Principles
(Part XVIII)

• **In Relation to Process** *(cont'd)*
—*The Optimality-Nonoptimality Principle*
(On the Nature of Highly Favorable Options)
  • Both optimality and non-optimality are important, in relation to the mind, nature, culture, and society, albeit in different ways. There is no optimality without nonoptimality—and vice versa.
  • Optimality (in terms of highly favorable options) is not perfect and can be realized in different degrees.
  • "Maximization" does not necessarily entail "optimization," as shown in the problem of "negative externalities" in economics.
  • Non-optimality can come in all shapes and sizes, in different degrees, like "maximizing" in economics vs. "satisficing" in sociology.
  • Optimality can be more feasible in the longer term of technological improvement.
  • Optimality should not be confused with the beauty of simplicity, since the more optimal a process is, the more complicated (not necessarily the simpler) it can be.
  • Family resemblance: e.g., optimality-satisfaction, optimality-maximization, optimality-heuristicness, idealness-realisticness, and the like.
  • Sources: First worked out in *FPHMORP*. See also my later books.

(continued on next page)

Table 4.4. The Syntax of Existential Dialectics I:
The Principles
(Part XIX)

• **In Relation to Process** *(cont'd)*
—*The Simultaneity-Nonsimultaneity Principle*
(On the Sequence of Time)
  • Both simultaneity and nonsimultaneity are important, in relation to the mind, nature, culture, and society, albeit in different ways. There is no simultaneity without nonsimultaneity—and vice versa.
  • An event B can occur after the occurrence of another event A in a causal situation. But A and B can also occur simultaneously in a different situation, and this is important, because, in quantum mechanics (as addressed in *FPHPT*), for instance, particles move so fast that, for all practical purposes, A and B can be treated as occurring simultaneously.
  • In conventional wisdom, A and its negation ~A are different and do not coexist simultaneously. But in certain circumstances, it is also important to consider A and ~A simultaneously, as shown in the interactions between two opposites in the nature vs. nature debate (as addressed in *BNN*) and in the ritual/speech coevolution debate as well as the coarticulation debate (as addressed in *FPHPHON*).
  • Simultaneity does not have to be absolute, as it can be more or less so for two entities to occur simultaneously.
  • On one end of the line is exteme simultaneity and on the other end is extreme nonsimultaneously, and between the two are different degrees or gradations of simultaneity or nonsimultaneity.
  • Family resemblance: e.g., simultaneity-sequence, simultaneity-consecutiveness, contemporaneity-successiveness, sychronicity-sequence, and the like.
  • Sources: First worked out in *FPHPHON*. See also my later books.

(continued on next page)

Table 4.4. The Syntax of Existential Dialectics I:
The Principles
(Part XX)

• **In Relation to Process** *(cont'd)*
—*The Isolation-Interaction Principle*
  (On the Interaction among Entities)
  • Both isolaiton and interaction are important, in relation to the mind, nature, culture, and society, albeit in different ways. There is no isolation and interaction—and vice versa.
  • Isolation and interactions are not perfect and can be realized in different degrees.
  • Isolation and interaction take time to develop.
  • Interaction can have different outcomes over time (e.g., "merging," "split," "loss," etc. in sound change).
  • The isolation-interaction pair should not be confused with the absoluteness-relativeness pair, although both concern the issue of autonomy, but there are different opposites in relation to autonomy (in the contexts of method, process, etc.).
  • Family resemblance: e.g., isolation-exchange, isolation-intercourse, autonomy-trade, aloneness-interrelationship, autarky-commerce, insulation-interaction, secludedness-interrelationship, segregation-interaction , and the like.
  • Sources: First worked out in *FPHACCO*. See also my later books.

• **In Relation to Agency**
—*The Theory-Praxis Principle*
  (On the Duality of Knowledge))
  • This has to do with the duality of knowledge in existential dialectics, in that, if there is theoretical construction, there is likewise its practical application, both technical and normative. There is no theory without praxis—and vice versa.
  • Family resemblance: e.g., discovery-application, knowledge-action, invention-innovation, knowledge-motivation, theory-intentionality, universality-particularity, discourse-action, knowledge-interest, potentiality-actuality, theory-practice, etc.
  • Source: Especially from *FPHE*. See also my later books.

(continued on next page)

**Table 4.4. The Syntax of Existential Dialectics I:
The Principles
(Part XXI)**

• **In Relation to Agency** *(cont'd)*
—*The Convention-Novelty Principle*
(On the Nature of Creative Thinking)
 • If there is conventional wisdom, there is likewise novel challenge, to
 the extent that both convergent and divergent thinking are part of
 life. There is no convention without novelty—and vice versa.
 • In addition, in this context of the convention-novelty principle, there
 are, in the absence of better words, what I want to call (a) *creative
 techniques* and (b) *creative traits*, which, when satisfied—in
 relation to the larger context of the mind, nature, society, and
 culture—can be used to enhance creative works. The list of
 creative techniques and traits (as summarized in *Table 4.1* of
 FPHCT) are not exhaustive, of course, but the examples here
 constitute a great beginning of understanding the structure of
 creative thinking.
 • Yet, lest the reader gets carried away by the euphoria about creative
 thinking in our time, it should be reminded that creative thinking
 has its own possibilities and limits (as shown in *Table 2.1* of
 FPHCT on invention), just as it has its own promises and pitfalls
 (as shown in *Table 3.1* of *FPHCT* on innovation). In the end, it
 should also be stressed that creative thinking has its own
 desirability and dark sides (as shown in *Table 4.2* of *FPHCT*,
 BNN, and *FPHMIG*).
 • This has important daily implications for an average individual, and
 the word "average" here allows different degrees of variation
 from one individual to another in a population, at any given point
 in history.
 • Family resemblance: e.g., normalness-nonnormalness, conformity-
 nonconformity, convergence-divergence, familiarity-freshness,
 inertia-newness, equilibrium-disturbance, etc.
 • Sources: First from *FPHCT*. See also my later books.

(*continued on next page*)

**Table 4.4. The Syntax of Existential Dialectics I:
The Principles
(Part XXII)**

• **In Relation to Agency** *(cont'd)*
—*The Evolution-Transformation Principle*
(On the Multiple Kinds of Agency)
• This principle (and the symmetry-asymmetry principle) are both about *the agency of change.* The word "agency," in a formal definition, refers to "a person or thing through which power is exerted or an end is achieved." (MWD 2007b) It therefore does not have to necessarily involve an intelligent lifeform.
• Because of this dual meaning in agency, the evolution-transformation principle is more concerned with *the multiple kinds of agency,* that is, both about the *evolution* in the state of nature (e.g., an object of natural beauty) and the *transformation* in the world of intelligent lifeforms (e.g., a work of art, an air-conditioner, etc.). There is no evolution without transformation—and vice versa.
• And the transformative part of the principle precisely refers to the other dimension in the dual meaning of agency, in giving technology a major role to play in the change of the world, which is something that I extensively analyzed in *FHC* in the context of the technophilic lifeworld, espeically though not exclusively since modern times. The same theme is also elaborated in other books of mine.
• Family resemblance: e.g., nonwillingness-willingness, naturalness-technologicalness, evolution-creation, naturalness-nonnaturalness, inorganicness-volition, naturalness-artificialness, inorganicness-motivation, etc.
• Sources: Especially from *FAE.* See also other books of mine.

(continued on next page)

Table 4.4. The Syntax of Existential Dialectics I:
The Principles
(Part XXIII)

• **In Relation to Agency** *(cont'd)*
  —*The Symmetry-Asymmetry Principle*
  (On the Relationships among Existents)
  • There is no symmetry without asymmetry—and vice versa.
  • For instance, the Same can be symmetric and asymmetric towards the Others. But in case of asymmetry, oppression and self-oppression can occur. So, when the Same is asymmetric towards the Others, the Same can also be relatively asymmetric towards itself in self-oppression, just as the Others can be likewise towards themselves.
  • The subsequent oppressiveness is dualistic, as much by the Same against the Others and itself, as by the Others against the Same and themselves.
  • Both oppression and self-oppression can be achieved by way of downgrading differences between the Same and the Others and of accentuating them.
  • This is true, even though not all forms of asymmetry have to be about oppression and self-oppression.
  • In addition, from Chapter Three of *FPHG*, symmetry is not perfect, to be understood in an approximate sense under many life circumstances.
  • Family resemblance: e.g., balance-extremity, reflexiveness-unreflexiveness, balance-unbalance, equality-inequality, center-periphery, compatibility-incompatibility, proportion-disproportion, harmoniousness-unharrmoniousness, etc.
  • Sources: From all my books, starting with *FHC*. First named in *BCPC*. See, for instance, *FCD* for more details on the Same and the Others.

(*continued on next page*)

Table 4.4. The Syntax of Existential Dialectics I:
The Principles
(Part XXIV)

• **In Relation to Agency** *(cont'd)*
—*The Softness-Hardness Principle*
(On the Force of Change)
  • This has to do with *the force of change* under the category about agency in existential dialectics, in that any change by an agent, be it organic (like humans) or non-organic (like natural objects), can occur in a forceful (aggressive) or gentle (pacific) way, which can come in all shapes and sizes, of course. There is no softness without hardness—and vice versa.
  • Family resemblance: e.g., peacefulness-violence, cooperation-competition, acceptance-discrimination, love-hatred, peace-war, pacificity-aggression, dovishness-hawkishness, reward-punishment, kindness-hostility, admiration-belittlement, inclusion-exclusion, friendliness-unfriendliness, like-dislike, cooperation-predation, courteousness-violence, polishedness-harshness, integration-rivalry, bribery-killing, femininity-masculinity, absorption-resistance, amicality-animosity, etc.
  • Sources: Especially from *ALD*. See also my later books.

(continued on next page)

Table 4.4. The Syntax of Existential Dialectics I:
The Principles
(Part XXV)

• **In Relation to Agency** *(cont'd)*
—*The Seriousness-Playfulness Principle*
(On the Extent of Seriousness)
  • If there is seriousness, there is also playfulness, especially for any agent with some kind of intelligence life, be it about humans, animals, or, later, post-humans. There is no seriousness without playfulness—and vice versa.
  • Lest any misunderstanding occurs, the word "playfulness" here should not be confused with other terms like "laughter," "smile," "joke," "tickleness," and "laugh-like vocalization" (in some animals), for instance.
  • Being playful can come in all shapes and sizes and therefore is not necessarily tied up with any of these terms, although it can result from any of them, or a combination of them, or something else altogether.
  • This principle, together with some other principles (especially though not exclusively, like the formalness-informalness principle), have important implications for what constitutes rationality, be it about "rationality of application" at the practical level or "rationality of knowledge" at the meta-theoretical level (as summarized in *Sec. 4.20* of *FPHH*).
  • Family resemblance: e.g., seriousness-jokingness, seriousness-humorousness, seriousness-wittiness, seriousness-nonseriousness, seriousness-relaxedness, seriousness-restingness, Apollo-Dionysus, seriousness-clownishness, criticalness-imaginativeness, etc.
  • Sources: First from *FPHH* & *FPHGAM* See also my later books.

(continued on next page)

Table 4.4. The Syntax of Existential Dialectics I:
The Principles
(Part XXVI)

• **In Relation to Agency** *(cont'd)*
—*The Activeness-Inactiveness Principle*
(On the Extent of Activeness)
  • If there is activeness, there is also inactiveness, especially (though not exclusively) for any agent with some kind of intelligence life, be it about humans, animals, or, later, post-humans. There is no activeness without inactiveness—and vice versa.
  • Being active can come in all shapes and sizes, as a person can be inactive because he is tired, old, sick, sleepy, uninterested, etc., just as an object can be inactive because it is at rest, out of work, etc.
  • This principle, together with some other principles (especially though not exclusively, like the formalness-informalness principle and seriousness-playfulness principle), have important implications for what constitutes rationality, be it about "rationality of application" at the practical level or "rationality of knowledge" at the meta-theoretical level (as summarized in *Sec. 4.20* of *FPHH*).
    • Family resemblance: e.g., alertness-unalertness, activeness-decrepidness, alertness-sleepiness, awakenness-hibernatedness, activeness-tiredness, alertness-uninterestedness, alertness-unwareness, soberness-unawareness, soberness-inactiveness, alertness-inactiveness, activeness-passiveness, etc.
  • Sources: First from *FPHTRAN*.

(*continued on next page*)

**Table 4.4. The Syntax of Existential Dialectics I:
The Principles
(Part XXVII)**

• **In Relation to Agency** *(cont'd)*
—*The Selfness-Otherness Principle*
(On the Magnitude of Self-Centeredness)
  • If there is the tendency to be mostly centered on one's self or group, there is likewise the tendency to be mostly centered on others, especially (though not exclusively) for any agent with some kind of intelligence life, be it about humans, animals, or, later, post-humans. There is no selfness without otherness—and vice versa.
  • Being self-centered and being other-centered do not have to be mutually exclusive, as the two can come in all shapes and sizes, or in different degrees. And other-centeredness does not entail desirability, any more than self-centeredness implies non-desirability, as both can go either way.
  • In addition, whether self-centeredness constitutes a moral alternative or, conversely, an alternative to morality is of course debatable (as addressed in my other book titled *Beyond Ethics to Post-Ethics*).
  • Good examples of family resemblance in relation to the principle are egoisticness-altruisticness, selfishness-unselfishness, selfness-selflessness, egocentricness-othercentricness, parasiticalness-helpfulness, take-give, and so on.
  • Source: First from *FPHCA*

(continued on next page)

Table 4.4. The Syntax of Existential Dialectics I:
The Principles
(Part XXVIII)

• **In Relation to Outcome**
—*The Regression-Progression Principle*
(On the Direction of History)
• Neither the cyclical nor the linear views are adequate for explaining many phenomena at all levels. There is regression without progression—and vice versa.
• History progresses to more advanced forms, but with a regressive touch. Examples include no freedom without unfreedom, no equality without inequality, and no civilization without barbarity.
• This is not an inevitable law, but merely a highly likely empirical trend.
• Family resemblance: e.g., cost-benefit, undesirability-desirability, badness-goodness, risk-opportunity, dysfunctionality-functionality, cyclicity-linearity, failure-success, setback-progress, reversal-linearity, etc.
• Sources: From all my books, starting with *FHC*. First named in *BCPC*.

—*The Same-Difference Principle*
(On the Metamorphosis of Change)
• An entity, as it evolves over time, can be both different from and similar to its opposing alternatives and does not have to be solely more different from them over time. There is no similarity without difference—and vice versa.
• Opposites are not absolute in a black-or-white fashion; so, an entity can become relatively more similar to (or more different from) its opposite over time.
• Family resemblance: e.g., homogeneity-heterogeneity, we-they, similarity-contrast, assimilation-dissimilation, etc.
• Sources: Especially from ALD. See also my later books

(continued on next page)

Table 4.4. The Syntax of Existential Dialectics I:
The Principles
(Part XXIX)

- **In Relation to Outcome** *(cont'd)*
  —*The Stability-Reaction Principle*
  (On the Feedback Mechanism for Further Changes)
  - Once an outcome becomes stabilized over time (which varies from case to case), there is resistance to it, such that it undergoes further changes in its multifaceted interactions with the outside world (e.g., with other entities, energy, space, and so on).
  - There is no stability without reaction (to stability for further changes)—and vice versa.
  - Family resemblance: e.g., stability-forwardness, balance-reaction, balance-forwardness, rest-motion, normalcy-feedback, stability-breakup, consolidation-modification, etc.
  - Sources: First from *FPHCHEM.*

(*continued on next page*)

**Table 4.4. The Syntax of Existential Dialectics I:
The Principles
(Part XXX)**

• **In Relation to Outcome** *(cont'd)*
—*The Functionality-Nonfunctionality Principle
(On the Presence of Function)*
  • If there is the presence of action for which something or someone is fitted, there is likewise the relative lack of action for which something or someone is fitted. There is no functionality without nonfunctionallity—and vice versa.
  • A *function* should not be confused with an *alternative function*, which is just another kind of function; just as *nonfunction* should not be confused with *dysfunction* (which has more to do with malfunction and is thus related more to the regression-progression principle).
  • In addition, being functional (or useful) and being nonfunctional (or useless) do not have to be mutually exclusive, as the two can come in all shapes and sizes, or in different degrees. And what is functional at one time may become nonfunctional at another time, and vice-versa.
  • Good examples of family resemblance in relation to the principle are usefulness-nonusefulness, usefulness-uselessness, valueness-nonvalueness, and the like.
  • Source: First from *FPHCA*

(*continued on next page*)

Table 4.4. The Syntax of Existential Dialectics I:
The Principles
(Part XXXI)

• **In Relation to Outcome** *(cont'd)*
—*The Intentionality-Nonintentionality Principle*
(On the Planning for Outcomes)
 • If there is the planning or design of something for a certain outcome, there is likewise the relative absence of planning or design of something for a certain outcome. There is no intentionality without nonintentionallity—and vice versa.
 • An intention for an outcome does not have to be certain, so the outcome can even be counter-intentional in being the opposite of what was originally planned. In this sense, counter-intentionality is a special case of non-intentionality; in other words, there are unintended consequences which can be just the opposite of what was originally planned.
 • An intention for an outcome is mostly relevant to intelligent life, but there are non-intelligent life and non-living matter in the universe too, so nonintentionality is also important.
 • In addition, an intention does not have to be obvious or straightforward, as William Shakspeare once famously said: "I must be cruel only to be kind."
 • Especially, works on unintended consequences (like *FPHAERO*) have contributed to the understanding of nonintentionality.
 • Good examples of family resemblance in relation to the principle are purposiveness-nonpurposiveness, intention-accidentalness, design-randomness, awareness-unawareness, etc.
 • Source: First from *FPHW*

(continued on next page)

Table 4.4. The Syntax of Existential Dialectics I:
The Principles
(Part XXXII)

• **In Relation to Outcome** *(cont'd)*
—*The Survivability-Nonsurvivability Principle*
  (On the Survival of things)
  • If there are some entities which survive at certain times, there are
    likewise other entities which do not survive. There is no
    survivability without nonsurvivability—and vice versa. In nature,
    for illustration, there are some animals which survive in hard times,
    whereas others do not—and this is true, not just among different
    species but also among different members of the same species (and
    the phenomenon of "selection" in evolutionary biology has much to
    say on this, as already addressed in *BNN*).
  • Of course, the principle is not restricted solely to the animal world,
    since it can be used to other cases concerning non-animals too (e.g.,
    trees, lakes, etc. in the natural world—or empires, companies, etc. in
    the human world).
  • But one should not confuse this principle with the expansion-
    contraction principle, since those entities which survive, say, can
    still expand or contract over time (e.g., those animals which survive
    can be more capable in some activities but not in others, for
    instance).
  • Nor should this principle be confused with the stability-reaction
    principle, in that the condition of both survivability and non-
    survivability may lead to further changes later on (as shown in the
    emergence of new species after the extinction of some old ones, as
    already explained in *BNR*).
  • Good examples of family resemblance in relation to the principle are
    survival-extinction, life-death, existence-nonexistence, and the like.
  • Source: First from *FPHPROB*

(*continued on next page*)

Table 4.4. The Syntax of Existential Dialectics I:
The Principles
(Part XXXIII)

• **In Relation to Outcome** *(cont'd)*
  —*The Materiality-Nonmateriality Principle*
  (On the Impact of Spirituality)
  • If there are material entities which evolve over time, there are likewise nonmaterial entities which become developed over time. There is no materiality without nonmateriality—and vice versa.
  • Entities do not have to be of material existence only (e.g., space-time, matter-energy, Having, etc.), as there are also non-material ones (e.g., Being, Belonging, etc.).
  • Non-material entities need not be narrowly understood in religious terms only (e.g., faith, praying, etc.), as there are non-religious spiritual types too (e.g., fasting, meditation, communality, etc.).
  —Non-material entities do not have to be misleadingly trapped within the now debunked old-fashioned analytical framework of teleology (as they are constrained by the predictability-unpredictability principle, the functionality-nonfunctionality principle, and so on).
  —Non-material entities can become more developed in outcome over time, but they can be both desirable and undesirable (as constrained by the regression-progression principle, for instance).
  • Non-material entities do not just stay constant but undergo changes over time (as constrained by the change-constancy principle, the stability-reaction principle, and so on).
  • Non-material entities can take different forms and contents over time (as constrained by the same-difference principle, for instance), and good examples are the visions in relation to the mind, nature, culture, and society (as proposed in my previous books aforecited).
  • Good examples of family resemblance in relation to the principle are materiality-mentality, physicality-suprasensibility, materiality-spirituality, mundaneness-sacredness, etc.
  • Source: First from *FPHETIO*

Notes: The examples here are solely illustrative (not exhaustive). The comparison is also relative (not absolute), nor are they mutually exclusive. As generalities, they allow exceptions.

Table 4.5. The Syntax of Existential Dialectics II:
The Principles as Short Cuts
(Part I)

• The principles should be treated with caution, lest misunderstanding occurs, since they do not constitute rigid dualities (or dichotomies).

• The reason is that each pair in an ontological principle consists of two opposites, which are, however, merely short cuts both for multiple variations and degrees, as well as for different interactions with multiple other entities unlike them. In this light, each pair can end up having hundred (or even thousand, if not more) different versions, which interact with hundred (or even thousand, if not more) other entities. There are two clarifications here.

• Firstly, this conception of shortcuts is not mutually exclusive nor absolute, in that the opposites can come in all shapes and sizes, with different degrees. For instance, by analogy, just as there are different degrees of the two colors "white" and "black"—there are likewise different degrees of the opposites in each ontological pair, to the extent that there can be multiple entities (not only two) interacting with each other in each pair.

• And secondly, this conception of shortcuts do not ignore other possible entities in interacting with the two opposites (with their different versions) in each pair. For instance, by analogy, there are not only the two colors "white" and "black" as opposites, since there are other colors too besides them like "yellow," "green," "purple," or else. The same logic can be applied to each ontological pair, in that they also interact with other entities, not with only two of them (with their different versions).

• Therefore, with these two clarifications in mind—each pair in an ontological principle serves only as an abbreviation for something more complicated and, therefore, although it contains two opposites, it should not be confused as a duality (dualism).

(continued on next page)

Table 4.5. The Syntax of Existential Dialectics II:
The Principles as Short Cuts
(Part II)

• Existential dialectics rejects any dualism (or dichotomy) as too rigid and instead allows the multiplicity of entities, to the extent that between the two opposites in each pair exist many other alternatives to choose from. They are named in that short form for aesthetic elegance, instead of listing all possible entities between the two opposites in the title.

• To be dialectic is to go beyond any rigid dichotomy and transcend into something different altogether in the long haul. One may be tempted to call the dialectic logic here with a different name like existential "multilectics" (instead of "dialectics"), but this naming is incorrect (or even misleading), for the two reasons aforestated.

• After all, each ontological pair come in all shapes and sizes (with different degrees) and do not exist by themselves but also interact with other entities unlike them. The virtue of revealing an ontological pair is to show how they relate within themselves (in multiple versions) and also interact with others unlike them (also in multiple versions).

• This will be clear in the table on "the dialectic constraints imposed by the principles."

Source: From Ch.1 of *FPHK*

The Future of Post-Human Etiology

Table 4.6. The Syntax of Existential Dialectics III:
The Principles as Family Resemblances

• Each ontological principle is generic, with some other comparable ontological pairs to be put in the same family (like a *family resemblance*). Ludwig Wittgenstein (1953) once suggested the idea of "family resemblance" in explaining different games classified under the same family called *games.*

• Why should, for instance, playing football and chess as playing "games," when it is well understood that football is not the same as chess? The answer is that, although each game is different and has different rules, many of them (though not all) share, more or less, some commonalites (e.g., scoring as necessary for winning).

• And this is so, even though some games share more than some others in any given selection of critieria, and no two games are exactly identical. So, his point here is that there is no essential core which is common to all games, and the best that one can look for is some characteristics which are common to many (but not all) games. (A. Biletzki 2006)

• By the same logic—in the previous section on selection criteria, the flexibility-inflexibility pair can be put in the family resemblance of the simpleness-complicatedness principle, although the two pairs are not exactly identical. Likewise, the directness-indirectness pair can be put in the family resemblance of the preciseness-vagueness principle, although, again, the two pairs are not exactly identical.

• In this sense, which specific pair in a family should be used to designate the name of the family can be at times a bit arbitrary, but with good reason.

• For illustration, in the context of method, the partiality-totality principle can take the different form like individualisticness-holisticness, just as the explicability-inexplicability principle can take the different form like underlyingness-regularness—although each two pairs are not exactly identical and have slightly different meanings and usages. A more comprehensive listing of this family resemblance for all other principles is shown in the table on the syntax of existential dialectics.

Source: From Ch.1 of *FPHK*

**Table 4.7. The Syntax of Existential Dialectics IV:
The Dialectic Constraints Imposed by the Principles
(Part I)**

• **Co-Existent and Asymmetric**
—The principles, as they constitute the syntax of existential dialectics, are dialectic in character, such that, when they are applied, they impose dialectic constraints on how reality is to be understood. Consider, say, the symmetry-asymmetry principle as an illustration here, in order to summarize two main characters of the dialectic constraints in question.
—Firstly, to be dialectic here is to go beyond the narrow dichotomies (and, for that matter, any rigid multi-dimensional classificatory scheme), be they about "self" vs. "world," "freedom" vs. "unfreedom," "barbarity" vs. "civilization," "individuality" vs. "communality," and so on.
—One way to do so (to go beyond) is to consider them all in terms of co-existence (without favoring one over the rest). For instance, my theory of "post-civilization" (to be summarized later in the section on the pragmatics of existential dialectics) is to go beyond barbarity and civilization in terms of understanding barbarity and civilization as being co-existent. And the same logic can be said in relation to my theories of "post-democracy," "post-capitalsm," and others (also to be introduced later in the section on the pragmatics of existential dialectics), in regard to freedom vs. unfreedom, equality vs. inequality, communality vs. individuality, spirituality vs. materiality, and so on.
—But to consider them all (in the dichotomies—and, for that matter, in any rigid multi-dimensional classifactory schme) as co-existent is not the same as to imply that the opposites in any classificatory scheme are all equal, since, in accordance to the symmetry-asymmetry principle (as an illustration here), if they are equal in terms of being considered as co-existent, they are asymmetric in terms of being unequal in dialectic interaction (e.g., X can be more dominant than Y in case A, or Y is more dominant than X in case B).

(continued on next page)

Table 4.7. The Syntax of Existential Dialectics IV:
The Dialectic Constraints Imposed by the Principles
(Part II)

—For this reason, there are different versions of "post-democracy" and "post-capitalism" in my theories. As an illustration, in version I of the theory of post-democracy, freedom is more dominant than equality, whereas in version II of the theory of post-democracy, equality is more so than freedom.

—But this "X more than Y" has to be understood in the context of dialectic logic (not in conventional logic), in that both "X" and "Y" are important in post-democracy (in the context of dialectic logic), but in an asymmetry way. By contrast, in conventional logic, it often favors one over the other—be it in regard to privileging freedom over equality in Fascism, favoring freedom relatively more than equality in Liberal Democracy, or favoring equality relatively more than freedom in Socialist Democracy. In the latter two cases (about Liberal Democracy and Socialist Democracy), the difference between dialectic logic and conventional logic can be one in degree, not in kind—in this sense, albeit not in other senses.

—The same logic can be said about the relatonships between individuality and communality, between spirituality and materiality, and between formal legalism and informal legalism in the different versions of my theory of post-capitalism.

• **Transcendent**
—Secondly, to be dialectic is to go beyond the narrow dichotomies (and, for that matter, any rigid multi-dimensional classificatory scheme) in another way, this time, in a transcendent way, that is, in exploring other possibilities or even other issues not considered within the narrow confines of narrow dichotomies (and, for that matter, any rigid multi-dimensional classificatory scheme).

(continued on next page)

Table 4.7. The Syntax of Existential Dialectics IV:
The Dialectic Constraints Imposed by the Principles
(Part III)

—As an analogy, to go beyond the narrow color dichotomy of "black" and "white" is not just to choose both "black" and "white" (as in the first meaning) but also to explore other color options (e.g., "green," "purple," "blue," etc.—and, alternatively, "shade," "line," "curve," etc.). By the same logic, to go beyond "democracy" is to transcend democracy (as in version III of the theory of "post-democracy") and to explore other possibilties of lifeforms (e.g., floating consciousness, hyper-spatial consciousness, etc., to live beyond the narrow obsession with freedom and equality).

—This dialectic character of the principles in existential dialectics has important implications for the pragmatics of existential dialectics (as will be clear shortly, in the section on the pragmatics of existential dialectics).

Notes: The examples here are solely illustrative (not exhaustive). The comparison is also relative (not absolute), nor are they mutually exclusive. As generalities, they allow exceptions.

Sources: First explicitly stated in *ALD*. Also from all other books of mine.

**Table 4.8. The Syntax of Existential Dialectics V:
Further Clarifications
(Part I)**

• **Pioneering**
—Firstly, the total number of ontological principles is unknown, to be discovered later, as our knowledge of the world becomes more advanced.
—Consequently, the principles as introduced in my books are not exhaustive, with new ones being added, whenever more of them are discovered in later research.
—At least, future generations can pick up where I leave off and continue the discovery.
—In this sense, my work should be treated as a pioneering effort for the development of a systematic, comprehensive analysis of a new general ontology for the future of knowledge.

• **Flexible**
—Secondly, the principles are not rigidly classified, as they can be reclassified in a different way.
—For instance, the preciseness-vagueness principle is classified under the category of "structure" but can be reclassified under the category of "method," although in so doing, it has a different meaning in the context of method.
—The same logic applies to the same-difference principle under the category of "outcome," which can be reclassified under the category of "structure," although in so doing, once more, it has a different meaning in the context of structure.

• **Mutually Constraining**
—Thirdly, the principles are to be understood together, not that each prinicple is to be analyzed independently of others. After all, the principles are mutually constraining, in that they work together as a whole.

(continued on next page)

Table 4.8. The Syntax of Existential Dialectics V:
Further Clarifications
(Part II)

• **Selectively Useful**
—Fourthly, the principles are relevant to all subject matters, but some principles are more useful to some subject matters than others—as implied in the symmetry-asymmetry principle. This is true, even if different studies of the same kind can yield different views about the degree of relevance for each ontological principle, depending on the specific nature of a research in question, needless to say.

• **Anti-Reductionistic**
—And fifthly, the principles constitute only two levels of analysis, this time, at the ontological and methodological levels—while other levels of analysis (from the perspectives of the mind, nature, society, and culture) are also needed, in order to understand reality in its totality (as explained in the section on "sophisticated methodological holism," so as to avoid the dual dangers of reductionism and reverse-reductionism).

Notes: The examples here are solely illustrative (not exhaustive). The comparison is also relative (not absolute), nor are they mutually exclusive. As generalities, they allow exceptions.
Sources: From my previous books like *FHC, FCD, FPHC, BDPD, BCPC, BNN, FC, FAE*, and so on.

Table 4.9. The Syntax of Existential Dialectics VI:
The Dilemma of Specific vs. General Ontology
(Part I)

• Ontology is often more complicated and imposes some seemingly insurmountable difficulties concerning what constitutes a kind of ontology which can be valid enough to be accepted by the wider intellectual community in question. An excellent example concerns what I want to call *the dilemma of ontology* in relation to the relationship between "specific ontology" and "general ontology." (M. Bunge 1999; R. Corazzon 2007)

• On the one hand, "general ontology," as Mario Bunge (1999) put it, "studies all existents." But, on the other hand, "special ontology studies one genus of thing or process—physical, chemical, biological, social, etc." (M. Bunge 1999; R. Corazzon 2007)

• Consequently, the relationship between the former and the latter is that, as an illustration, "whereas general ontology studies the concepts of space, time, and event, the ontology of the social investigates such general sociological concepts as those of social system, social structure, and social change." (M. Bunge 1999; R. Corazzon 2007)

• With this formal definition in mind, the relationship between the two forms of ontology only poses *the dilemma of ontology*, in that general ontology is possible to the extent that its general contructs must be broad enough to serve as the "lowest common denominator" for all disciplines, but this character of the lowest common denominator is not only hard to find but also its usefulness is limited. (WK 2008b)

• But specific ontology fares no better either, in that its specific constructs primarily serve a specific discipline in question, although other disciplines can appropriate them for their own purposes, but in a different context (especially, though not exclusively, when used as a metaphor from one field to another). For instance, the Kantian category of understanding under the heading of "quantity" constitutes a type of specific ontology, which is specific to the discipline of mathematics, although other disciplines can make use of the categories in their own context.

(continued on next page)

Table 4.9. The Syntax of Existential Dialectics VI:
The Dilemma of Specific vs. General Ontology
(Part II)

• A solution lies in my proposal of "sophisticated methodological holism," which requires all levels of analysis in any subject matter. See the tables on sophisticated methodological holism, and on reductionism and reverse-reductionism, for more details.

Source: From *Sec. 1.4* of *FPHK*

Table 4.10. The Syntax of Existential Dialectics VII:
Types of Inappropriate Family Resemblances
(Part I)

• **Inadequate Family Resemblances**
—Ex: consistency-inconsistency: the formalness-informalenss principle
—Ex: cognition-noncognition: the formalness-informalness principle

• **Compound Family Resemblances**
—Ex: reality-nonreality: the formalness-informalness principles, the absoluteness-relativeness principle
—Ex: normality-abnormality: the symmetry-asymmetry principle, the density-emptiness principle, the convention-novelty principle, the same-difference principle
—Ex: structure-context: the simpleness-complicatedness principle, the theory-praxis principle
—Ex: freedom-unfreedom: the expansion-contraction principle
—Ex: morality-immorality: the denseness-emptiness principle, the symmetry-asymmetry, the same-difference principle
—Ex: particularness-universalness: the preciseness-vagueness principle, the simpleness-complicatedness principle
—Ex: pureness-mixedness: the absoluteness-relativeness principle, the simpleness-complicatedness principle, the same-difference principle
—Ex: shortsightedness-foresightedness: the partiality-totality principle, the simpleness-complicatedness principle
—Ex: shorttermness-longtermness: the partiality-totality principle, the simpleness-complicatedness principle, the slowness-quickness principle
—Ex: smoothness-roughness: the softness-hardness principle, the symmetry-asymmetry principle
—Ex: warmth-coldness: the finiteness-transfiniteness principle, the softness-hardness principle.

• **One-Sided Family Resemblances**
—Ex: sound-silence: asymmetry (in the symmetry-asymmetry principle)
—Ex: vision-blindness: asymmetry (in the symmetry-asymmetry principle)

(continued on next page)

Table 4.10. The Syntax of Existential Dialectics VII:
Types of Inappropriate Family Resemblances
(Part II)

• **Vague Family Resemblances**
—Ex: shortness-longness, narrowness-broadness, smallness-largeness, smallness-greatness, microness-macroness, and littleness-muchness: three different possibilities, namely, (a) finiteness (in the finiteness-transfiniteness principle), if both opposites are defined on a finite scale, (b) transfiniteness (in the finiteness-transfiniteness principle) if both opposites are defined on a transfinite scale, and (c) the finiteness-transfiniteness principle if one opposite is defined on a finite scale and the other opposite is defined on a transfinite scale.

• **One-Sided and Compound Family Resemblances**
—Ex: extroversion-introversion: one-sided, as part of the side (category) of "normality" in the normality-abnormality pair. And compounded, because the normality-abnormality pair is in turn related to the symmetry-asymmetry principle, the density-emptiness principle, the convention-novelty principle, the same-difference principle
—Ex: organizedness-spontaneousness: one-sided, as part of the side (category) of "normality" in the normality-abnormality pair. And compounded, because the normality-abnormality pair is in turn related to the symmetry-asymmetry principle, the density-emptiness principle, the convention-novelty principle, the same-difference principle
—Ex: risk-caution: one-sided, as part of the side (category) of "normality" in the normality-abnormality pair. And compounded, because the normality-abnormality pair is in turn related to the symmetry-asymmetry principle, the density-emptiness principle, the convention-novelty principle, the same-difference principle

Notes: The examples here are solely illustrative (not exhaustive). The comparison is also relative (not absolute), nor are they mutually exclusive. As generalities, they allow exceptions.
Source: First summarized in *BEPE* (and updated in later books)

Table 4.11. The Semantics of Existential Dialectics
(Part I)

• **Abstract Structure vs. Specific Meanings**
—The syntax of existential dialectics so understood in terms of
ontological principles only gives us the structure of ontology in the
world, in an abstract (general) sense. These principles by themselves
do not tell us the specific meanings in a given context.
—In order to grasp the specific meanings of the principles in a given
context, it is necessary to study the semantics of existential dialectics.
And the analysis of the ontological principles as family resemblances
in the section on syntax is only a starting point (and thus overlaps a bit
with the semantics of existential dialectics here).
—With this caveat in mind, the reason that I have often gone in great
lengths in my previous books on different subjects is to explain the
specific meanings of the principles when applied in different contexts.

• **Specific Meanings in Specific Fields**
—For instance, in *FPHST*, I used the first three principles (i.e., the
change-constancy principle, the regression-progression principle, and
the symmetry-asymmetry principle) to propose "the perspectival
theory of space-time," for a better way to understand space and
time—especially, though not exclusively, in relation to future post-
human history (as summarized in *Table 3.6*, *Table 3.7*, *Table 3.8*, and
Table 3.9). In so doing, I had to introduce concepts and theories
specific to the field of physics and other related fields (e.g., "absolute
space" and "absolute time" in "classical mechanics" and "relative
space-time" in "the theory of relativity").
—In *BNN*, I also exploited the three principles to propose the
"transcendent" approach to the study of genes and memes as a new
way to understand the interaction between nature and nurture. In so
doing, I had to explore concepts and theories in the world of
evolutionary theory (e.g., "mutation," "variation," "adaptation,"
"selection," and "inheritance" in Darwinian evolutionary theory) and
neural biology (e.g., "chromosome," "gene," "DNA," "RNA,"
"protein," "neuron," "neural network," and "behavior").

(continued on next page)

Table 4.11. The Semantics of Existential Dialectics
(Part II)

- **Two Types of Translation (Interpretation)**
  —In the technical jargons of semantics, these exercises in my books perform two essential functions of translation (or interpretation), namely, (a) "intensive" interpretation (about the properties or relations of the principles in existential dialectics), and (b) "extensive" interpretation (about the classes or cases to which the properties and relations of the principles in existential dialectics are applied). (WK 2011oo)

- **Limits of Translation (Interpretation)**
  —But there are limits of translation (or interpretation), and an excellent example is that "there is a problem with the 'objectivity' of translation, as it is relative to different cultural (or sub-cultural) contexts. For instance, one of the still unresolved problems in linguistics is: 'Is there an objective gauge for the quality of translation?'" (*FPHCOM* & WK 2011pp)
  —This is one serious problem about the logic of translation and interpretation that I already addressed in *Sec. 3.5.1* of *FPHCOM* (and also, for that matter, in *FHC*, in the context of hermeneutics).

Notes: The categories and examples in each are solely illustrative (not exhaustive). The comparison is also relative (not absolute), nor are they mutually exclusive. As generalities, they allow exceptions.
Sources: First explicitly stated in *ALD* (and later revised in *FPHCOM*). Also from all other books of mine.

Table 4.12. The Pragmatics of Existential Dialectics
(Part I)

• **The Two-Way Street Connecting Theory and Meta-Theory**
—The pragmatics of existential dialectics is not a one-way street (that is, using the ontological principles for theoretical insights in praxis) but a two-way one, that is, (a) from meta-theory to theory, and (b) from theory to meta-theory.
—(a) On one side of the street, the ontological principles can inspire some theoretical insights in praxis, that is, in relation to some specific fields.
—(b) On the other (opposing) side of the street, however, the study of a subject matter in the specific fields in turn reveals some more hitherto unknown ontological principles to be discovered and identified. For this reason, three new principles were added in *FC*, one in *FAE*, and two in *ALD*, on top of the original three in *BCPC*—after some research on the specific subject matters.

• **Direct and Indirect Applications**
—*Direct*
  • The logic of existential dialectics can shed some theoretical insights on diverse phenomena in the world, and good instances are the pertinent use of the principles of existential dialectics for the theoretical insights on the freedom/unfreedom dialectics, the equality/inequality dialectics, and the wealth/poverty dialectics in my previous works.
  • My latest books like *FPHST* and *BNN* also use the principles to reveal some theoretical insights on the perspectives of space and time (as in *FPHST*) and of nature and nurture (as in *BNN*).
—*Indirect*
  • The theoretical insights can further be used to reveal other phenomena directly from them (viz., the theoretical insights) and therefore indirectly from the principles themselves. A good instance is the use of the theoretical insights on the freedom/unfreedom and equality/inequality dialectics for the understanding of the civilization/barbarity dialectics.

(continued on next page)

**Table 4.12. The Pragmatics of Existential Dialectics
(Part II)**

• **Direct and Indirect Applications (*cont'd*)**
  • Even in indirect applications, however, a phenomenon under study can still be directly related back to the principles themselves. In the example as cited above, the civilization/barbarity dialectics can be directly related to the principles of existential dialectics without the intermediate role of the freedom/unfreedom and equality/inequality dialectics.

• **Multiple Levels of Application**
  —The theoretical insights can be applied to different levels of analysis, even though in a given example, it may refer to one level only. For instance, in the example concerning the freedom/unfreedom dialectics, it can be used at the structural level (e.g., in relation to the theory of cyclical progression of hegemony), but it can be exploited as well for other levels (e.g., the theory of post-capitalism at the institutional level).

Notes: The categories and examples in each are solely illustrative (not exhaustive). The comparison is also relative (not absolute), nor are they mutually exclusive. As generalities, they allow exceptions.
Sources: From Ch.6 of *BCPC*. See also other books of mine.

Table 4.13. The Freedom-Unfreedom Dialectics
(Part I)

• **On Having**
—*In Relation to the Technological*
(1) if freer from submission to Nature, then less free from ecological degradation (Deep and Social Ecology), even if in a hi-tech form
(2) if freer from technological inconvenience / backwardness, then less free from technological control and the loss of privacy
(3) if freer from technological (material) backwardness, then less free from the abusive (barbaric) maltreatment of the primitive Others
—*In Relation to the Everyday*
(1) if freer from abject poverty, then less free from artificial needs/discontents (Frankfurt School)
(2) if freer from sensual suppression, then less free from violent sublimation (Freud)
(3) if freer from the snobbishness of high culture, then less free from the shabbiness (leveling-off effect) of mass culture (Tocqueville)
(4) if freer from the inefficiency of traditional "compassionate economy," then less free from the bondage of a "ruthless [competitive] economy" (Keynes)
(5) if freer from anarchy in the state of nature (system fragmentation), then less free from government regulations and controls in system integration

(continued on next page)

Table 4.13. The Freedom-Unfreedom Dialectics
(Part II)

• **On Belonging**
—*In Relation to the Good and the Just*
(1) if freer from disciplinary society, then less free from society of control (Foucault)
(2) if freer from the tyranny of one or a few, then less free from the tyranny of the majority (or sometimes, minority veto)
(3) if freer from elitist decision making, then less free from political gridlock/cleavage
(4) if freer from arbitrary (discretionary) administration, then less free from bureaucratic irrationality (Weber) and legal trickery (loopholes)

• **On Being**
—*In Relation to the True*
(1) if freer from unscientific dogmas, then less free from instrumental abyss (nihilism). Or conversely, if freer from meaninglessness, then less free from dogmas.
(2) if freer from the bondage of partiality/partisanship (e.g., prejudice, discrimination), then less free from the danger of impartiality and neutrality (e.g., opportunism, unrealisticness, lack of compassion, inaction)
(3) if freer from making generalizations, then less free from being unable to understand much of anything
—*In Relation to the Holy*
(1) if freer from collective conscience, then less free from social loneliness
(2) if freer from religious absoluteness, then less free from spiritual emptiness
—*In Relation to the Beautiful/Sublime*
(1) if freer from artistic non-autonomy, then less free from aesthetic disillusion (deconstruction)

(continued on next page)

Table 4.13. The Freedom-Unfreedom Dialectics
(Part III)

Notes: The examples in each category are solely illustrative (not exhaustive), and the comparison is relative (not absolute), nor are they necessarily mutually exclusive. And some can be easily re-classified elsewhere. As generalities, they allow exceptions.

Sources: A reconstruction from Ch.10 of *FCD*, based on *FHC*

Table 4.14. The Equality-Inequality Dialectics
(Part I)

• On Having
—*In Relation to the Technological*
(1) if more equal in treating Nature with spiritual unity, then less equal in suppressing the dominant drive to transcend it altogether
—*In Relation to the Everyday*
(1) if more equal in building social plurality, then less equal in leveling-off effects (e.g., the subsequent relative intolerance of high/intellectual ethos in mass culture industry)
(2) if more equal in socioeconomic distribution beyond a certain point, then less equal in efficiency (e.g. resentment, the erosion of work ethics)
(3) if more equal in urging an affirmative action program, then less equal in creating victim mentality (in oneself), stigma (from others), reverse discrimination (against the once privileged), and mediocracy (against the more able)

• On Belonging
—*In Relation to the Good and the Just*
(1) if more equal in banning monarchic/oligarchic exclusion, then less equal in producing "the tyranny of the majority" or of "minority veto"
(2) if more equal in encouraging participatory decision making, then less equal in inducing political divisiveness (gridlock/cleavage in power blocs) and organizational oligarchy
(3) if more equal in institutionalizing a decentralized bureaucracy, then less equal in falling into more territorial/turf politics (intrigues)

(continued on next page)

Table 4.14. The Equality-Inequality Dialectics
(Part II)

• **On Being**
  —In Relation to the Beautiful / Sublime
  (1) if more equal in accepting diverse styles ("anything goes" mentality), then less equal in artistic good quality (in leveling-off effects against the best)
  —In Relation to the True
  (1) if more equal in tolerating multiple viewpoints (no matter how extreme), then less equal in epistemic standards
  —In Relation to the Holy
  (1) if more equal in celebrating any cults and sects (no matter how questionable), then less equal in spiritual depth and authenticity

Notes: The examples in each category are solely illustrative (not exhaustive), and the comparison is relative (not absolute), nor are they mutually exclusive. And some can be easily reclassified elsewhere. As generalities, they allow exceptions.

Sources: A reconstruction from Ch.10 of *FCD*, based on *FHC*

Table 4.15. The Duality of Oppression in Existential Dialectics:
Oppression and Self-Oppression
(Part I)

• **From the Same to the Others and Itself**
—The Oppression by the Same against the Others
  • *By way of downgrading differences*
    –Ex: on judiciary caprice for corporate crimes (*Sec.2.2.1.2.1*)
    –Ex: on the deceptive politics of liberation (*Sec.3.5*)
    –Ex: on the humanitarian mystique (*Sec.4.4*)
    –Ex: on the fad of emotional intelligence (*Sec.5.3*)
  • *By way of accentuating differences*
    –Ex: on the legal sophistry of self-defense (*Sec.2.3*)
    –Ex: on the legal semantics of proportionality (*Sec.2.4*)
    –Ex: on the tricky politics of external threat (*Sec.3.4*)
    –Ex: on the appeal of the Far Right for democracy (*Sec.5.4*)
    –Ex: on the democratic axis of evil (*Sec.5.5*)
    –Ex: on the democratic way of brutality and revenge (*Sec.5.6*)
    –Ex: on democratic autocracy (*Sec.6.4*)
—The Oppression by the Same against Itself
  • *By way of downgrading differences*
    –Ex: on the politics of fear (*Sec.2.2*)
    –Ex: on the trickery of compassionate conservatism (*Sec.3.2*)
    –Ex: on the deceptive politics of patriotism (*Sec.3.3*)
  • *By way of accentuating differences*
    –Ex: on the caprice of due process on domestic suspects (*Sec.2.2*)
    –Ex: on the false security/freedom dilemma (*Sec.6.5.2*)

(continued on next page)

**Table 4.15. The Duality of Oppression in Existential Dialectics:
Oppression and Self-Oppression
(Part II)**

• **From the Others to the Same and Themselves**
—The Oppression by the Others against the Same
  • *By way of downgrading differences*
    –Ex: on judiciary caprice in the reverse direction (*Sec.2.2.1.2.2*)
    –Ex: on equal pay (*Sec.6.2.1.1*)
    –Ex: on equal representation (*Sec.6.2.1.2*)
    –Ex: on affirmative action program (*Sec.6.3.1.1*)
    –Ex: on same-sex marriage (*Sec.6.3.1.2*)
  • *By way of accentuating differences*
    –Ex: on sexual harassment (*Sec.6.2.2.1*)
    –Ex: on physical violence (*Sec.6.2.2.2*)
    –Ex: on sexual exploitation (*Sec.6.2.2.3*)
—The Oppression by the Others against Themselves
  • *By way of downgrading differences*
    –Ex: on the reverse-class mystique (*Sec.4.2*)
    –Ex: on the reverse-black mystique (*Sec.4.3*)
    –Ex: on self-discrimination by downgrading (*Sec.6.3.2.2*)
  • *By way of accentuating differences*
    –Ex: on self-discrimination by accentuating (*Sec.6.3.2.1*)

Notes: The examples are solely illustrative (not exhaustive), nor are they mutually exclusive. As generalities, they allow exceptions. Also, both forms of oppression co-exist in all of the examples, so the listing of them are only meant in a relative, not absolute, sense.
Source: A summary of the sections (as cited) in Chs.2-6 of *BDPD*. See text for more info and references.

Table 4.16. The Structure of Existential Dialectics I:
The Freedom/Unfreedom and Equality/Inequality Dialectics

• Each freedom and equality produces its own unfreedom and inequality, regardless of whether the pair occurs in political society (with the nation-state), in civil society (with some autonomy from the state), or elsewhere (e.g., in the private sphere of individual homes)—and regardless of whether freedom and equality are understood as "negative" or "positive."

• Oppression is dualistic, as much by the Same against the Others and itself, as by the Others against the Same and themselves.

• Both forms of oppression and self-oppression can be achieved by way of downgrading differences (between the Same and the Others) and of accentuating them.

• The relationships are relatively asymmetric between the Same and the Others and relatively symmetric within them. This is true, even when the Same can be relatively asymmetric towards itself in self-oppression, just as the Others can be likewise towards themselves.

• Symmetry and asymmetry change over time, with ever new players, new causes, and new forms.

Notes: The examples in each category are solely illustrative (not exhaustive) nor necessarily mutually exclusive, and the comparison is relative (not absolute). As generalities, they allow exceptions. "Negative" freedom is freedom "from" (e.g., freedom from poverty), whereas "positive" freedom is freedom "to" (e.g., freedom to the state of enlightenment). "Negative" equality is "procedural" equality (e.g., equality of opportunity), while "positive" equality is "substantive" equality (e.g., equality of outcome). Existential dialectics impose constraints on freedom and equality in democracy, non-democracy, and post-democracy. There is no utopia, in the end; even should there be one, dystopia would exist within it.
Sources: From *Table 1.5* of *BDPD*—and also from *FHC*, *FCD*, and *FPHC*

Table 4.17. The Structure of Existential Dialectics II:
The Wealth/Poverty Dialectics

• There is no wealth without poverty, just as there is no poverty without wealth.

• The wealth/poverty dialectics occurs in the realms of having, belonging, and being, in relation to the material, relational, and spiritual.

• The wealth/poverty dialectics also expresses itself at the multiple levels of analysis in accordance to methodological holism, be they about the micro-physical, the chemical, the biological, the psychological, the organizational, the institutional, the structural, the systemic, the cultural, and the cosmological.

• The wealth/poverty dialectics is a different manifestation of existential dialectics in general, subject to the principles in its logic of ontology—just as the freedom/unfreedom and equality/inequality dialectics are likewise.

• There is no economic utopia, in the end; even should there be one, dystopia would exist within it.

Notes: The main points here are solely illustrative (not exhaustive) nor necessarily mutually exclusive, and the comparison is relative (not absolute). As generalities, they allow exceptions.
Sources: From *BCPC*. See also *FCD* and *FHC*.

Table 4.18. The Structure of Existential Dialectics III:
The Civilization/Barbarity Dialectics

• There is no civilization without barbarity.

• The civilization/barbarity dialectics applies in the four civilizing processes (e.g., the rationalizing process, the pacifying process, the stewardizing process, and the subliming process).

• The civilization/barbarity dialectics is another (different) manifestation of existential dialectics in general, subject to the principles in its logic of ontology—just as the freedom/unfreedom and equality/inequality dialectics and the wealth/poverty dialectics are likewise.

• There is no utopia, in the end; even should there be one, dystopia would exist within it.

Notes: The main points here are solely illustrative (not exhaustive) nor necessarily mutually exclusive, and the comparison is relative (not absolute). As generalities, they allow exceptions.
Sources: From *BCIV*. See also *FCD*, *FHC*, and *BDPD*.

Table 4.19. The Double Sides of Virtual Organizations (Part I)

• **Psychological**
—Ex: virtual psychosis
—Ex: impersonality and loneliness in quaternary social relations

• **Organizational**
—Ex: the race for power and interests
—Ex: the world of unequal successes
—Ex: the bureaucratic life of its own
—Ex: lesser accountability and transparency

• **Economic**
—Ex: the economic divides
—Ex: the erosive impact of commercialization

• **Political**
—Ex: the anti-authoritarian myth
—Ex: different power struggles among groups (e.g., Conservative, Reformist, Radical)

• **Structural**
—Ex: different localities (e.g., climates, scenery)
—Ex: divided domains (e.g., core, peripheral, sub-peripheral)
—Ex: substitution effect of social capital

• **Systemic**
—Ex: uneven advances in transportation and communications, and geographical migration

• **Cultural**
—Ex: conflicting civilizational fabrics (e.g., Confucian, Islamic, Western)
—Ex: the bias of the Liberal Democratic agenda
—Ex: the addiction to moral fanaticism

(continued on next page)

Table 4.19. The Double Sides of Virtual Organizations
(Part II)

Notes: These categories and examples are solely illustrative (not exhaustive), and some of the items can be reclassified somewhere else. Nor are they mutually exclusive. Since they are generalities, exceptions are expected.

Source: From Ch.7 of *FCD*

**Table 4.20. Beyond the World of Titans,
and the Remaking of the World Order**

• **Hyper-Empires**
   —Ex: The Chinese Union
   —Ex: The Indian Union

• **Meso-Empires**
   —Ex: The European Union
   —Ex: The North American Union

• **Micro-Empires**
   —Ex: The Latin American Union
   —Ex: The Middle Eastern Union

• **The Rest of the World**
   —Odd Powers
      • Ex: Japan
      • Ex: Russia
   —The Poor Club
      • Ex: The African Union
   —Ambivalent Regions
      • Ex: Southeast Asia
      • Ex: Oceania
      • Ex: South Asia
      • Ex: Central Asia
      • Ex: Southern/Eastern Europe
      • Ex: North Africa
      • Ex: Central America
      • Ex: Others (e.g., the Korean peninsula)

Source: A summary of Chs.2-5 (of *BWT*)

Table 4.21. The Origins
of Authoritarian Liberal Democracy

• **The Geopower of Nature (Ch.4 of *ALD*)**
—Ex: Power Character and Geographical Strategy
—Ex: Living Space and Territorial Expansion
—Ex: Strategic Heartland and Containment

• **The Biopsychology of the Mind (Ch.5 of *ALD*)**
—Ex: The Bell Curve and Mass Intelligence
—Ex: Group Analysis and Mass Knowledge
—Ex: Groupthink and Elite (Mis)calculation

• **The Disciplinary Control of Society (Ch.6 of *ALD*)**
—Ex: Social Organizations of Ruthlessness
—Ex: Social Institutions of Greed
—Ex: Social Structure of Exclusion
—Ex: Social Systems of Violence

• **The Molding Force of Culture (Ch.7 of *ALD*)**
—Ex: The Tradition of Conquest
—Ex: The Rationalization of Unreason

Notes: The examples in each category are solely illustrative (not exhaustive), and they are also relative (not absolute), nor are they mutually exclusive. As generalities, they allow exceptions.
Source: A summary of Chs.4-7 of *ALD*

Table 4.22. The Theory of Post-Democracy I:
The Priority of Freedom over Equality
(Part I)

• **Differences**
  —*For the aggressive Lions (the strong Elitists)*
  •Setting up rank distinctions among unequals (e.g., between inferior
    humans and superior post-humans, or later among inferior post-
    humans and superior ones, relatively speaking)
  •Yearning for being not only distinguished from unequals, but also
    the first among equals (the best of the very best)
  •Soul-searching for a   high spiritual culture (not the trashy one
    for the masses). Mass culture is a dirty joke for them.
  —*For the manipulative Foxes (the weak Counter-Elitists)*
  •Seeking a gentle hegemony by way of more communitarian concerns
    (for inferior humans and, later, inferior post-humans)
  •Being more sympathetic to less formal-legalistic institutions and
    values

• **Similarities**
  —*For both Lions and Foxes*
  •Exploring different spheres of non-human consciousness in the
    cosmos (something vastly superior than the human one)
  •Recognizing the democratic illusions (e.g., no freedom without
    unfreedom, no equality without inequality, or simply no justice
    without injustice, and vice versa)

(continued on next page)

Table 4.22. The Theory of Post-Democracy I:
The Priority of Freedom over Equality
(Part II)

Notes: The two callings and examples in each category are solely illustrative (not exhaustive), since there will be many different post-human value ideals in the distant future of post-human civilization. The comparison is also relative (not absolute) towards post-democracy, so this is not just a version of free-market democracy (nor Fascism/Nazism, as shown in the table later on democracy, non-democracy, and post-democracy). Nor are they mutually exclusive. As generalities, they allow exceptions. And the specific forms of post-human post-democratic ideals need to be further developed in future after-postmodern history, as they will be different from the ones we now know. The point here is to solely give an extremely rough picture of a small part of the world to come that we have never known.

Source: From Ch.10 of *FCD*. Refer to text for more info and references.

Table 4.23. The Theory of Post-Democracy II: The Priority of Equality over Freedom

• **Hybrid Versions of**
—Ex: the Trans-Feminine Calling
—Ex: the Trans-Sinitic Calling
—Ex: the Trans-Islamic Calling
—Ex: the Trans-Outerspace Calling

• **Qualifications**
—These four versions of post-capitalist value ideals need not automatically be post-democratic, just as capitalism does not necessarily mean democracy. They are two different entities—though closely related.
—But up to a certain threshold of elevating equality at the farther expense of freedom, the democratic ideals will be overcome and cease to exist.
—The overcome will not be socialist or communist, but post-democratic with no freedom without unfreedom and no equality without inequality, subject to the constraints of existential dialectics.

Notes: The callings are solely illustrative (not exhaustive), since there will be many different post-human value ideals in the distant future of post-human lifeforms. The comparison is also relative (not absolute), nor are they mutually exclusive. As generalities, they allow exceptions. And the specific forms of post-human post-democratic ideals need to be further developed in future after-postmodern history, as they will be different from the ones we now know. The point here is to solely give an extremely rough picture of a small part of the world to come that we have never known.
Source: From Ch.10 of *FCD*. Refer to text for more info and references.

Table 4.24. The Theory of Post-Democracy III:
The Transcendence of Freedom and Equality
(Part I)

• **Transcending Freedom in Floating Existence**
—*Freedom*: seeking an ultimate elimination of the body. Being without the body. The aim is to transcend freedom in the end into a metaphysical state (i.e., beyond the physique).
—*Unfreedom*: yet facing difficult trade-offs. The sacrifice of bodily existence and its joyfulness. An eternal boredom in floating existence in dark deep space, though with alternative pleasures. There is no free lunch even in the state of transcending freedom.

• **Transcending Equality in the Rivalry of Cosmic Hegemony**
—*Inequality*: competing to outlast other lifeforms in floating existence, or just marginalizing them for one's hegemonic expansiveness in the rest of the cosmos (and even beyond). Universalism is only for the mediocre.
—*Equality*: accepting only those of one's rank as equal partners in the vast spacetime for cosmic supremacy. Even here, the aim is to transcend equality into a metaphysical state.

(continued on next page)

Table 4.24. The Theory of Post-Democracy III:
The Transcendence of Freedom and Equality
(Part II)

Notes: Do not confuse this transcendence of freedom and equality (as one version of post-democracy) with the naïve temptation to transcend the freedom/unfreedom and equality/inequality dialectics. Existential dialectics hold true for freedom and equality in all cultures and societies—past, present, or future (i.e., democracy, non-democracy, and post-democracy), regardless of whether freedom and equality are conventionally understood as "negative" or "positive."

Also, the two features and examples in each are solely illustrative (not exhaustive), since there will be many different post-human value ideals in the distant future of post-human lifeforms. The comparison is also relative (not absolute), nor are they mutually exclusive. As generalities, they allow exceptions. And the specific forms of post-human ideals even for these radically alien floating lifeforms (and others unknown to us) need to be further developed in future after-postmodern history, as they will likely be different from the ones herein illustrated. The point here is to solely give a very rough picture of a small part of the extremely alien world to come that we have never known.

Source: From Ch.10 of *FCD*. Refer to text for more info and references.

**Table 4.25. Democracy, Non-Democracy, and Post-Democracy
(Part I)**

• **Democracy**
—*Theoretical Constructs*
•The pursuit of freedom and equality (in various degrees), regardless of whether freedom and equality can be understood as "negative" or "positive"
    (1) more equality than freedom: The relative priority of the good over the right
    (2) more freedom than equality: The relative priority of the right over the good
—*Types*
•Only (1): Different versions of communitarian moral universalism
•Only (2): Different versions of liberal moral universalism
•(1) or (2): Different versions of anarchic (non-nation-state) moral universalism
•(1) or (2): Different versions of postmodern moral localism

• **Non-Democracy**
—*Theoretical Constructs*
•The focus on (1') equality or (2') freedom, but not both, regardless of whether freedom and equality can be understood as "negative" or "positive"
—*Types*
•Only (1'): Different versions on the Far Left (e.g., Stalinism, Robespierrianism)
•Only (2'): Different versions on the Far Right (e.g., Nazism, absolute monarchism)

(continued on next page)

Table 4.25. Democracy, Non-Democracy, and Post-Democracy
(Part II)

• **Post-Democracy**
—*Theoretical Constructs*
•The priority of (1'') equality over freedom, or (2'') freedom over equality, or (3'') the transcendence of freedom and equality, regardless of whether freedom and equality are "negative" or "positive." In degree, (1'') or (2'') is less than (1') or (2') but more than (1) or (2)—respectively.
•Like democracy and non-democracy, post-democracy is also subject to the freedom/unfreedom and equality/inequality dialectics (or existential dialectics in general). Unlike them, post-democracy acknowledges the constraints of existential dialectics and no longer value freedom and equality as sacred virtues. There is no utopia, in the end; even were there one, dystopia would exist within it.
—*Types*
•(1''): Different versions of trans-Sinitic value ideals
•(1''): Different versions of trans-feminine value ideals
•(1''): Different versions of trans-Islamic value ideals
•(1''): Different versions of trans-outerspace value ideals
•(2''): Different versions of post-human elitist value ideals
•(3''): Different versions of the value ideals of floating consciousness (etc.)

(continued on next page)

Table 4.25. Democracy, Non-Democracy, and Post-Democracy (Part III)

Notes: The examples are solely illustrative (not exhaustive), nor are they mutually exclusive. As generalities, they allow exceptions. "Negative" freedom is freedom "from" (e.g., freedom from poverty), whereas "positive" freedom is freedom "to" (e.g., freedom to the state of enlightenment). "Negative" equality is "procedural" equality (e.g., equality of opportunity), while "positive" equality is "substantive" equality (e.g., equality of outcome). Existential dialectics impose constraints on freedom and equality in democracy, non-democracy, and post-democracy, regardless of whether freedom and equality can be understood as "negative" or "positive" in conventional discourse. Therefore, do not confuse the transcendence of freedom and equality in (3") with the naïve temptation to transcend existential dialectics. There is no utopia, in the end; even should there be one, it would not exist without dystopia embedded within it.

Sources: A summary, based on my previous works, especially Ch.5 of *FHC*, Chs.5-10 of *FCD*, Chs.2-4 of *FPHC*, and Chs.1 & 7 of *BDPD*. The reader should consult the books for more analysis, as this is only a summary here.

Table 4.26. Multiple Causes of the Emergence of Post-Democracy
(Part I)

• **At the Micro-Physical Level**
—Ex: intelligent life without the human physical-chemical system
—Sources: Ch.7 of *FHC*; Chs.9-10 of *FCD*; Ch.1 of *FPHC*

• **At the Chemical Level**
—Ex: space radiation and toxins
—Sources: Ch.7 of *FHC*; Chs.9-10 of *FCD*

• **At the Bio-Psychological Level**
—Ex: exo-biological evolution in deep space
—Ex: genetic engineering of new beings
—Ex: limits of cognitive partiality
—Ex: illusions of emotional neutrality
—Ex: human biological inequality
—Ex: the rise of unfolding unconsciousness
—Sources: Ch.2 & Chs.9-10 of *FCD*; Ch.7 of *FHC*; Ch.4 of *BCPC*;
  FPHU

• **At the Institutional Level**
—Ex: the flawed logic of equality
—Ex: the conflicting nature of governance
—Sources: Ch. 5 of *FHC*; Chs. 6 & 10 of *FCD*; Ch. 3 of *FPHC*;
  Chs.2-5 of *BDPD*

• **At the Organizational Level**
—Ex: e-civic alienation
—Ex: the dark sides of formal-legalistic routines
—Sources: Ch.3 of *FHC*; Ch.7 of *FCD*; Ch.3 of *FPHC*

• **At the Structural Level**
—Ex: ever new forms of inequities, at home and abroad
—Ex: the emergence of China, women, and Islam as major actors
—Sources: Chs.5-6 of *FHC*; Chs.7, 9 & 10 of *FCD*; Chs.4-5 of *BDPD*

(continued on next page)

Table 4.26. Multiple Causes of the Emergence of Post-Democracy (Part II)

• **At the Cultural Level**
—Ex: freedom/unfreedom dialectics
—Ex: equality/inequality dialectics
—Ex: system fragmentation and integration
—Sources: Ch.5 of *FHC*; Chs. 3, 9 & 10 of *FCD*; Ch.4 of *FPHC*; Ch.1 of *BDPD*; Ch.4 of *BCPC*

• **At the Systemic Level**
—Ex: space habitats (in zero-gravity) and colonization
—Ex: ultra advanced future info systems
—Ex: qualitative demography
—Sources: Ch.7 of *FHC*; Chs.9 &10 of *FCD*

• **At the Cosmological Level**
—Ex: the colonization of multiverses
—Ex: the alteration of space-time and the creation of new matter-energy
—Ex: the expansion of floating consciousness
—Ex: the spread of hyper-spatial consciousness
—Sources: Ch.7 of *FHC*; Chs.9 &10 of *FCD*; Ch.4 of *FPHC*; *FPHST*

Notes: The examples in each category are solely illustrative (not exhaustive), and some of the items can be reclassified somewhere else. Nor are they always mutually exclusive. Since they are generalities, exceptions are expected.
Sources: Especially from *FHC, FCD, FPHC, BCPC, BDPD, FPHST*, and *FPHU*. See also other books and my perspectives on civilizational holism.

**Table 4.27. Some Clarifications
about Post-Capitalism and Post-Democracy
(Part I)**

• The prefix "trans-" in the first category of post-capitalism (with its four versions) refers to something "going beyond" (not "uniting" or "combining"). Ex: *Sec.10.3.3* of *FCD*; *Sec.2.4* & *Sec.4.4* of *FPHC*; *Sec.7.2* of *BCPC*

• Such terms like "post-democracy," "post-capitalism," "post-human elitist," "trans-feminine calling," and the like as used in my works are more for our current intellectual convenience than to the liking of future humans and post-humans, who will surely invent more tasteful neologisms to call their own eras, entities, and everything else, for that matter. But the didactic point here is to use the terms to foretell what the future might be like, not that its eras and entities must be called so exactly and permanently. Ex: *Sec.11.1* of *FCD*; *Sec.7.2* of *BCPC*

• The four versions in the first category of post-capitalist value ideals need not automatically be post-democratic, just as capitalism does not necessarily mean democracy. They are two different entities—though closely related. But up to a certain threshold of elevating equality at the farther expense of freedom, the democratic ideals will be overcome and cease to exist. The same is true for the post-human elitist calling in the second category of post-capitalism in relation to post-democracy, depending on the extent to which freedom is elevated at the expense of equality. Ex: *Sec.10.4.3.3* of *FCD*; *Table 3.9* of *FPHC*; *Table 7.6* of *BDPD*

• The comparison in each of the three realms of existence in all forms of post-capitalism is not absolute, but relative. Examples include "communal" vs. "individualistic," and the like. Ex: Notes in *Table 10.8, Table 10.9, Table 10.10,* & *Table 10.11* of *FCD*; Chs.2-4 of *FPHC*; *Sec.7.2* of *BCPC*

(continued on next page)

**Table 4.27. Some Clarifications
about Post-Capitalism and Post-Democracy
(Part II)**

• The emergence of post-capitalism (and post-democracy, for that matter) has multiple causes (to not be reduced to one or only a few).
Ex: Ch.10 of *FCD*, Chs.2-4 of *FPHC*; *Sec.1.3* & *Sec.7.2* of *BCPC* (or *Table 1.8* & *Table 7.11*)

• The specific forms of post-capitalism (and post-democracy, for that matter) need to be further developed in future after-postmodern history, as they will be different from the ones we now know. The point here is to solely give an extremely rough sketch of a world to come that we have never known.
Ex: *Sec.10.3.3* & *Sec.10.4.3.3* of *FCD*; *Table 10.14* & *Table 10.15* of *FCD*; *Sec.7.2* of *BCPC*

• All forms of post-capitalism are not part of a "teleological law," but of "historical trends" only. The same is also true for all forms of post-democracy.
Ex: *Sec.7.1* of *FHC*; *Sec.9.5.3.2* & *Sec.10.3.4.2* of *FCD*; *Sec.7.2* of *BCPC*

• Post-capitalism is not better than capitalism in an "absolute" sense but only fits in better, on the basis of the historical contingency of culture, society, nature, and the mind in some future eras. The same is true for post-democracy in relation to democracy. The term "better" is historically relative.
Ex: *Sec.10.3.3* of *FCD*; *Sec.1.7* of *BDPD*; *Sec.1.5* of *BCPC*

(continued on next page)

**Table 4.27. Some Clarifications
about Post-Capitalism and Post-Democracy
(Part III)**

• All forms of post-capitalism and post-democracy are subject to the constraints of existential dialectics. In the process, the dialectic direction is to go beyond the conventional "either-or" dichotomies (e.g., freedom vs. unfreedom, equality vs. inequality, freedom vs. equality, individuality vs. communality, spirituality vs. materiality, formal legalism vs. informal legalism, etc.). As is true in post-civilization, to go beyond the dichotomies is to acknowledge the co-existence of both in each dichotomy, although the degree of scaling one over the over varies from case to case (e.g., the theory of post-capitalism I, the theory of post-capitalism II, the theory of post-democracy I, the theory of post-democracy II, etc.)—but is not to be extreme in largely favoring one over the other, *on average* (all things considered). There is no utopia to be had in the end; even should there be one, dystopia would exist within it.
Ex: Ch.5 of *FHC*; *Sec.10.4.4.2* of *FCD*; *Sec.1.5* of *BDPD*; *Sec.1.3* of *BCPC*; *BCIV*

• All forms of post-capitalism, however different from each other though they are, share one common feature, in that they all inspire for a higher spiritual culture. The same is also true for post-democracy.
Ex: *Sec.10.3*, *Sec.10.4* & *Sec.10.5* of *FCD*; *Chs.2-4* of *FPHC*; *Sec.7.2* of *BCPC*

• All forms of post-capitalism try to avoid the excess in capitalist consumerism by favoring more basic than artificial needs in having, but the quality and quantity of these "basic" needs will be measured by future standards, not by our current ones. Standards are historically relative.
Ex: *Sec.10.3*, *Sec.10.4* & *Sec.10.5* of *FCD*; *Ch.2* of *FPHC*; *Sec.7.2* of *BCPC*

(continued on next page)

**Table 4.27. Some Clarifications
about Post-Capitalism and Post-Democracy
(Part IV)**

• All forms of post-capitalism make use of a different degree of political authority with advanced info systems in future history and strives for higher spiritual cultures (especially in the post-human age), while acknowledging the constraints of existential dialectics and no longer valuing free market (as in capitalism) and economic control (as in non-capitalism) as sacred virtues.
Ex: *Sec.10.3.4.2*, *Sec.10.3*, *Sec.10.4* & *Sec.10.5* of *FCD*; Chs.2-4 of *FPHC*; *Sec.1.5* of *BDPD*; *Sec.7.2* of *BCPC*

Notes:: The main points here are solely illustrative (not exhaustive) nor necessarily mutually exclusive, and the comparison is relative (not absolute). As generalities, they allow exceptions. The sections as cited are only illustrative (not exhaustive).
Sources: From *FHC*, *FCD*, *FPHC*, and *BDPD*

Table 4.28. The Theory of Post-Capitalism I.1:
By Group—
Ex: Spiritual/Communal in the Trans-Feminine Calling

• **More Communal Than Individual**
—*Sharing*: learning from others, as different ideas mutually enrich
—*Cooperative*: encouraging a sense of shared leadership and teamwork

• **More Informal-Legalistic Than Formal-Legalistic**
—*Specific*: listening more from the heart than from the head, to know a person as a concrete, not as an abstract, unit
—*Affective*: thinking and acting with others on a more affective tone. Business can mix with an emotional touch.
—*Ascriptive*: hiring (or firing) can be done on the basis of merit (or lack of it), but deep solidarity (sisterhood) is important too.
—*Particularistic*: making decisions on the basis of cost-benefit analysis, but a given group relationship is vital

• **More Spiritual Than Secular**
—*Long-Term Looking*: sharing for a long-term relationship (e.g., love, friendship), not just for a short-term gain
—*Loving/Caring*: showing compassion for the sufferings of others, without quickly blaming and pre-judging
—*Respectful*: showing acceptance about others' feelings (and thoughts)

Notes: The categories and examples are solely illustrative, since there can be different versions, and the comparison is relative (not absolute), nor are they mutually exclusive. As generalities, they allow exceptions. The specific forms of the trans-feminine version need to be further developed in future after-postmodern history, as they will be different from the ones we now know, since the prefix "trans-" here means going beyond or deconstructing the feminine values, while using them as the inspirational point at the beginning.
Source: From Ch.10 of *FCD*. Refer to text for more info and references.

Table 4.29. The Theory of Post-Capitalism I.2:
By Nation-State—
Ex: Spiritual/Communal in the Trans-Sinitic Calling

• **More Communal Than Individualistic**
—*Centralized*: being more top-down in management
—*Collective*: encouraging more group cooperation
—*Social*: investing in trust and connection

• **More Informal-Legalistic Than Formal-Legalistic**
—*Specific*: knowing more of those related or connected
—*Affective*: behaving in a paternalistic, hierarchical way
—*Ascriptive*: favoring family members and those related
—*Particularistic*: building connection (guanxi) as imperative

• **More Spiritual Than Secular**
—*Expansionist*: diffusing civilizational values (e.g., the superiority complex of civilizationalism)
—*Holistic*: synthesizing things into a panoramic horizon
—*Historical*: learning from the lessons of the ancient past
—*Respectful*: deferential to elders and superiors

Notes: The categories and examples are solely illustrative, since there can be different versions, and the comparison is relative (not absolute), nor are they mutually exclusive. As generalities, they allow exceptions. The specific forms of the trans-Sinitic version need to be further developed in future after-postmodern history, as they will be different from the ones we now know, since the prefix "trans-" here means going beyond or deconstructing the Sinitic values, while using them as the inspirational point at the beginning.

Source: From Ch.10 of *FCD*. Refer to text for more info and references.

Table 4.30. The Theory of Post-Capitalism I.3:
By Region—
Ex: Spiritual/Communal in the Trans-Islamic Calling

• **More Communal Than Individualistic**
 —*Collective*: building the webs of relationships to bind individuals
 —*Sharing*: cultivating the established "wisdom" through common experience
 —*Cooperative*: stressing harmony, solidarity, and commonality

• **More Informal-Legalistic Than Formal-Legalistic**
 —*Specific*: making efforts to know well the participants (family and larger community) in matters of common concern
 —*Affective*: mixing work with language and ritual on explicit religious (Islamic) ideals, texts, stories, and examples
 —*Ascriptive*: privileging local history and custom on relationships among kinship groups
 —*Particularistic*: preferring an unbiased insider with ongoing connections to all parties

• **More Spiritual Than Secular**
 —*Historical*: learning from the lessons of the past as a source of stability and guidance
 —*Deferential*: showing respect for age, experience, status, and leadership in communal affairs
 —*Honorable*: emphasizing face, dignity, prestige, and fairness
 —*Compassionate*: giving mercy and charity ("Zahah") to others

Notes: The categories and examples are solely illustrative (not exhaustive), and the comparison is relative (not absolute), nor are they mutually exclusive. As generalities, they allow exceptions. The specific forms of the trans-Islamic version need to be further developed in future after-postmodern history, as they will be different from the ones we now know, since the prefix "trans-" here means going beyond or deconstructing the Islamic values, while using them as the inspirational point at the beginning.
Sources: From Ch.10 of *FCD*. Refer to text for more info and references, especially from the works by George Irani (2000) and C. Murphy (September 19, 2001).

**Table 4.31. The Theory of Post-Capitalism I.4:
By Universe—
Ex: Spiritual/Communal in the Trans-Outerspace Calling**

- **More Communal Than Individual**
  —*Cooperative*: requiring teamwork in small space habitats
  —*Sharing*: learning from, and enjoying being with, each other in a small group in outer space

- **More Informal-Legalistic Than Formal-Legalistic**
  —*Specific*: knowing more about each other to facilitate living and working together in space, both as fellow astronauts and space-mates
  —*Affective*: being friendly and social to each other as vital to working and living in small space quarters
  —*Ascriptive*: nurturing comaraderie among fellow astronauts as if they are family members over time
  —*Particularistic*: building work relationship with enduring memory in a space mission

- **More Spiritual Than Secular**
  —*Long-Term*: looking beyond selfish materialistic concerns in a precarious space environment with potential life or death
  —*Loving/Caring*: cultivating deep bondage for the success of a long term space mission
  —*Transcendent*: searching for life meaning in outer space

Notes: The calling and examples in each category are solely illustrative (not exhaustive), since there will be many different outer-space value ideals in the distant future of space colonization. The comparison is also relative (not absolute), nor are they mutually exclusive. As generalities, they allow exceptions. And the specific forms of trans-outer-space calling need to be further developed in future after-postmodern history, as they will be different from the ones we now know, since the prefix "trans-" here means going beyond or deconstructing the current outer-space values, while using them as the inspirational point at the beginning. The point here is to solely give an extremely rough picture of a small part of the world to come that we still do not know much about.
Source: From Ch.10 of *FCD*. Refer to text for more info and references.

Table 4.32. The Theory of Post-Capitalism II:
Spiritual/Individualistic in the Post-Human Elitist Calling
(Part I)

• **More Individualistic Than Communal**
—Setting up rank distinctions among unequals (e.g., between inferior humans and superior post-humans, or later among inferior post-humans and superior ones, relatively speaking)
—Yearning for being not only distinguished from unequals, but also the first among equals (the best of the very best)
—Recognizing the constraints of equality/inequality dialectics (or existential dialectics in general)

• **More Spiritual Than Secular**
—Soul-searching for a high spiritual culture (not the trashy one for the masses). Mass culture is a dirty joke for them.
—Exploring different spheres of non-human consciousness in the cosmos (something vastly superior than the human one)
—Recognizing the constraints of freedom/unfreedom dialectics (or existential dialectics in general)

• **Qualifications**
—Although post-human elitist post-democracy is comparable to post-human elitist post-capitalism in some respects, the former does not necessarily imply the latter (post-human elitist post-capitalism), just as democracy does not have to entail capitalism. They are two different (though related) entities.
—But up to a certain threshold of incorporating government intervention with advanced info systems in future civilizations for higher spiritual concerns at the expense of the free market and materialist pursuit, the capitalist ideal will be overcome.
—The overcome will not be Fascist or feudalistic, but post-capitalist, subject to the constraints of existential dialectics.

(continued on next page)

Table 4.32. The Theory of Post-Capitalism II:
Spiritual/Individualistic in the Post-Human Elitist Calling
(Part II)

Notes: The calling and examples in each category are solely illustrative (not exhaustive). The comparison is also relative (not absolute), nor are they mutually exclusive. As generalities, they allow exceptions. And the specific forms of post-human elitist post-capitalism need to be further developed in future after-postmodern history, as they will be different from the ones we now know, while using them as the inspirational point at the beginning. The point here is to solely give an extremely rough picture of a small part of the world to come that we still do not know much about.

Sources: From Ch.10 of *FCD* (and also *FPHC*, *BDPD*, and *BCPC*). Refer to the text for more info and references.

**Table 4.33. Capitalism, Non-Capitalism, and Post-Capitalism
(Part I)**

• **Capitalism**
—*Theoretical Constructs*
  •Allocation of scarce resources among alternative wants largely by free market for competition (whose characteristics in its ideal form include, for instance, no barrier to entry or exit, homogeneity, perfect information, a large number of buyers/sellers, and perfect factor mobility)
  •More formal-legalistic than informal-legalistic, more individualistic than communal, and more material (secular) than spiritual
  •Either (1) minimal government or (2) relatively active government
—*Types*
  •Only (1): Different versions of market capitalism (e.g., the U.S.)
  •Only (2): Different versions of welfare capitalism (e.g., Sweden)

• **Non-Capitalism**
—*Theoretical Constructs*
  •Allocation of scarce resources among alternative wants mainly by political authority for policies (which can be regulative, redistributive, symbolic, and participatory)
  •More informal-legalistic than formal-legalistic
  •Either (1') more individualistic (for the elites), often (though not always) for material (secular) concerns, or (2') more communal (for the masses), often (though not always) for spiritual concerns
—*Types*
  •Only (1'): Different versions on the Right (e.g., Fascist corporate-state economy for the glory of the new Rome, medieval lord-vassal-serf economy for the power of the feudalistic order)
  •Only (2'): Different versions on the Left (e.g., Soviet command economy for the creation of the New Socialist Man)

(continued on next page)

Table 4.33. Capitalism, Non-Capitalism, and Post-Capitalism (Part II)

• **Post-Capitalism**
—*Theoretical Constructs*
•Allocation of scarce resources among alternative wants largely by political authority with advanced info systems in future civilizations, subject to existential dialectics. In degree of allocating by authority, post-capitalism is more than capitalism but less than non-capitalism.
•More spiritual than secular (material)
•Either (1'') more individualistic or (2") more communal
•Like capitalism and non-capitalism, post-capitalism is also subject to the freedom/unfreedom and equality/inequality dialectics (or existential dialectics in general). There is no utopia, in the end; even were there one, dystopia would exist within it.
•Unlike capitalism and non-capitalism, post-capitalism makes use of a different degree of political authority with advanced info systems in future civilizations and strives for higher-spiritual cultures (especially in the post-human age), while acknowledging the constraints of existential dialectics and no longer valuing free market (as in capitalism) and economic control (as in non-capitalism) as sacred virtues.
—*Types*
•Only (1"): Different versions of post-human elitist value ideals
•Only (2''): Different versions of trans-Sinitic value ideals
•Only (2''): Different versions of trans-feminine value ideals
•Only (2''): Different versions of trans-Islamic value ideals
•Only (2''): Different versions of trans-outerspace value ideals

(continued on next page)

Table 4.33. Capitalism, Non-Capitalism, and Post-Capitalism (Part III)

Notes: The calling and examples in each category are solely illustrative (not exhaustive). The comparison is also relative (not absolute), nor are they mutually exclusive. As generalities, they allow exceptions. And the specific forms of each calling need to be further developed in future after-postmodern history, as they will be different from the ones we now know, while using them as the inspirational point at the beginning. The point here is to solely give an extremely rough picture of a small part of the world to come that we still do not know much about.

Source: From Ch.10 of *FCD*. Refer to the text for more info and references.

Table 4.34. Multiple Causes of the Emergence of Post-Capitalism (Part I)

• **At the Micro-Physical Level**
 —Ex: intelligent life without the human physical-chemical system
 —Ex: mastering of quantum mechanics, electromagnetism, and other fields for the understanding of a broad range of anomalous experiences and the application for artificial intelligence for spiritual quest
 —Sources: Ch.7 of *FHC*; Chs.9-10 of *FCD*; Ch.1 of *FPHC*

• **At the Chemical Level**
 —Ex: space radiation and toxins
 —Sources: Ch.7 of *FHC*; Chs.9-10 of *FCD*

• **At the Bio-Psychological Level**
 —Ex: exo-biological evolution in deep space
 —Ex: genetic engineering of new beings
 —Ex: limits of human cognition
 —Ex: the rise of unfolding unconsciousness
 —Sources: Ch.2 & Chs.9-10 of *FCD*; Ch.7 of *FHC*; *FPHU*

• **At the Institutional Level**
 —Ex: the flawed logic of the free market
 —Ex: the need of a post-autistic economics
 —Sources: Ch.10 of *FCD*

• **At the Organizational Level**
 —Ex: the dark sides of formal-legalistic routines
 —Sources: Ch.3 of *FHC*; Ch.7 of *FCD*; Ch.3 of *FPHC*

• **At the Structural Level**
 —Ex: ever new forms of inequities, at home and abroad
 —Ex: the emergence of China, women, and Islam as major actors
 —Sources: Chs.5-6 of *FHC*; Chs.7, 9 & 10 of *FCD*; Chs.4-5 of *BDPD*

(continued on next page)

Table 4.34. Multiple Causes of the Emergence of Post-Capitalism (Part II)

• **At the Cultural Level**
—Ex: freedom/unfreedom dialectics
—Ex: equality/inequality dialectics
—Sources: Ch.5 of *FHC*; Chs.3 & 10 of *FCD*; Ch.4 of *FPHC*; Ch.1 of *BDPD*

• **At the Systemic Level**
—Ex: space habitats (in zero-gravity) and colonization
—Ex: ultra advanced future info systems
—Ex: qualitative demography
—Sources: Ch.7 of *FHC*; Chs. 9 & 10 of *FCD*

• **At the Cosmological Level**
—Ex: the colonization of multiverses
—Ex: the alteration of space-time and the creation of new matter-energy
—Ex: the expansion of floating consciousness
—Ex: the spread of hyper-spatial consciousness
—Sources: Ch.7 of *FHC*; Chs. 9 & 10 of *FCD*; Ch.4 of *FPHC*; *FPHST*

Notes: The examples in each category are solely illustrative (not exhaustive), and some of the items can be reclassified somewhere else. Nor are they always mutually exclusive. Since they are generalities, exceptions are expected.

Sources: Especially from *FHC, FCD, FPHC, BCPC, BDPD, FPHST*, and *FPHU*. See also other books and my perspectives on civilizational holism.

Table 4.35. The Theoretical Debate on Civilization

• **The Progressive Theory of Civilization**
  —*Thesis*: The "civilizing" process is "good," as opposed to the "barbarizing" process as something "bad," relatively speaking.
  —*Discourse*: Especially, though not exclusively, in the Enlightenment era and a bit before. Example: Thomas Hobbes—in that the tribes in primitive societies were "savages."

• **The Romantic Theory of Barbarity**
  —*Thesis*: The "civilizing" process is "bad," as opposed to the "barbarizing" process as something "good," relatively speaking.
  —*Discourse*: Especially, though not exclusively, in the Counter-Enlightenment circle. Example: Jean-Jacques Rousseau—in that civilization "corrupts" men, and the "savages" are in fact "noble."

• **The Moderate Theory of Civilization**
  —*Thesis*: The "civilizing" process is "good," but there is a price to pay, especially in systematic (compulsive) self-control.
  —*Discourse*: Especially, though not exclusively, in some late modern and postmodern circles. Example: Norbert Elias—in that social manners become more refined in the civilizing process, but self-control also becomes more systematic.

• **The Theory of Post-Civilization**
  —*Thesis*: The civilizing process is as evil and good as barbarity, and each cannot exist without the other, to be eventually superseded by post-civilization unto the post-human age.
  —*Discourse*: Proposed by Peter Baofu. See the rest of *BCIV* for more analysis.

Source: From *BCIV* on the theoretical debate

**Table 4.36. No Freedom Without Unfreedom
in the Civilizing Processes
(Part I)**

• **The Rationalizing Process (at the Level of Culture)**
—if freer from the dominance of unreason (as in barbarism) in the civilizing process, then less free from the rationalizing process (be it in the form of the principle of either transcendence or immanence)
—if freer from the principle of immanence in the rationalizing process, then less free from the inclination to commit terror in the name of reason and the relative underdevelopment of non-reason (e.g., in relation to yoga and meditation)
—if freer from the principle of transcendence in the rationalizing process, then less free from the relative underdevelopment of reason (e.g., in relation to systematic methodology) and the occurrence of oppression in the name of non-reason

• **The Pacifying Process (at the Level of Society)**
—if freer from the dominance of pillage (as in savagery) in the civilizing process, then less free from the pacifying process (be it in the form of external control or self-control)
—if freer from self-control in the pacifying process, then less free from the temptation of expansionist oppression and rebellious mindset in external control
—if freer from external control in the pacifying process, then less free from the gruesome psychological self-torture and conformism in self-control

• **The Stewardizing Process (at the Level of Nature)**
—if freer from the dominance of nature (as in the state of nature) in the civilizing process, then less free from the stewardizing process (be it in the form of the stewardship of creation or the covenant with nature)
—if freer from the stewardship of creation in the stewardizing process, then less free from material underdevelopment, relatively speaking, and spiritual exclusion in the covenant with nature
—if freer from the covenant with nature in the stewardizing process, then less free from ecological degradation and spiritual disconnection from nature in the stewardship of creation

(continued on next page)

**Table 4.36. No Freedom Without Unfreedom
in the Civilizing Processes
(Part II)**

• **The Subliming Process (at the Level of the Mind)**
—if freer from the dominance of spontaneity (as in the wild state of the mind) in the civilizing process, then less free from the subliming process, be it in the form of (cyclical-centric) self-refinement or (linear-centric) self-discipline
—if freer from (cyclical-centric) self-refinement in the subliming process, then less free from the (linear-centric) self-regimen (as a form of neurosis)
—if freer from (linear-centric) self-discipline in the subliming process, then less free from the (cyclical-centric) self-torture (equally as a form of neurosis)

Notes: The examples in each category are solely illustrative (not exhaustive), and the comparison is relative (not absolute), nor are they necessarily mutually exclusive. And some can be easily re-classified elsewhere. As generalities, they allow exceptions.
Sources: From *BCIV*. See also *FHC*, *FCD*, *FPHC*, *BDPD*, and *BCPC*.

Table 4.37. No Equality Without Inequality in the Civilizing Processes (Part I)

• **The Rationalizing Process (at the Level of Culture)**
—if more equal for the role of rationalization in the rationalizing process (of civilizational making), then less equal for that of mythicization (as in barbarism)
—if more equal for the principle of transcendence in (linear-centric) rationalizing process, then less equal for the principle of immanence
—if more equal for the principle of immanence in (cyclical-centric) rationalizing   process,   then   less   equal   for   the   principle   of transcendence

• **The Pacifying Process (at the Level of Society)**
—if more equal for pacification in civilizational making, then less equal for the institution of pillaging and others (as in savagery)
—if more equal for external control, relatively speaking, in pacifying process, then less equal for self-control
—if more equal for self-control, relatively speaking, in   pacifying process, then less equal for external-control

• **The Stewardizing Process (at the Level of Nature)**
—if more equal for stewardship in the stewardizing process (of civilizational making), then less equal for reverent (submissive) existence (as in barbarism)
—if more equal for the stewardship of creation in (linear- centric) stewardizing process, then less equal for the (cyclical-centric) covenant with nature for harmonious co-existence
—if more equal for the (cyclical-centric) covenant with nature in the stewardizing process, then less equal for the (linear-centric) stewardship of nature for domination

(continued on next page)

Table 4.37. No Equality Without Inequality in the Civilizing Processes (Part II)

• **The Subliming Process (at the Level of the Mind)**
— if more equal for the role of reason in the subliming process, then less equal for that of unreason (as in the natural state of wildness)
— if more equal for the primacy of reason in (linear-centric) subliming process, then less equal for other faculties (e.g., intuition, existential feelings, and analogous thinking) in cyclical-centric one
— if more equal for the exercise of other faculties (e.g., intuition, existential feelings, and analogous thinking) in cyclical-centric subliming process, then less equal for the role of reason in linear-centric counterpart

Notes: The examples in each category are solely illustrative (not exhaustive), and the comparison is relative (not absolute), nor are they mutually exclusive. And some can be easily reclassified else-where. As generalities, they allow exceptions.
Sources: From *BCIV*. See also *FHC*, *FCD*, *FPHC*, *BDPD*, and *BCPC*.

Table 4.38. Five Theses on Post-Civilization

• Post-civilization no longer treats civilization as good and barbarity as evil (relatively speaking), nor does it nostalgically regard barbarity as good and civilization as evil (relatively speaking again). Civilization is as evil and good as barbarity.

• Post-civilization also no longer accepts the dichotomy between civilization and barbarity. Civilization cannot exist without barbarity. It is no longer necessary to preserve civilization, any more than it is imperative to destroy barbarity. To go beyond civilization and barbarity is to acknowledge the co-existence of both, although the degree of scaling one over the over varies from case to case—but is not to be extreme in largely favoring one over the other, *on average* (subject to the constraints of existential dialectics).

• Post-civilization is thus subject to the constraints of existential dialectics. There is no freedom without unfreedom, and no equality without inequality, for instance. There will be no utopia; even should there be one, there would be dystopia embedded within it.

• Post-civilization will eventually replace civilization (as a form of life settlement), to be dominated by post-capitalist and post-democratic lifeforms here on earth and in deep space (besides other alien lifeforms that we have never known), unto the post-human age in multiverses. Those few post-humans who keep civilization will live in a "post-human civilization," while the rest (the majority), who choose post-civilization, will evolve towards the state of "post-human post-civilization." One therefore should not confuse "post-human civilization" with "post-human post-civilization," as the two are not the same.

• Post-civilization will confront psychosis as a primary problem in the culture of virtuality unto the post-human age, just as civilization has neurosis as a primary one of its own (although both neurosis and psychosis are major problems in both).

Notes: The comparison in each category is relative (not absolute), nor are they necessarily mutually exclusive. And some can be easily re-classified elsewhere. As generalities, they allow exceptions.
Sources: From *BCIV*. See also *FHC*, *FCD*, *FPHC*, *BDPD*, and *BCPC*.

Table 4.39. Barbarity, Civilization, and Post-Civilization

• **The Rationalizing Process (at the Level of Culture)**
—*Barbarity*
  • More mythicizing than rationalizing, relatively speaking
—*Civilization*
  • More rationalizing than mythicizing, relatively speaking
—*Post-Civilization*
  • Beyond the dichotomy, subject to existential dialectics

• **The Pacifying Process (at the Level of Society)**
—*Barbarity*
  • More pillaging than pacifying, relatively speaking
—*Civilization*
  • More pacifying than pillaging, relatively speaking
—*Post-Civilization*
  • Beyond the dichotomy, subject to existential dialectics

• **The Stewardizing Process (at the Level of Nature)**
—*Barbarity*
  • More revering than stewardizing, relatively speaking
—*Civilization*
  • More stewardizing than revering, relatively speaking
—*Post-Civilization*
  • Beyond the dichotomy, subject to existential dialectics

• **The Subliming Process (at the Level of the Mind)**
—*Barbarity*
  • More impulsing than subliming, relatively speaking
—*Civilization*
  • More subliming than impulsing, relatively speaking
—*Post-Civilization*
  • Beyond the dichotomy, subject to existential dialectics

Notes: The comparison in each category is relative (not absolute), nor are they necessarily mutually exclusive. And some can be easily re-classified elsewhere. As generalities, they allow exceptions.
Sources: From *BCIV*. See also *FHC, FCD, FPHC, BDPD,* and *BCPC*.

Table 4.40. Types of Super Civilization in the Cosmos
(Part I)

• **Type I**
—a civilization which gains control of and uses the total energy output "falling on its planet from its sun for interstellar communication" (or, in general, space colonization). For N. Kardashev, who proposed the first three types, human civilization is currently Type Zero (Type O), which is below even Type I, since its present energy consumption for all purposes, let alone for interstellar communication, is still 10,000 times less.

• **Type II**
—a civilization which gains control of and uses directly the total energy output of its sun for interstellar communication (or, in general, space colonization).

• **Type III**
—a civilization which gains control of and uses the total energy output of its galaxy for interstellar communication (or, in general, space colonization).

• **Type IV**
—a civilization which gains control of and uses the total energy output of its cluster of galaxies for interstellar communication (or, in general, space colonization).

• **Type V**
—a civilization which gains control of and uses the total energy output of its supercluster of galaxies for interstellar communica-tion (or, in general, space colonization).

(continued on next page)

Table 4.40. Types of Super Civilization in the Cosmos (Part II)

• **Type...n**
—So continues the series in what I call the cyclical progression of hegemony in the cosmos and beyond.

Notes: The Russian astrophysicist Nikolai Kardashev proposed the first three types of super civilization in terms of total energy out-put for interstellar communication. (CSM 1979) I extend his argument further to propose Type IV, Type V, Type VI, and Type...n, in the context of my claim about the cyclical progression of he-gemony in the cosmos and beyond.

Sources: From *Table 9.4* of *FCD*. See *FHC*, *FCD*, and *FPHC* for more info.

Table 4.41. The Civilizational Project
from Pre-Modernity to After-Postmodernity
(Part I)

	Pre-Modern	Modern	Postmodern	After-Postmodern
Main narratives	•Sacralness •Courtliness •Vitalism •Animism	•Freedom •Equality •Fraternity	•Multiplicity •Hybridization	•Naked contingency •Cyclical progression of hegemony
Main institutions	•Monarchy •Aristocracy •Feudalism •Holy order •Primitivism	•Capitalism •Liberalism •Socialism •Nazism •Fascism	•Capitalism •Liberalism •Postmodern politics of difference	•Post-Capitalism •Post-Democracy •Others
Main technological and economic revolutions	•Agricultural	•Service •Industrial	•Informational	•Biological •Material •Energy •Space •Others

(continued on next page)

Table 4.41. The Civilizational Project
from Pre-Modernity to After-Postmodernity
(Part II)

	Pre-Modern	*Modern*	*Postmodern*	*After-Postmodern*
Main agents	•Males •Upper strata •Mini-states	•Males •Upper strata •Whites •Empires	•Males •Upper strata •Whites •Others •Supra-states •IO's	•Post-humans •Humans •Others
Main impacts	•Local	•Inter-national	•Global	•Outer-space •Multiverse
Main outcomes	•Towards moderntiy •Rise of linear- & cyclical-centric civiliza-tions	•Towards post-modernity •Dominance of linear-centric civilization	•Towards after-post-moderntiy •Linear-centric civiliza-tion in crisis	•Towards human (& maybe post-human) extinction •Rise of post-civiliza-tion, especially in post-human forms of space-time

Notes: The examples in each category are solely illustrative (not exhaustive) nor necessarily mutually exclusive, and the comparison is relative (not absolute). As generalities, they allow exceptions.
Sources: From *Table 10.16* of *FCD*—and also from *BCIV* on post-civilization (and *FPHST*)

Table 4.42. Civilizational Holism
(Part I)

• **At the Micro-Physical Theoretical Level**
—Ex: Mastering of quantum mechanics, electromagnetism, and other fields for the understanding of a broad range of anomalous experiences and theapplication for artificial intelligence (*Sec.1.4.1* of *FPHC*)

• **At the Chemical Theoretical Level**
—Ex: Unprecedented expansion of (and violence to) the mind through ever new forms of drugs (and virtual technologies, for that matter) (Ch.9 of *FCD*)

• **At the Biological Theoretical Level**
—Ex: Humans are not biologically equal, on the basis of race, gender, ethnicity, age, and whatnot. (*Sec.2.6* & Ch.10 of *FCD*; *BNN*) And post-humans will experience the same fate, in an even more amazing way.

• **At the Psychological Theoretical Level**
—Ex: Human cognitive impartiality and emotional neutrality are quite limited. (*Secs.2.4-2.5* of *FCD*)
—Ex: Rise of Floating Consciousness (Ch.10 of *FCD*; Chs.1 & 4 of *FPHC*) and Unfolding Unconsciousness (*FPHU*)

• **At the Organizational Theoretical Level**
—Ex: Administrative colonization of deep space, with less legal-formalism in some corners. (Chs.9-10 of *FCD*)

• **At the Institutional Theoretical Level**
—Ex: Both capitalism and democracy will not last, to be superseded by different versions of post-capitalism and post-democracy in after-postmodernity. (Ch.10 of *FCD*)

(continued on next page)

Table 4.42. Civilizational Holism
(Part II)

• **At the Structural Theoretical Level**
—Ex: Social stratification reappears in ever new forms, also with new causes and new players in the cyclical progression of hegemony. (Chs.8-10 of *FCD*)
—Ex: The world of hyper-empires, and the union of the unions (*BWT*)

• **At the Systemic Theoretical Level**
—Ex: Outerspace expansion: local → regional → global → solar → galactic → clustery → multiversal (Ch.9 of *FCD*)
—Ex: Demographic transition: human extinction, and the rise of post-humans (e.g., cyborgs, thinking machines, thinking robots, genetically altered superior beings, floating consciousness, hyper-spatial consciousness) (Ch.4 of *FPHC*; Ch.10 of *FCD*; & Ch.7 of *FHC*)
—Ex: New technological forces in material sciences, electronic and communication sciences, energy sciences, biosciences, manufacturing and engineering sciences, and space sciences (Ch.10 of *FCD* & Ch.7 of *FHC*)
—Ex: Systematic dominance towards nature for space colonization (Chs.9-10 of *FCD*; Chs.2 & 7 of *FHC*)

• **At the Cultural Theoretical Level**
—Ex: The post-human transcendence of freedom and equality (Ch.10 of *FCD*)
—Ex: Methodological Holism (Ch.1 of *FCD*; Ch.1 of *FPHC*; *Sec.2.1* & *Sec.2.5* of *BCPC*)
—Ex: The Evolution from Barbarity to Post-Civilization (*BCIV*)

• **At the Cosmological Theoretical Level**
—Ex: Mastering of dark matter and dark energy, and the exploration of multiverses (Ch.4 of *FPHC*; Ch.10 of *FCD*; & Ch.7 of *FHC*)
—Ex: Alternation of space-time (*FPHST*)
—Ex: The emergence of hyper-spatial consciousness (*FPHC*)

(continued on next page)

Table 4.42. Civilizational Holism
(Part III)

• **At Other Levels**
—Ex: Historical: pre-modernity → modernity → postmodernity → after-postmodernity (human distinction, and the rise of post-humans, including floating consciousness, hyper-spatial consciousness, and unfolding unconsciousness) (Ch.7 of *FHC*; Ch.10 of *FCD*; *FPHC*; *FPHU*)

Notes: These examples are solely illustrative (not exhaustive), and some of the items can be reclassified somewhere else. Nor are they always mutually exclusive. Since they are generalities, exceptions are expected. And the comparison is relative, not absolute.
Sources: From *Table 5.1* of *FPHC*—with details from *FHC*, *FCD*, and the rest of my books. Not every aspect in each category as discussed in all my books are presented here, since there are too many issues. For more info, also consult the table on theories on civilizational holism and, of course, the books themselves.

Table 4.43. Theories on Civilizational Holism
(Part I)

I. Theories in Relation to Nature
—At the Chemical Theoretical Level
- 73. Constructivist Theory of Aerology (Peter Baofu)
  (*FPHAERO*)
- 72. Creational Theory of Chemistry (Peter Baofu)
  (*FPHCHEM*)
- (• 67). Resilient Theory of Natural Resources (Peter Baofu)
  (*BNR*)

—At the Macro-Physical (Cosmological) Theoretical Level
- (• 73.) Constructivist Theory of Aerology (Peter Baofu)
  (*FPHAERO*)
- 71. Resettlement Theory of Geology (Peter Baofu)
  (*FPHGEOL*)
- 70. Theory of Post-Cosmology (Peter Baofu)
  (*BCOS*)
- 69. Theory of Hyper-Spatial Consciousness (Peter Baofu)
  (Ch.4 of *FPHC*; *FPHG*)
- (• 67). Resilient Theory of Natural Resources (Peter Baofu)
  (*BNR*)
- (• 66). Panoramic Theory of Transportation (Peter Baofu)
  (*FPHTRAN*)
- (• 64). Multilateral Theory of Acoustics (Peter Baofu)
  (*FPHA*)
- (• 63). Selective Theory of Geometry (Peter Baofu)
  (*FPHG*)
- (• 62). Perspectival Theory of Space-Time (Peter Baofu)
  (*FPHST*)
- (• 61). Dialectic Theory of Complexity (Peter Baofu)
  (*FC*)
- (• 32). Theory of Floating Consciousness (Peter Baofu)
  (Ch.10 of *FCD*; Chs.1 & 4 of *FPHC*)
- 68. Theory of the Geopower of Nature (Ch.4 of *ALD*)—
  refined as the Interventive-Reshaping Theory of
  Geography (Peter Baofu) (*FPHGEOG*)

(continued on next page)

Table 4.43. Theories on Civilizational Holism
(Part II)

I. Theories in Relation to Nature (*cont'd*)
—At the Micro-Physical Theoretical Level
- 67. Resilient Theory of Natural Resources (Peter Baofu)
  (*BNR*)
- 66. Panoramic Theory of Transportation (Peter Baofu)
  (*FPHTRAN*)
- 65. Transcendent Theory of Architecture (Peter Baofu)
  (*FPHARCH*)
- 64. Multilateral Theory of Acoustics (Peter Baofu)
  (*FPHA*)
- 63. Selective Theory of Geometry (Peter Baofu)
  (*FPHG*)
- 62. Perspectival Theory of Space-Time (Peter Baofu)
  (*FPHST*)
- 61. Dialectic Theory of Complexity (Peter Baofu)
  (*FC*)

II. Theories in Relation to Culture
—At the Cultural Theoretical Level
- 60. Pluralist Theory of Etiology (Peter Baofu)
  (*FPHETIO*)
- 59. Inclusivist Theory of Phonology (Peter Baofu)
  (*FPHPHON*)
- 58. Ephemeral Theory of the Visual Arts (Peter Baofu)
  (*FPHVA*)
- 57. Sequential Theory of Thanatology (Peter Baofu)
  (*FPHTHAN*)
- 56. Fusional Theory of Morphology (Peter Baofu)
  (*FPHMORP*)
- 55. Modificative Theory of Sports (Peter Baofu)
  (*FPHSPORT*)
- 54. Inquisitive Theory of Culinary Art (Peter Baofu)
  (*FPHCA*)
- 53. Interactive Theory of Semantics (Peter Baofu)
  (*FPHSEM*)

(continued on next page)

Table 4.43. Theories on Civilizational Holism
(Part III)

II. Theories in Relation to Culture (*cont'd*)
*—At the Cultural Theoretical Level (*cont'd*)*
- 52. Transdicsiplinary Theory of Performing Arts (Peter Baofu)
  (*FPHPA*)
- 51. Comparative-Impartial Theory of Literature (Peter Baofu)
  (*FPHLIT*)
- 50. Mediative-Variative Theory of Chess (Peter Baofu)
  (*FPHCHESS*)
- 49. Theory of Post-Ethics (Peter Baofu) (*BEPE*)
- 48. Dualistic Theory of Mass Culture (Peter Baofu)
  (Ch.2 of *FHC*)
- 47. Comparative Theory of Religion—also known as the
  Comparative-Substitutive Theory of Religion (Peter Baofu)
  (Ch.3 of *FHC*; Ch.9 of *FCD*; Ch.1 of *FPHK*; *FPHR*)
- 46. Theory of Post-Civilization (Peter Baofu)
  (*BCIV*)
- 45. Theory of the Trinity of Modernity to Its After-Postmodern
  Counterpart (Peter Baofu)
  (*FHC*; Ch.10 of *FCD*)
- 44. Transformative Theory of Aesthetic Experience (Peter Baofu)
  (*FAE*)
- (• 21). Theory of Post-Capitalism (Peter Baofu)
  (Ch.10 of *FCD*; Chs.2 & 4 of *FPHC*; *BCPC*)
- (• 20). Theory of Post-Democracy (Peter Baofu)
  (Ch.10 of *FCD*; Chs.3 & 4 of *FPHC*; *BDPD*)
- (• 5). Theory of Methodological Holism (Peter Baofu)
  (Ch.1 of *FCD*; Ch.1of *FPHC*; *Sec.2.1* & *Sec.2.5* of *BCPC*;
  FC; *FPHK*; etc.)
- (• 4). Theory of Existential Dialectics,
  or the Holistic Theory of Knowledge (Peter Baofu)
  (*FHC*; *FCD*; *FPHC*; *BDPD*; *FC*; *FAE*; *ALD; FIA; FPHK*; etc,)
- (• 3). Contrastive Theory of Rationality (Peter Baofu)
  (*FPHML*)

(continued on next page)

Table 4.43. Theories on Civilizational Holism
(Part IV)

III. Theories in Relation to the Mind
—*At the Biological Theoretical Level*
- 43. Interconnected Theory of Health Care (Peter Baofu)
  (*FPHHC*)
- 42. Theory of Contrastive Advantages (Peter Baofu)
  (*Sec.2.6* & Ch.10 of *FCD; BNN*)
- (• 32).Theory of Floating Consciousness (Peter Baofu)
  (Ch.10 of *FCD*; Chs.1 & 4 of *FPHC*)
—*At the Psychological Theoretical Level*
- 41. Complex Theory of Data Analysis (Peter Baofu)
  (*FPHDA*)
- 40. Supersession Theory of Computing (Peter Baofu)
  (*FPHCOM*)
- 39. Metamorphic Theory of Humor (Peter Baofu)
  (*FPHH*)
- 38. Contrarian Theory of Personality (Peter Baofu)
  (*FPHP*)
- 37. Theory of Virtual Sexuality (Peter Baofu)
  (*FPHS*)
- 36. Expansive-Contractive Theory of Martial Arts (Peter Baofu)
  (*FPHMA*)
- 35. Multilogical Theory of Learning (Peter Baofu)
  (*FPHL*)
- 34. Comprehensive Theory of Creative Thinking (Peter Baofu)
  (*FPHCT*)
- 33. Theory of Unfolding Unconsciousness—also known as the
  Unfolding Theory of Anomalous Experience (Peter Baofu)
  (*FPHU*)
- 32. Theory of Floating Consciousness (Peter Baofu)
  (Ch.10 of *FCD*; Chs.1 & 4 of *FPHC*)
- 31. Theory of Cognitive Partiality (Peter Baofu)
  (*Sec.2.4* of *FCD*; *Sec.4.5.1.1* of *BCPC*)

(continued on next page)

Table 4.43. Theories on Civilizational Holism
(Part V)

III. Theories in Relation to the Mind (*cont'd*)
—*At the Psychological Theoretical Level* (*cont'd*)
• 30. Theory of Emotional Non-Neutrality (Peter Baofu)
  (*Sec.2.5* of *FCD*; *Sec.4.5.2* of of *BCPC*)
• 29. Theory of Behavioral Alteration (Peter Baofu)
  (*Sec.4.5.3* of *BCPC*)

IV. Theories in Relation to Society
—*At the Organizational Theoretical Level*
• 28. Theory of E-Civic Alienation (Peter Baofu)
  (Ch.7 of *FCD*)
• 27. Combinational Theory of Organization (Peter Baofu)
  (*FPHO*; Ch.6 of *ALD*)
—*At the Institutional Theoretical Level*
• 26. Double-Sided Theory of Accounting (Peter Baofu)
  (*FPHACCO*)
• 25. Reflective Theory of Criminality (Peter Baofu)
  (*FPHCRIM*)
• 24. Detached Theory of Gambling (Peter Baofu)
  (*FPHGAM*)
• 23. Heterodox Theory of Education (Peter Baofu)
  (*FPHEDU*)
• 22. Reconstruction Theory of Law (Peter Baofu)
  (*FPHLAW*)
• 21. Theory of Post-Capitalism (Peter Baofu)
  (Ch.10 of *FCD*; Chs.2 & 4 of *FPHC*; *BCPC*)
• 20. Theory of Post-Democracy (Peter Baofu)
  (Ch.10 of *FCD*; Chs.3 & 4 of *FPHC*; *BDPD*)
• 19. Dynamic Theory of Comparative Political Systems
  (Peter Baofu) (*ALD*)
(• 9.) Theory of the Cyclical Progression of Empire-Building
  (Peter Baofu) (*BWT*)

(continued on next page)

Table 4.43. Theories on Civilizational Holism
(Part VI)

IV. Theories in Relation to Society (cont'd)
—*At the Systemic Theoretical Level*
- 18. Transfigurative Theory of Waste (Peter Baofu)
  (*FPHW*)
- 17. Theory of the Cyclical Progression of Migration (Peter Baofu)
  (*FPHMIG*)
- (• 71). Resettlement Theory of Geology (Peter Baofu)
  (*FPHGEOL*)
- 16. Contingent Theory of Urban Planning (Peter Baofu)
  (*FPHUP*)
- 15. Totalistic Theory of Communication (Peter Baofu)
  (*FPHMM*; *FCD*; *FHC*)
- 14. Ambivalent Theory of Technology (Peter Baofu)
  (*FPHE*; *FCD*; *FHC*)
- 13. Multifaceted Theory of War and Peace (Peter Baofu)
  (Ch.9 of *FCD*; Ch.1 of *FPHK*)
- 12. Theory of Post-Humanity (Peter Baofu)
  (Ch.7 of *FHC*; Chs.3, & 10 of *FCD*; Chs.1, 3 & 4 of *FPHC*;
  and other books of mine)
- 11. Theory of the Cyclical Progression of System Integration
  and Fragmentation (Peter Baofu) (Chs.9-10 of *FCD*)
- 10. Synthetic Theory of Information Architecture (Peter Baofu)
  (*FIA*)

—*At the Structural Theoretical Level*
- 9. Theory of the Cyclical Progression of Hegemony
  (Peter Baofu)
  (Chs.9-10 of *FCD*; Chs.1, 3 & 4 of *FPHC*; *BDPD*)
- 8. Theory of the Cyclical Progression of Empire-Building
  (Peter Baofu)
  (*BWT*)

(continued on next page)

Table 4.43. Theories on Civilizational Holism
(Part VII)

V. Meta-Theories (in Relation to Theories)
—At the Methodological Meta-Theoretical Level
(• 53).Interactive Theory of Semantics (Peter Baofu)
(*FPHSEM*)
(• 41). Complex Theory of Data Analysis (Peter Baofu)
(*FPHDA*)
• 7.   Interpretivist Theory of Probability (Peter Baofu)
(*FPHROB*)
• 6.   Critical-Dialectic Theory of Formal Science (Peter Baofu)
(*FPHFS*)
• 5.   Theory of Methodological Holism (Peter Baofu)
(Ch.1 of *FCD*; Ch.1of *FPHC*; *Sec.2.1 & Sec.2.5* of *BCPC*; *FC*;
FPHK; etc.)
—At the Ontological Meta-Theoretical Level
• 4.   Theory of Existential Dialectics,
or the Holistic Theory of Knowledge (Peter Baofu)
(*FHC*; *FCD*; *FPHC*; *BDPD*; *FC*; *FAE; ALD; FIA; FPHK*; etc,)
• 3.   Contrastive Theory of Rationality (Peter Baofu)
(*FPHML*)

VI. Theories in Relation to the Rest
—At the Meta-Historical Level
• 2. Multifold Theory of History (Peter Baofu)
(*FPHHIST*)
—At the Empirical-Historical Level
• 1. Theory of the Evolution from   Pre-Modernity to After-
Postmodernity (Peter Baofu)
(*FHC*; Ch.9-10 of *FCD*; *FPHC*)

Notes: All these theories are my constructions, as some of the main contributions of my grant project on civilization and its future. These examples are solely illustrative (not exhaustive), and some of the items can be reclassified somewhere else. Nor are they always mutually exclusive. Since they are generalities, exceptions are expected.
Sources: From my previous books.

Table 4.44. Three Great Future Transformations of Mind Games

• **Virtual Games**
—Ex: online chess
—Ex: virtual experience

• **Novel Games**
—Ex: new chess variants
—Ex: new chess engines

• **Post-Human Mind Games**
—Ex: the quest for broader/deeper mental benefits of chess playing
—Ex: games designed for the evolution of the mind into different body-less forms (e.g., "floating consciousness," "hyper-spatial consciousness," "unfolding unconsciousness")

Notes: The examples in the categories are solely illustrative (not exhaustive), and the comparison is relative (not absolute), nor are they necessarily mutually exclusive. And some can be easily re-classified elsewhere. As generalities, they allow exceptions.
Sources: From *Sec. 4.16* of *FPHCHESS*. See text for more info. Also, consult *FCD* for strategy and tactics in warfare and *FPHO* for strategy and tactics in organization.

BIBLIOGRAPHY

Adams, F. C. & G. Laughlin. 1997. "A DYING UNIVERSE: The Long Term Fate and Evolution of Astrophysical Objects" (January 18). *Rev.Mod.Phys.*, 69:337. <http://arxiv.org/pdf/astro-ph/9701131v1.pdf>.

Allen, John; Doreen B. Massey; & Michael Pryke. 1999. *Unsettling Cities*. NY: Routledge.

Allcock, J. 1969. "The Time of Arrival in Quantum Mechanics I. Formal Considerations." *Annals of Physics*, 53 (2): 253–285. <http://adsabs.harvard.edu/abs/1969AnPhy..53..253A>.

Allport, G. 1950. "The Role of Expectancy." *The Tensions That Cause Wars*. In H. Cantrill, ed. Urbana, IL: University of Illinois.

Andrew, Sluyter. 2003. "Neo-Environmental Determinism, Intellectual Damage Control, and Nature/Society Science." *Antipode*, 4 (35).

Ariely, D. 2008. *Predictably Irrational: The Hidden Forces that Shape our Decisions*. New York, NY: HarperCollins.

Bailyn, M. 1994. *A Survey of Thermodynamics*, New York, NY: American Institute of Physics.

Baofu, Peter. 2014. *The Future of Post-Human Public Administration: Towards a New Theory of Policy and Implementation.*

_____.2014a. *The Future of Post-Human Etiology: Towards a New Theory of Cause and Effect*. Volume 2. Hauppauge, NY: Nova Science Publishers, Inc.

_____.2014b. *The Future of Post-Human Etiology: Towards a New Theory of Cause and Effect*. Volume 1. Hauppauge, NY: Nova Science Publishers, Inc.

_____,2014c. *The Future of Post-Human Accounting: Towards a New Theory of Addition and Subtraction in Information Management*. Charlotte, NC: Information Age Publishing.

_____,2014d. *The Future of Post-Human Phonology: Towards a New Theory of Generality and Specificity*. Hauppauge, NY: Nova Science Publishers, Inc.

_____.2014e. *The Future of Post-Human Aerology: Towards a New Theory of Predictaiblity and Nonpredictability*. Volume 2. Hauppauge, NY: Nova Science Publishers, Inc.

_____.2014f. *The Future of Post-Human Aerology: Towards a New Theory of Predictaiblity and Nonpredictability*. Volume 1. Hauppauge, NY: Nova

Science Publishers, Inc.

_____.2014g. *The Future of Post-Human Visual Arts: Towards a New Theory of Techniques and Spirits.*

_____.2014h. *Beyond Human Resources to Post-Human Resources: Towards a New Theory of Quantity and Quality in Demographics.*

_____.2013. *The Future of Post-Human Thanatology: Towards a New Theory of Death and After-Death.* Berlin, Germany: Logos Verlag Berlin.

_____.2013a. *The Future of Post-Human Health Care: Towards a New Theory of Mind and Body.* Hauppauge, NY: Nova Science Publishers, Inc.

_____.2013b. *The Future of Post-Human Morphology: Towards a New Theory of Typologies and Rules.* Hauppauge, NY: Nova Science Publishers, Inc.

_____.2013c. *The Future of Post-Human Probability: Towards a New Theory of Objectivity and Subjectivity.* Hauppauge, NY: Nova Science Publishers, Inc.

_____.2013d. *The Future of Post-Human Sports: Towards a New Theory of Training and Winning.* Cambridge, England: Cambridge Scholars Publishing.

_____.2013e. *Beyond Natural Resources to Post-Human Resources: Towards a New Theory of Diversity and Discontinuity.* Cambridge, England: Cambridge Scholars Publishing.

_____.2012. *The Future of Post-Human Waste: Towards a New Theory of Uselessness and Usefulness.* Cambridge, England: Cambridge Scholars Publishing.

_____.2012a. *The Future of Post-Human Culinary Art: Towards a New Theory of Ingredients and Techniques.* Cambridge, England: Cambridge Scholars Publishing.

_____.2012b. *The Future of Post-Human Transportation: A Preface to a New Theory of Networks and Operations.* Cambridge, England: Cambridge Scholars Publishing.

_____.2012c. *The Future of Post-Human Migration: A Preface to a New Theory of Sameness, Otherness, and Identity.* Cambridge, England: Cambridge Scholars Publishing.

_____.2012d. *The Future of Post-Human History: A Preface to a New Theory of Universality and Relativity.* Cambridge, England: Cambridge Scholars Publishing.

_____.2012e. *The Future of Post-Human Criminality: A Preface to a New Theory of Heroes and Villains.* Cambridge, England: Cambridge International Science Publishing, Ltd.

_____.2012f. *The Future of Post-Human Architecture: A Preface to a New Theory of Form and Function.* Cambridge, England: Cambridge International Science Publishing, Ltd.

_____.2012g. *The Future of Post-Human Semantics: A Preface to a New Theory of*

Internality and Externality. Cambridge, England: Cambridge Scholars Publishing.

_____.2012h. *The Future of Post-Human Performing Arts: A Preface to a New Theory of the Body and its Presence.* Cambridge, England: Cambridge Scholars Publishing.

_____.2011. *The Future of Post-Human Geography: A Preface to a New Theory of Environments and their Interactions.* Cambridge, England: Cambridge International Science Publishing, Ltd.

_____.2011a. *The Future of Post-Human Data Analysis: A Preface to a New Theory of Quantitative and Qualitative Research.* Cambridge, England: Cambridge International Science Publishing, Ltd.

_____.2011b. *The Future of Post-Human Chemistry: A Preface to a New Theory of Substances and their Changes.* Cambridge, England: Cambridge Scholars Publishing.

_____.2011c. *The Future of Post-Human Literature: A Preface to a New Theory of Fiction and Non-Fiction.* Cambridge, England: Cambridge International Science Publishing, Ltd.

_____.2011d. *The Future of Post-Human Computing: A Preface to a New Theory of Hardware, Software, and the Mind.* Cambridge, England: Cambridge International Science Publishing, Ltd.

_____.2011e. *The Future of Post-Human Gambling: A Preface to a New Theory of Risk and Caution.* Cambridge, England: Cambridge International Science Publishing, Ltd.

_____.2011f. *The Future of Post-Human Acoustics: A Preface to a New Theory of Sound and Silence.* Cambridge, England: Cambridge International Science Publishing, Ltd.

_____.2011g. *The Future of Post-Human Humor: A Preface to a New Theory of Joking and Laughing.* Cambridge, England: Cambridge International Science Publishing, Ltd.

_____.2011h. *Beyond Ethics to Post-Ethics: A Preface to a New Theory of Morality and Immorality.* Charlotte, NC: Information Age Publishing.

_____.2011i. *The Future of Post-Human Education: A Preface to a New Theory of Teaching and Learning.* Cambridge, England: Cambridge International Science Publishing, Ltd.

_____.2010. *The Future of Post-Human Religion: A Preface to a New Theory of Spirituality.* Cambridge, England: Cambridge International Science Publishing, Ltd.

_____.2010a. *The Future of Post-Human Chess: A Preface to a New Theory of Tactics and Strategy.* Cambridge, England: Cambridge International Science Publishing, Ltd.

_____.2010b. *The Future of Post-Human Geology: A Preface to a New Theory of Statics and Dynamics*. Cambridge, England: Cambridge International Science Publishing, Ltd.

_____.2010c. *Beyond Cosmology to Post-Cosmology: A Preface to a New Theory of Different Worlds*. Cambridge, England: Cambridge International Science Publishing, Ltd.

_____.2010d. *The Future of Post-Human Personality: A Preface to a New Theory of Normality and Abnormality*. Cambridge, England: Cambridge International Science Publishing, Ltd.

_____.2010e. *The Future of Post-Human War and Peace: A Preface to a New Theory of Aggression and Pacificity*. Cambridge, England: Cambridge Scholars Publishing.

_____.2010f. *The Future of Post-Human Formal Science: A Preface to a New Theory of Abstraction and Application*. Cambridge, England: Cambridge Scholars Publishing.

_____.2010g. *The Future of Post-Human Law: A Preface to a New Theory of Necessity, Contingency, and Justice*. Cambridge, England: Cambridge Scholars Publishing.

_____.2010h. *The Future of Post-Human Sexuality: A Preface to a New Theory of the Body and Spirit of Love Makers*. Cambridge, England: Cambridge Scholars Publishing.

_____,2009. *The Future of Post-Human Martial Arts: A Preface to a New Theory of the Body and Spirit of Warriors*. Cambridge, England: Cambridge Scholars Publishing.

_____.2009a. *The Future of Post-Human Organization: A Preface to a New Theory of Communication, Decision-Making, and Leadership*. Cambridge, England: Cambridge Scholars Publishing.

_____.2009b. *The Future of Post-Human Language: A Preface to a New Theory of Structure, Context, and Learning*. Cambridge, England: Cambridge Scholars Publishing.

_____.2009c. *The Future of Post-Human Urban Planning: A Preface to a New Theory of Density, Void, and Sustainability*. Cambridge, England: Cambridge Scholars Publishing.

_____.2009d. *The Future of Post-Human Geometry: A Preface to a New Theory of Infinity, Symmetry, and Dimensionality*. Cambridge, England: Cambridge Scholars Publishing.

_____.2009e. *The Future of Post-Human Creative Thinking: A Preface to a New Theory of Invention and Innovation*. Cambridge, England: Cambridge Scholars Publishing.

_____.2009f. *The Future of Post-Human Mass Media: A Preface to a New Theory of Communication*. Cambridge, England: Cambridge Scholars Publishing.

_____.2009g. *The Future of Post-Human Engineering: A Preface to a New Theory of Technology.* Cambridge, England: Cambridge Scholars Publishing.

_____.2008. *The Future of Post-Human Mathematical Logic: A Preface to a New Theory of Rationality.* Cambridge, England: Cambridge Scholars Publishing.

_____.2008a. *The Future of Post-Human Knowledge: A Preface to a New Theory of Methodology and Ontology.* Oxford, United Kingdom: Chandos Publishing (Oxford) Ltd.

_____.2008b. *The Future of Post-Human Unconsciousness: A Preface to a New Theory of Anomalous Experience.* Cambridge, England: Cambridge Scholars Publishing.

_____.2008c. *The Future of Information Architecture: Conceiving a New Way to Understand Taxonomy, Network, and Intelligence.* Oxford, United Kingdom: Chandos Publishing (Oxford) Ltd.

_____.2007. *The Rise of Authoritarian Liberal Democracy: A Preface to a New Theory of Comparative Political Systems.* Cambridge, England: Cambridge Scholars Publishing.

_____.2007a. *The Future of Aesthetic Experience: Conceiving a Better Way to Beauty, Ugliness, and the Rest.* Cambridge, England: Cambridge Scholars Publishing.

_____.2007b. *The Future of Complexity: Conceiving a Better Way to Understand Order and Chaos.* London, United Kingdom: World Scientific Publishing Co.

_____.2007c. *Beyond the World of Titans, and the Remaking of World Order: A Preface to a New Logic of Empire-Building.* Cambridge, England: Cambridge Scholars Publishing.

_____.2006. *Beyond Nature and Nurture: Conceiving a Better Way to Understand Genes and Memes.* Cambridge, England: Cambridge Scholars Publishing.

_____.2006a. *The Future of Post-Human Space-Time: Conceiving a Better Way to Understand Space and Time.* New York: Peter Lang Publishing, Inc.

_____.2006b. *Beyond Civilization to Post-Civilization: Conceiving a Better Model of Life Settlement to Supersede Civilization.* New York: Peter Lang Publishing, Inc.

_____.2005. *Beyond Capitalism to Post-Capitalism: Conceiving a Better Model of Wealth Acquisition to Supersede Capitalism.* New York: The Edwin Mellen Press.

_____.2004. *The Future of Post-Human Consciousness.* New York: The Edwin Mellen Press.

_____.2004a. *Beyond Democracy to Post-Democracy: Conceiving a Better Model of Governance to Supersede Democracy.* Volume 1. New York: The Edwin Mellen Press.

_____.2004b. *Beyond Democracy to Post-Democracy: Conceiving a Better Model of Governance to Supersede Democracy*. Volume 2. New York: The Edwin Mellen Press.

_____.2002. *The Future of Capitalism and Democracy*. Maryland: The University Press of America.

_____.2000. *The Future of Human Civilization*. Volume 1. New York: The Edwin Mellen Press.

_____.2000a. *The Future of Human Civilization*. Volume 2. New York: The Edwin Mellen Press.

Baron, J. 2007. *Thinking and Deciding*. New York, NY: Cambridge University Press.

Barrow, John D. 1998. *Impossibility: The Limits of Science and the Science of Limits*. Oxford: Oxford University Press.

Barry, Patrick. 2006. "What's Done is Done... or is It?" (August 28). *New Scientist.* <http://www.newscientist.com/article/mg19125710.900-whats-done-is-done-or-is-it.html>.

Basener, William F. 2006. *Topology and its Applications*. New York, NY: Wiley.

BBC. 2001. "Aspirin Heart Warning" (February 15). <http://news.bbc.co.uk/2/hi/health/1168850.stm>.

_____.1954. "1954: Peace Deal Ends Indo-China War" (July 21). <http://news.bbc.co.uk/onthisday/hi/dates/stories/july/21/newsid_3894000/38 94175.stm>.

Beauchamp, Tom L.; & Alexander Rosenberg. 1981. *Hume and the Problem of Causation*. Cambridge, England: Oxford University Press.

Beaumont, Peter. 2012. "Why 'blowback' is the Hidden Danger of War" (September 08). *The Observer*. <http://www.theguardian.com/world/2002/sep/08/september11.terrorism1>.

Beebee, Helen. 2006. *Hume on Causation*. New York, NY: Routledge.

Berger J. M.; & B. Mandelbrot. 1963. "A New Model for Error Clustering in Telephone Circuits." *I.B.M. Journal of Research and Development*, 7: 224–236.

Berry, Michael. 1989. "Quantum Chaology, Not Quantum Chaos." *Physica Scripta* 40 (3): 335. <http://adsabs.harvard.edu/abs/1989PhyS...40..335B>.

Biletzki, Anat; & Anat Matar. 2006. "Ludwig Wittgenstein" (Nov. 17). *Stanford Encyclopedia of Philosophy*. <http://plato.stanford.edu/entries/wittgenstein/>.

Black, Max. 1956. "Why Cannot an Effect Precede Its Cause." *Analysis*, 16 (16): 49–58. <http://analysis.oxfordjournals.org/content/16/3/49>.

Boot, Max. 2007. "Another Vietnam?" (August 24). *The Wall Street Journal*. <http://online.wsj.com/news/articles/SB118792232818807567?mg=reno64-wsj&url=http%3A%2F%2Fonline.wsj.com%2Farticle%2FSB1187922328188

07567.html>.

Booth, Anna Birgitta. 1984. "Creation Myths of the North American Indians." *Sacred Narrative: Readings in the Theory of Myth*. Alan Dundes, ed. Berkeley, CA: University of California Press.

Brameld, T. 1972. "Education as Self-Fulfilling Prophecy." *Phi Beta Kappa*, 54 (1): 8–11, 58–61.

Brandt, Andres von. 1972. *Fish Catching Methods of the World*. London, England: Fishing News.

Buldyrev, S. V.; A. Goldberger; S. Havlin; C. Peng; & H. Stanley. 1994. "Fractals in Biology and Medicine: From DNA to the Heartbeat." *Fractals in Science*. Armin Bunde; & Shlomo Havlin, eds. Germany: Springer.

Bunge, Mario. 1999. *Dictionary of philosophy*. Amherst, MA: Prometheus Books.

Burkert, Walter. 1979. *Structure and History in Greek Mythology and Ritual*. Berkeley, CA: University of California Press.

Calame, Claude. 2003. *Myth and History in Ancient Greece: The Symbolic Creation of a Colony*. Daniel W. Berman, tr. Princeton, NJ: Princeton University Press.

Callen, H. B. 1960/1985. *Thermodynamics and an Introduction to Thermostatistics*, New York, NY: Wiley.

Cameron, M; A. Vulcan; C. Finch; & S. Newstead. 1994. "Mandatory Bicycle Helmet Use following a Decade of Helmet Promotion in Victoria, Australia— an Evaluation." *Accident Analysis and Prevention*, 26 (3): 325–327. <http://www.sciencedirect.com/science/article/pii/000145759490006X>.

Carroll; Jennifer Chen. 2005. "Does Inflation Provide Natural Initial Conditions for the Universe?." *Gen.Rel.Grav.*, 37: 1671-1674. <http://arxiv.org/abs/gr-qc/0505037>.

Carroll, Robert Todd. 2013. "Law of Attraction" (December 19). *The Skeptic's Dictionary*. <http://www.skepdic.com/lawofattraction.html>.

Chase, Scott. 1993. "Tachyons" (March). *Physics FAQ*. <http://math.ucr.edu/home/baez/physics/ParticleAndNuclear/tachyons.html>.

Chomsky, Noam. 1992. "The Threat of a Good Example." <http://www.chomsky. info/books/unclesam01.htm>.

Chou, R., & M. Helfand. 2005. "Challenges in Systematic Reviews that Assess Treatment Harms." *Ann Intern Med*, 142 (12 Pt 2): 1090-0. <http://www.ncbi.nlm.nih.gov/pubmed/15968034>.

Christ Church City Libraries (CHR). 2014. "Rabbits—Introduction into New Zealand" (February 05). <http://christchurchcitylibraries.com/Kids/ NZBirdsAnimals/Rabbits/>.

Connolly, Kate. 2009. "From Iron Curtain to Green Belt" (July 04). <http://www.theguardian.com/travel/2009/jul/04/germany-green-line-iron-

curtain>.

Copi, Irving M. 1968. *Introduction to Logic*. New York, NY: Macmillian.

Corazzon, Raul. 2007. "Definitions of Ontology: From Nicolai Hartmann to the Present Time." <http://www.formalontology.it/section_4_two.htm>.

Corbett, Dan. 2008. "Introduction to String Theory" (November 23). *ThinkQuest*. <http://library.thinkquest.org/27930/stringtheory1.htm>.

Costa de Beauregard, Olivier. 1977. "Time Symmetry and the Einstein Paradox." *Il Nuovo Cimento* (42B). <http://www.costa-de-beauregard.com/fr/wp-content/uploads/2011/11/OCB-1977-5.pdf>.

De Jong, Piet. 2009. "Evaluating the Health Benefit of Mandatory Bicycle Helmet Laws" (October 26). <http://papers.ssrn.com/sol3/papers.cfm?abstract_id=1368064>.

de Melo-Martín, I. 2005. "Firing up the Nature/Nurture Controversy: Bioethics and Genetic Determinism." *J Med Ethics*, 31 (9): 526–30. <http://www.ncbi.nlm.nih.gov/pmc/articles/PMC1734214/>.

Degasperis, A.; & L. Fonda; & G. Ghirardi. 1974. "Does the Lifetime of an Unstable System Depend on the Measuring Apparatus?." *Il Nuovo Cimento A*, 21 (3): 471–484. <http://adsabs.harvard.edu/abs/1974NCimA..21..471D>.

Donelson, Forsyth. 1987. "Social Psychology." Stamford, CT: Brooks/Cole Publishing.

Druckman, Daniel; & John A. Swets, eds. 1988. *Enhancing Human Performance: Issues, Theories, and Techniques*. Washington, DC: National Academy Press.

Dudley, Will. 2002. *Hegel, Nietzsche, and Philosophy: Thinking Freedom*. Cambridge, UK: Cambridge University Press.

Dummett, Michael. 1954. "Can an Effect Precede its Cause." *Proceedings of the Aristotelian Society* (Supp. 28).

Echanobe, J.; A. Del Campo; & J. Muga. 2008. "Disclosing Hidden Information in the Quantum Zeno Effect: Pulsed Measurement of the Quantum Time of Arrival." *Physical Review A*, 77 (3): 032112. <http://arxiv.org/abs/0712.0670>.

Edmunds, Lowell. 1990. *Approaches to Greek Myth*. Baltimore, MD: Johns Hopkins University Press.

Elaydi, Saber N. 1999. *Discrete Chaos*. Boca Raton, FL: Chapman & Hall/CRC,

Eliade, Mircea. 1976. *A History of Religious Ideas: Volume 1: From the Stone Age to the Eleusinian Mysteries*. Willard R. Trask, tr. Chicago,IL: The University of Chicago Press.

_____.1963. *Myth and Reality*. Willard Trask, tr. New York, NY: Harper & Row.

Elitzur, A.; S. Doley; & N. Kolenda, eds. 2005. *Quo Vadis Quantum Mechanics?*. New York, NY: Springer.

Ellerman, David.. 2012. "A Common Fallacy in Quantum Mechanics: Why Delayed Choice Experiments do NOT imply Retrocausality" (December 16). <http://www.ellerman.org/a-common-fallacy/>.

Epstein, J. M.; & R. Axtell. 1996. *Growing Artificial Societies—Social Science from the Bottom*. Cambridge, MA: MIT Press.

Everett, Hugh. 1957. "'Relative State' Formulation of Quantum Mechanics" (July). *Reviews of Modern Physics*, vol. 29, no.3. <http://www.univer.omsk.su/omsk/Sci/Everett/paper1957.html>.

Facchi, P.; & S. Pascazio. 2002. "Quantum Zeno Subspaces." *Physical Review Letters*, 89 (8): 080401. <http://adsabs.harvard.edu/abs/2002PhRvL..89h0401F>.

Falcon, Andrea. 2008. "Aristotle on Causality." *Stanford Encyclopedia of Philosophy*. <http://plato.stanford.edu/entries/aristotle-causality/#FouCau>.

Faye, Jan. 2001. "Backward Causation" (August 27). *Stanford Encyclopedia of Philosophy*. <http://plato.stanford.edu/entries/causation-backwards/>.

_____; Uwe Scheffler; & Max Urchs, eds. 1994. *Logic and Causal Reasoning*. Germany: Wiley-VCH.

Federation of American Scientists (FED). 1998. "Red Army Faction." <http://www.fas.org/irp/world/para/raf.htm>.

_____.1998a. "Brigate Rosse." <http://www.fas.org/irp/world/para/br.htm>.

_____.1997. "KGB Active Measures." <http://www.fas.org/irp/world/russia/kgb/su0523.htm>.

Feinberg, Gerald. 1967. "Possibility of Faster-Than-Light Particles." *Physical Review*, 159 (159): 1089. <http://adsabs.harvard.edu/abs/1967PhRv..159.1089F>.

Feynman, Richard. 1965. "The Development of the Space-Time View of Quantum Electrodynamics." *Nobel Lecture*. <http://nobelprize.org/nobel_prizes/physics/laureates/1965/feynman-lecture.html>.

_____.1949. "The Theory of Positrons." *Physical Review*, 76 (76): 749.

Firehammer, Reginald. 2005. "Basic Principles of Ontology" (January 05). <http://usabig.com/autonomist/philosophy/ontology2.html>.

Fischer, M.; B. Gutiérrez-Medina; & M. Raizen. 2001. "Observation of the Quantum Zeno and Anti-Zeno Effects in an Unstable System." *Physical Review Letters*, 87 (4): 040402. <http://arxiv.org/abs/quant-ph/0104035>.

Flew, Anthony. 1954. "Can an Effect Precede its Cause." *Proceedings of the Aristotelian Society* (Supp. 28).

Forero, Juan. 2006. "Colombia's Coca Survives U.S. plan to uproot it" (August 19). *The New York Times*.

Franson, J.; B. Jacobs; & T. Pittman. 2006. "Quantum Computing Using Single Photons and the Zeno Effect." *Physical Review A*, 70 (6): 062302. <http://arxiv.org/abs/quant-ph/0408097>.

Gao, J. & J. Delos. 1992. "Closed-Orbit Theory of Oscillations in Atomic Photoabsorption Cross Sections in a Strong Electric Field. II. Derivation of

Formulas." *Phys. Rev. A*, 46 (3): 1455–1467. <http://adsabs.harvard.edu/abs/1992PhRvA..46.1455G>.

Ghirardi, G. C.; C. Omero; A. Rimini; & T. Weber. 1979. "Small Time Behaviour of Quantum Nondecay Probability and Zeno's Paradox in Quantum Mechanics." *Il Nuovo Cimento A*, 52 (4): 421. <http://adsabs.harvard.edu/abs/1979NCimA..52..421G>.

Gigerenzer, G.; & D. Goldstein. 1996. "Reasoning the Fast and Frugal Way: Models of Bounded Rationality." *Psychological Review*, 103: 650–669.

Gilpin, A. 1996. *Dictionary of Environment and Sustainable Development.* Hoboken, NJ: John Wiley and Sons.

Gleick, James. 1987. *Chaos: Making a New Science.* London, England: Cardinal.

Glimm, J.; & D. Sharp. 1999. "Stochastic Differential Equations: Selected Applications in Continuum Physics." Stochastic Partial Differential Equations: Six Perspectives. R. A. Carmona and B. Rozovskii, ed. Providence, RI: American Mathematical Society.

Golan, Zev. 2007. *God, Man and Nietzsche: A Startling Dialogue between Judaism and Modern Philosophers.* Bloomington, IN: iUniverse.

Goldhill, Simon. 1991. *The Poet's Voice: Essays on Poetics and Greek Literature.* Cambridge, England: Cambridge University Press.

Gott, J. Richard. 2002. *Time Travel in Einstein's Universe.* Boston : Houghton Mifflin.

Gott, Richard. 2005. "Rough Draft of History: 'All Right, Let's Get the @#!*% Out of Here'" (August 11). <http://www.mindfully.org/Reform/2005/Che-Guevara-Gott11aug05.htm>.

Grandy, W. T., Jr. 2008. *Entropy and the Time Evolution of Macroscopic Systems.* Cambridge, England: Oxford University Press.

Greene, Brian. 2004. *The Fabric of the Cosmos.* New York, NY: Alfred A. Knopf.

Greenstein, G.; & A. Zajonc. 2005. *The Quantum Challenge: Modern Research on the Foundations of Quantum Mechanics.* Burlington, MA: Jones & Bartlett Publishers.

Griffiths, David J. 2005. *Introduction to Quantum Mechanics.* Upper Saddle River, NJ: Pearson Prentice Hall.

Griffin, J.; & I. Tyrrell. 2011. *Godhead: The Brain's Big Bang.* UK: HG Publishing.

Guth, Alan. 1997. *The Inflationary Universe: The Quest for a New Theory Of Cosmic Origins.* New York: Helix Books.

Gutzwiller, Martin C. 1990. *Chaos in Classical and Quantum Mechanics.* New York, NY: Springer-Verlag.

_____.1971. "Periodic Orbits and Classical Quantization Conditions." *Journal of Mathematical Physics*, 12 (3): 343. <http://scitation.aip.org/content/aip/journal/jmp/12/3/10.1063/1.1665596>.

Halliwell, J. J. et al (editors). 1994. *Physical Origins of Time Asymmetry*. Cambridge, England: Cambridge University Press.

Hawking, Stephen. 2012. "Archives: Meeting Dr. Stephen Hawking." The Bridge School. <http://web.archive.org/web/20080919031137/http://www.bridge school.org/about/about_hawking.html>.

_____.2010. *The Grand Design*. New York, NY: Bantam Books.

_____.1992. "The Chronology Protection Conjecture." *Physical Review D* 46 (46): 603. <http://adsabs.harvard.edu/abs/1992PhRvD.. 46..603H>.

_____.1985. "Arrow of Time in Cosmology." *Phys. Rev. D*. 32 (10): 2489–2495. <http://prd.aps.org/abstract/PRD/v32/i10/p2489_1>.

Heidegger, Martin. 1984. *Nietzsche. Volume II: The Eternal Recurrence of the Same*. David Farrell Krell, tr. New York, NY: Harper and Row.

Heller, E. J.; & S. Tomsovic. 1993. "Postmodern Quantum Mechanics" (July). *Physics Today*.

Hewstone, Miles; Jaspers Jos; & Frank D. Fincham, eds. 1983. *Attribution Theory and Research: Conceptual Developmental and Social Dimensions*. New York, NY: Academic Press.

High Court of Australia (HIGH). 1991. "March v Stramare (E & MH) Pty Ltd [1991] HCA 12; (1991) 171 CLR 506; (1991) 9 BCL 215 (24 April 1991)." <http://www.austlii.edu.au/cgi-bin/sinodisp/au/cases/cth/HCA/1991/12.html? stem=0&synonyms=0&query=title(march%20and%20stramare%20)>.

History Channel (HIST). 2013. "Mao Zedong Outlines the New Chinese Government" (December 5). <http://www.history.com/this-day-in-history/mao-zedong-outlines-the-new-chinese-government>.

Hollander, Jason. 2003. "Renowned Columbia Sociologist and National Medal of Science Winner Robert K. Merton Dies at 92" (March 06). <http://www.columbia.edu/cu/news/03/02/robertKMerton.html>.

Iannone, A. Pabl. 2001. "Determinism." *Dictionary of World Philosophy*. UK: Taylor & Francis.

Independent, the (IND). 2009. "From Iron Curtain to Green Belt: How New Life Came to the Death Strip" (May 17). <http://www.independent.co.uk/ environment/nature/from-iron-curtain-to-green-belt-how-new-life-came-to-the-death-strip-1686294.html>.

Ioannidis J. P.; & J. Lau. 2001. "Completeness of Safety Reporting in Randomized Trials: An Evaluation of 7 Medical Areas." *JAMA*, 285 (4): 437–43. <http://jama.jamanetwork.com/article.aspx?articleid=193489>.

Irwin, Robert. 2003. *The Arabian Nights: A Companion*. Tauris Parke Paperbacks.

Itano, W.; D. Heinzen; J. Bollinger; & D. Wineland. 1990. "Quantum Zeno Effect." *Physical Review A*, 41 (5): 2295–2300.

<http://adsabs.harvard.edu/abs/1990PhRvA..41.2295I>.

Jaslow, R. 2012. "CDC Sees Autism Rate Rise 25%" (March 29). *CBS News*. <http://www.cbsnews.com/news/cdc-sees-autism-rate-rise-25/>.

Jones, Nisbett. 1971. *The Actor and the Observer: Divergent Perceptions of the Causes of Behavior*. New York: General Learning Press.

Kahneman, D.; & A. Tversky. 1972. "Subjective Probability: A Judgment of Representativeness." *Cognitive Psychology*, 3 (3): 430–454. <http://www.sciencedirect.com/science/article/pii/0010028572900163>.

Kaku, Michio. 1994. *Hyperspace: A Scientific Odyssey Through Parallel Universes, Time Warps, and The Tenth Dimension*. Illustrations by Robert O'Keefe. Oxford: Oxford University Press.

Karkuszewski, Zbyszek P.; Christopher Jarzynski; & Wojciech H. Zurek. 2002. "Quantum Chaotic Environments, the Butterfly Effect, and Decoherence." *Physical Review Letters*, 89 (17): 170405. <http://arxiv.org/abs/quant-ph/0111002>.

Kassin, Fein. 2008. *Markus. Social Psychology*. Stamford, CT: Cengage Learning.

Kaufman, Michael T. 2003. "Robert K. Merton, Versatile Sociologist and Father of the Focus Group, Dies at 92" (February 24). *The New York Times*. <http://www.nytimes.com/2003/02/24/nyregion/robert-k-merton-versatile-sociologist-and-father-of-the-focus-group-dies-at-92.html>.

Kaufman, Michael T. 2003. "Robert K. Merton, Versatile Sociologist and Father of the Focus Group, Dies at 92" (February 24). *The New York Times*. <http://www.nytimes.com/2003/02/24/nyregion/robert-k-merton-versatile-sociologist-and-father-of-the-focus-group-dies-at-92.html>.

Kaufmann, Walter. 1974. Nietzsche: Philosopher, Psychologist, Antichrist. (Fourth Edition) Princeton University Press,

Kellert, Stephen H. 1993. *In the Wake of Chaos: Unpredictable Order in Dynamical Systems*. Chicago, IL: University of Chicago Press.

Kenrick, D. T., N/ Li; & J. Butner. 2003. "Dynamical Evolutionary Psychology: Individual Decision Rules and Emergent Social Norms." *Psychological Review*, 110: 3–28.

Khalfin, L. A. 1958. "Contribution to the Decay Theory of a Quasi-Stationary State." *Soviet Physics JETP*, 6: 1053. <http://en.wikipedia.org/wiki/Zeno_effect#cite_note-Khalfin-15>.

Kimball, Charles. 2008. "Creation Myths and Sacred Stories." *Comparative Religion*. Chantilly, VA: The Teaching Company.

Klein, Jacob. 1985. "Leibnitz, an Introduction." *Lectures and Essays*, Annapolis, MD: St Johns College Press.

Koshino, K.; & A. Shimizu. 2005. "Quantum Zeno Effect by General Measurements." *Physics Reports*, 412 (4): 191. <http://adsabs.harvard.edu/abs/2005PhR...412..191K>.

Kramer, Mark. 2010. "Stalin, Soviet Policy, and the Consolidation of a Communist Bloc in Eastern Europe, 1944-1953." <http://iis-db.stanford.edu/evnts/6186/Stalin_and_Eastern_Europe.pdf>.

Krasnikov, S. V. 1997. "Causality Violation and Paradoxes" (March). *Physical Review D*, 55 (6): 3427–3430. <http://prd.aps.org/abstract/PRD/v55/i6/p3427_1>.

Kouznetsov, D.; H. Oberst; A. Neumann; Y. Kuznetsova; K. Shimizu; J. Bisson; K. Ueda; & S. Brueck. 2006. "Ridged Atomic Mirrors and Atomic Nanoscope." *Journal of Physics B*, 39 (7): 1605–1623. <http://adsabs.harvard.edu/abs/2006JPhB...39.1605K>.

Kundera, Milan. 1999. *The Unbearable Lightness of Being*. New York, NY: Perennial Classics.

Lebowitz, Joel L. 1993. "Boltzmann's Entropy and Time's Arrow" (September). *Physics Today*, 46 (9): 32–38. <http://users.df.uba.ar/ariel/materias/FT3_2008_1C/papers_pdf/lebowitz_370.pdf>.

Lee, Jae-Seung; & A. K. Khitrin. 2004. "Quantum Amplifier: Measurement with Entangled Spins." *Journal of Chemical Physics*, 121 (9): 3949. <http://adsabs.harvard.edu/abs/2004JChPh.121.3949L>.

Leeming, David A. 2011. "Creation." *The Oxford Companion to World Mythology*. Oxford, England: Oxford University Press.

Leeming,

_____.2010. *Creation Myths of the World*. Santa Barbara, CA: ABC-CLIO.

_____; & Margaret Adams Leeming. 1994. *A Dictionary of Creation Myths*. Oxford, England: Oxford University Press.

Leibfried, D.; R. Blatt; C. Monroe; & D. Wineland. 2003. "Quantum Dynamics of Single Trapped Ions." *Reviews of Modern Physics*, 75: 281. <http://adsabs.harvard.edu/abs/2003RvMP...75..281l>.

Leibovici, L. 2001. "Effects of Remote, Retroactive Intercessory Prayer on Outcomes in Patients with Bloodstream Infection: Randomised Controlled Trial." *British Medical Journal*, 323 (7327): 1450–1. <http://www.ncbi.nlm.nih.gov/pmc/articles/PMC61047/>.

Leonard, Scott A; & Michael McClure. 2004. *Myth and Knowing*. NY: McGraw-Hill.

Lilienfeld, Scott O.; Steven Jay Lynn; Laura Namy; & Nancy Woolf. 2010. *Psychology: A Framework For Everyday Thinking*. Upper Saddle River, NJ: Pearson Education Incorporated.

Lindberg, David C. 1992. *The beginnings of Western Science*. Chicago, IL: University of Chicago Press.

Long, Charles H. 1963. *Alpha: The Myths of Creation*. New York: George Braziller.

Lorenz, Edward N. 1963. "Deterministic Non-Periodic Flow." *Journal of the Atmospheric Sciences*, 20 (2): 130–141.

Madrell, S.H.P. 1998. "Why are There No Insects in the Open Sea?" *The Journal of Experimental Biology*, 201:2461–2464.

Maier, Steven; & Martin Seligman. 1976. "Learned Helplessness:Theory and Evidence," *Journal of Experimental Psychology: General*, 105 (1): 3-46.

Malle, Bertram F. 2004. *How the Mind Explains Behavior: Folk Explanations, Meaning, and Social Interaction.* Cambridge, MA: The MIT Press.

Mandelbrot, Benoît. 1967. "How Long Is the Coast of Britain? Statistical Self-Similarity and Fractional Dimension." *Science*, 156 (3775): 636–8. <http://adsabs.harvard.edu/abs/1967Sci...156..636M>.

_____.1963. "The Variation of Certain Speculative Prices." *Journal of Business*, 36 (4): 394–419. <http://www.jstor.org/discover/10.2307/235097 0?uid=2&uid=4&sid=21103394743807>.

Mayr, Ernst W. 1992. "The Idea of Teleology." *Journal of the History of Ideas*, 53: 117–135.

McAleer, Neil. 1987. *The Mind-Boggling Universe.* New York: Doubleday & Co.

Medio, Alfredo; & Marji Lines. 2001. *Nonlinear Dynamics: A Primer.* Cambridge, England: Cambridge University Press.

Merriam-Webster's Collegiate Dictionary Online (MWD). 2014. "Cause" (January 27). <http://www.m-w.com/dictionary/cause>.

_____.2014a. "Effect" (January 27). <http://www.m-w.com/dictionary/effect>.

_____.2014b. "Convergence" (January 27). <http://www.m-w.com/dictionary/effect>.

_____.2007. "Agency" (March 20). <http://www.m-w.com/dictionary/agency>.

Merton, Robert K. 1996. "On Social Structure and Science." Chicago, IL: The University of Chicago Press.

_____.1936. "The Unanticipated Consequences of Purposive Social Action." *American Sociological Review*, 1 (6): 895. <http://www.d.umn.edu/ cla/faculty/jhamlin/4111/2111-home/CD/TheoryClass/Readings/MertonSocial Action.pdf>.

Motter, A. E.; & D. Campbell. 2013. "Chaos at Fifty." *Phys. Today*, 66(5), 27-33. <http://scitation.aip.org/content/aip/magazine/physicstoday/article/66/5/10.10 63/PT.3.1977>.

Munton, Silvester; & Hanks Stratton. 1999. "Attributions in Action." New York, NY: John Wiley & Sons.

Nakanishi, T.; K. Yamane; & M. Kitano. 2001. "Absorption-Free Optical Control of Spin Systems: the Quantum Zeno Effect in Optical Pumping." *Physical Review A*, 65 (1): 013404. <http://arxiv.org/abs/quant-ph/0103034>.

Nambu, Yoichiro. 1950. "The Use of the Proper Time in Quantum Electrodynamics I." *Progress in Theoretical Physics* (5).

National, the (NAT). 2009. "Life after Death on the Ocean Floor." <http://www.thenational.ae/apps/pbcs.dll/article?AID=/20090921/NATIONA L/709209873/1042/FOREIGN>.

NBC News (NBC). 2008. "Maryland Artificial Reef Initiative Celebrates 1 Year Anniversary" (February 07). <http://www.nbcnews.com/id/18853363/>.

Norton, Rob. 2008. "Unintended Consequences." *Concise Encyclopedia of Economics*. David R. Henderson, ed. Indianapolis, IN: Library of Economics and Liberty. <http://www.econlib.org/library/Enc/UnintendedConsequences. html>.

Nova Online (NO). 2000. "Time Can Vary." <http://www.pbs.org/ wgbh/nova/time/thinktime.html>.

Nowak A.; R. Vallacher; A. Tesser; & W. Borkowski. 2000. "Society of Self: The Emergence of Collective Properties in Self-Structure." *Psychological Review*, 107.

National Park Service (NPS). 2013. "The Quotable Quotes of Dwight D. Eisenhower" (December 5). <http://www.nps.gov/features/eise/jrranger/ quotes2.htm>.

Orrell, David. 2012. *Truth or Beauty: Science and the Quest for Order*. New, CT Haven: Yale University Press.

_____.2002. "Role of the Metric in Forecast Error Growth: How Chaotic is the Weather?." *Tellus*, 54A: 350–362.

_____; Leonard Smith; Jan Barkmeijer; & Tim Palmer. 2001. "Model Error in Weather Forecasting." *Nonlinear Proc. Geoph.* 9: 357–371.

Peres, A. 1995. *Quantum Theory: Concepts and Methods*. Dordrecht, Netherlands: Kluwer Academic.

Plutarch. 1976. *Plutarch's Moralia: Table-talk: Books I-III*. UK: Heinemann. <http://books.google.co.ma/books?id=k4fWAAAAMAAJ&q=%22the+proble m+about+the+egg+and+the+hen,+which+of+them+came+first%22&dq=%22 the+problem+about+the+egg+and+the+hen,+which+of+them+came+first%2 2&cd=5&hl=fr>.

Podesta, Don; & Douglas Farah. 1993. "Drug Policy in Andes Called Failure" (March 27). The Washington Post.

Popper, Karl. 1976. *Unended Quest: An Intellectual Autobiography*. LaSalle, IL: Open Court.

Poulin, David; Robin Blume-Kohout; Raymond Laflamme; & Harold Ollivier. 2004. "Exponential Speedup with a Single Bit of Quantum Information: Measuring the Average Fidelity Decay." *Physical Review Letters*. 92 (17): 177906. <http://adsabs.harvard.edu/abs/2004PhRvL..92q7906P>.

Price, Huw. 1997. *Time's Arrow and Archimedes' Point*. New York, NY: Oxford University Press.

Raizen, M. G.; S. Wilkinson; C. Bharucha; M. Fischer; K. Madison; P. Morrow;

Q. Niu; & B. Sundaram. 1997. "Experimental Evidence for Non-Exponential Decay in Quantum Tunnelling." *Nature*, 387 (6633): 575. <http://adsabs.harvard.edu/abs/1997Natur.387..575W>.

Raman, Shankar. 1997. Lectures on Literary Theory. Cambridge, MA: MIT (spring).

Rave, M. J. 2008. "Interpreting Quantum Interference Using a Berry's Phase-like Quantity." *Foundations of Physics*, 38: 1073–1081. <http://adsabs.harvard. edu/abs/2008FoPh...38.1073R>.

Renaud, Gabriel. 2005. "Protein Secondary Structure Prediction using Inter-Residue Contacts." <http://www.bioinformatics.uwaterloo.ca/~g2renaud/ thesis.pdf>.

Robinson, D. L. 2012. "Evaluating Head Injuries and Helmet Laws in Australia and New Zealand" (April). <http://cyclehelmets.org/1241.html>.

Rosenthal, R. 2003. "Covert Communication in Laboratories, Classrooms, and the Truly Real World." *Psychological Science*, 12: 151–155.

Rubin, Mark. 2001. "Locality in the Everett Interpretation of Heisenberg-Picture Quantum Mechanics." <http://arxiv.org/abs/quant-ph/0103079>.

Rudnick, Ze'ev. 2008. "What is...Quantum Chaos." *Notices of the American Mathematical Society*. <http://www.ams.org/notices/200801/tx080100032p. pdf>.

Sachs, Joe. 2005. "Aristotle: Motion and its Place in Nature." *Internet Encyclopedia of Philosophy*. <http://www.iep.utm.edu/aris-mot/>.

Sanderson, Catherine. 2010. *Social Psychology*. Hoboken, NJ: John Wiley & Sons, Inc.

Sarasvathy, Saras. 2014. "What Makes Entrepreneurs Entrepreneurial?" <http://www.effectuation.org/sites/default/files/research_papers/what-makes-entrepreneurs-entrepreneurial-sarasvathy_0.pdf>.

_____; et al. 2001. "Effectual Entrepreneurial Expertise: Existence and Bounds." <http://citeseerx.ist.psu.edu/viewdoc/download?doi=10.1.1.110. 2635&rep=rep1&type=pdf>.

Schmidt, Helmut. 1982. "Collapse of the State Vector and Psychokinetic Effect" (June). *Foundations of Physics*, 12.

_____.1978. "Can an Effect Precede its Cause? A Model of a Noncausal World" (June). *Foundations of Physics*, 8.

Segal, Robert A. 2004. *Myth: A Very Short Introduction*. Oxford, England: Oxford University Press.

_____.1996. *Theories of Myth: From Ancient Israel and Greece to Freud, Jung, Campbell, and Levi-Strauss: Philosophy, Religious Studies, and Myth*. Vol. 3. New York, NY: Garland.

Shlain, Leonard. 1991. *Art and Physics: Parallel Visions in Space,Time, and Light*.

New York: William Morrow and Co., Inc.

Shoup, Richard. 2002. "Anomalies and Constraints: Can Clairvoyance, Precognition, and Psychokinesis be Accommodated with Known Physics?." *Journal of Scientific Exploration*, 16.

Smith, Adam. 2009. *The Theory of Moral Sentiments*. Ryan Patrick Hanley, ed. New York, NY: Penguin Books.

Smith, Gaddis. 1995. *The Last Years of the Monroe Doctrine, 1945-1993*. New York, NY: Hill and Wang.

Smith, Ian. 2008. *Bitter Harvest: Zimbabwe and the Aftermath of Its Independence*. London, England: John Blake Publishing.

Society for Effectual Action (SOC). 2012. "Principles." Batten Institute, Darden School of Business. <http://www.effectuation.org/learn/principle/4>.

Sproul, Barbara C. 1979. *Primal Myths*. New York, NY: Harper Collins Publishers.

Stanford Encyclopedia of Philosophy (STAN). 2010. "Free Will" (October 29). <http://plato.stanford.edu/entries/freewill/>.

Stapp, H. P.; J. Schwartz; & M. Beauregard. 2005. "Quantum Physics in Neuroscience and Psychology: A Neurophysical Model of Mind-Brain Interaction." *Philosophical Transactions of the Royal Society B*, 360 (1458): 1309. <http://rstb.royalsocietypublishing.org/content/360/1458/1309>.

Steinhardt, P. J.; & N. Turok. 2004. "The Cyclic Model Simplified." *New Astron.Rev.*, 49 (2–6): 43–57. <http://arxiv.org/abs/astro-ph/0404480>.

Stenger, Victor J. 1990. *Physics and Psychics: The Search for a World Beyond the Senses*. Amherst, NY: Prometheus Books.

Stewart, James. 2008. *Calculus: Early Transcendentals*. Stamford, CT: Brooks/Cole.

Stolze, J.; & D. Suter. 2008. *Quantum Computing: a Short Course from Theory to Experiment*. New York, NY: Wiley-VCH. <http://books.google.co.ma/books?id=VkPGN1z15bcC&printsec=frontcover&dq=intitle:Quantum+intitle:Computing+inauthor:Stolze&hl=fr>.

Stoner, C. 2000. "Inquiries into the Nature of Free Energy and Entropy in Respect to Biochemical Thermodynamics." *Entropy*, 2 (3): 106–141.

Sudarshan, E. C. G.; & B. Misra. 1977. "The Zeno's Paradox in Quantum Theory." *Journal of Mathematical Physics*, 18 (4): 756–763. <http://adsabs.harvard.edu/abs/1977JMP....18..756M>.

Tanter, Raymond. 1999. *Rogue Regimes: Terrorism and Proliferation*. New York, NY: Macmillan.

Tarnas, Richard. 2006. *Cosmos and Psyche*. New York: Penguin Group.

TechNet Blogs (TECH). 2010. "Hacking Incidents 2009—Interesting Data" (March 12). <http://blogs.technet.com/b/rhalbheer/archive/2010/03/12/

hacking-incidents-2009-interesting-data.aspx>.

Teuscher, C.; & D. Hofstadter. 2004. *Alan Turing: Life and Legacy of a Great Thinker*. Germany: Springer.

Thalheimer, August. 2012. "6–Indian Materialism." *Introduction to Dialectical Materialism*. <http://webcache.googleusercontent.com/ search?q=cache:8TukAqIPIuQJ:www.marxists.org/archive/thalheimer /works/diamat/06.htm+eternal+recurrence&hl=en&start=5>.

Theosophy (THEO). 1939. "Ancient Landmarks: Plato and Aristotle." *Theosophy*, 27 (11): 483–491. <http://www.blavatsky.net/magazine/ theosophy/ww/additional/ancientlandmarks/PlatoAndAristotle.html>.

ThinkExist (TH). 2014. "People often find it easier to be a result of the past than a cause of the future" (January 28). <http://en.thinkexist.com/quotation/ people_often_find_it_easier_to_be_a_result_of_the/165744.html>.

_____.2014a. "Herman Melville" (February 03). <http://en.thinkexist.com /search/searchquotation.asp?search=effects>.

_____.2014b. "Phillip Gribble" (February 11). <http://en.thinkexist.com/ search/searchquotation.asp?search=effects&page=10>.

Thomas, W. I. 1928. *The Child in America: Behavior Problems and Programs*. New York, NY: Alfred A. Knopf.

Thorne, Kip. 1994. *Black Holes and Time Warps: Einstein's Outrageous Legacy*. New York, NY: W W Norton.

Tversky, A.,; & D. Kahneman. 1974. "Judgement under Uncertainty: Heuristics and Biases." *Sciences*, 185: 1124–1131.

University of Central Arkansas (UNIV). 2014. "French Indochina/Vietnam (1941-1954)" (February 07). <http://uca.edu/politicalscience/dadm-project/asia pacific-region/french-indochinavietnam-1941-1954/>.

U.S. Congress Office of Technology Assessment (USCOTA). 1994. "Saving Energy in U.S. Transportation." <http://en.wikipedia.org/wiki/Chicken_or_ the_egg#cite_ref-15>.

U.S. Food and Drug Administration (USFDA). 2014. "Thimerosal in Vaccines" (January 27). <http://www.fda.gov/BiologicsBloodVaccines/SafetyAvai lability/VaccineSafety/UCM096228>.

Van Huyssteen, Wentzel. 2003. "Theological Determinism." *Encyclopedia of Science and Religion*. UK: Macmillan Reference.

Vellekoop, Michel; & Raoul Berglund. 1994. "On Intervals, Transitivity = Chaos." *The American Mathematical Monthly*, 101 (4): 353–5.

von Neumann, J. 1955. *Mathematical Foundations of Quantum Mechanics*. Princeton, NJ: Princeton University Press.

van Inwagen, Peter. 2009. *The Powers of Rational Beings: Freedom of the Will.*

Oxford, England: Oxford University Press.

Vilenkin, Alex: 2006. *Many Worlds in One*. New York, NY: Hill and Wang.

Wald, R. 2006. "The Arrow of Time and the Initial Conditions of the Universe." *Studies in History and Philosophy of Science Part B: Studies in History and Philosophy of Modern Physics*, 37 (3): 394–398. <http://www.sciencedirect.com/science/article/pii/S1355219806000396>.

Wasilewska, Ewa. 2000. *Creation Stories of the Middle East*. Philadelphia, PA: Jessica Kingsley Publishers.

Watts, Robert G. 2007. *Global Warming and the Future of the Earth*. Morgan & Claypool.

Weaver, Mary Anne. 1996. "Blowback." <http://www.theatlantic.com/past/docs/issues/96may/blowback.htm>.

Weber, Max. 1930. *The Protestant Ethic and the Spirit of Capitalism*. Talcott Parsons, tr. New York: Scribner.

Weiner, B. 1992. *Human Motivation: Metaphors, Theories and Research*. Newbury Park, CA: Sage Publications.

Weiss, Roberto. 1973. *The Renaissance Discovery of Classical Antiquity*. Oxford, England: Blackwell.

Werndl, Charlotte. 2009. "What are the New Implications of Chaos for Unpredictability?." *The British Journal for the Philosophy of Science*, 60 (1): 195–220. <http://bjps.oxfordjournals.org/content/60/1/195.abstract>.

_____.2009a. "Are Deterministic Descriptions and Indeterministic Descriptions Observationally Equivalent?." *Studies in History and Philosophy of Modern Physics*, 40: 232-242.

Wharton, William R. 1998. "Backward Causation and the EPR Paradox." <http://arxiv.org/html/quant-ph/9810060>.

Wheeler, John; & Richard Feynman. 1945. "Interaction with the Absorber as the Mechanism of Radiation." *Review of Modern Physics*, (17).

Wheeler-Voegelin, Erminie; & Remedios W. Moore. 1957. "The Emergence Myth in Native North America." *Studies in Folklore, in Honor of Distinguished Service Professor Stith Thompson*. W. Edson Richmond, ed. IN: Indiana University Press.

Whittaker, S. 2007. "Secret Attraction." *The Montreal Gazette* (May 12). <http://www.canada.com/montrealgazette/story.html?id=78fc94dd-c0b2-4ade-891d-98770bfae388&k=70777>.

Wikipedia (WK). 2014. "Arrow of Time" (January 26). <http://en.wikipedia.org/wiki/Arrow_of_time>.

_____.2014a. "Retrocausality" (January 26). <http://en.wikipedia.org/wiki/Retrocausality>.

_____.2014b. "Causality" (January 26). <http://en.wikipedia.org/wiki/Causality>.

_____.2014c. "Etiology" (January 26). <http://en.wikipedia.org/wiki/Etiology>.

_____.2014d. "Myth of Origins" (January 27). <http://en.wikipedia.org/wiki/ Myth_of_origins>.

_____.2014e. "Factor" (January 27). <http://en.wikipedia.org/wiki/Factor>.

_____.2014f. "Environmental Factor" (January 27). <http://en.wikipedia.org/wiki/ Environmental_factor>.

_____.2014g. "Self-fulfilling Prophecy" (January 27). <http://en.wikipedia.org/ wiki/Self-fulfilling_prophecy>.

_____.2014h. "Result" (January 27). <http://en.wikipedia.org/wiki/Result>.

_____.2014i. "Convergence (Mathematics)" (January 27). <http://en.wikipedia. org/wiki/Convergence_(mathematics)>.

_____.2014j. "Unintended Consequence" (January 27). <http://en.wikipedia.org/ wiki/Unintended_consequence>.

_____.2014k. "Correlation" (January 27). <http://en.wikipedia.org/wiki/ Correlation>.

_____.2014l. "Synchronicity" (January 27). <http://en.wikipedia.org/wiki/ Synchronicity>.

_____.2014m. "Indeterminism" (January 27). <http://en.wikipedia.org/wiki/ Indeterminism>.

_____.2014n. "Attribution (Psychology)" (January 27). <http://en.wikipedia.org/ wiki/Attribution_(psychology)>.

_____.2014o. "Adverse Effect" (January 27). <http://en.wikipedia.org/wiki/ Adverse_effect>.

_____.2014p. "The Second Law of Thermodynamics" (January 27). <http://en.wikipedia.org/wiki/ Adverse_effect>.

_____.2014q. "Butterfly Effect" (January 27). <http://en.wikipedia.org/wiki/ Butterfly_effect>.

_____.2014r. "Causation (Law)" (January 27). <http://en.wikipedia.org/wiki/ Causation_(law)>.

_____.2014s. "Domino Theory" (January 27). <http://en.wikipedia.org/wiki/ Domino_theory>.

_____.2014t. "Creation Myth" (January 27). <http://en.wikipedia.org/wiki/ Creation_myth>.

_____.2014u. "Determinism" (January 27). <http://en.wikipedia.org/wiki/ Determinism>.

_____.2014v. "Suggestibility" (January 28). <http://en.wikipedia.org/wiki/ Suggestibility>.

_____.2014w. "Cognitive Bias" (January 28). <http://en.wikipedia.org/wiki/ Cognitive_bias>.

_____.2014x. "Self-Defeatiing Prophecy" (January 29). <http://en.wikipedia.org/wiki/Self-defeating_prophecy>.

_____.2014y. "First Law of Thermodynamics" (January 30). <http://en.wikipedia.org/wiki/First_law_of_thermodynamics>.

_____.2014z. "Entropy (Arrow of Time)" (January 30). <http://en.wikipedia.org/wiki/Entropy_(arrow_of_time)>.

_____.2014aa. "Eternal Recurrence" (January 30). <http://en.wikipedia.org/wiki/Eternal_recurrence>.

_____.2014bb. "Grandfather Paradox" (January 31). <http://en.wikipedia.org/wiki/Grandfather_paradox>.

_____.2014cc. "First Cause" (January 31). <http://en.wikipedia.org/wiki/First_cause>.

_____.2014dd. "Root Cause Analysis" (February 01). <http://en.wikipedia.org/wiki/Root_cause_analysis>.

_____.2014ee. "Incident Management" (February 01). <http://en.wikipedia.org/wiki/Incident_management>.

_____.2014ff. "Ishikawa Diagram" (February 01). <http://en.wikipedia.org/wiki/Ishikawa_diagram>.

_____.2014gg. "Continuous Improvement" (February 01). <http://en.wikipedia.org/wiki/Continuous_improvement>.

_____.2014hh. "Proximate Causation" (February 01). <http://en.wikipedia.org/wiki/Proximate_causation>.

_____.2014ii. "Four Causes" (February 01). <http://en.wikipedia.org/wiki/Four_causes>.

_____.2014jj. "Potentiality and Actuality" (February 02). <http://en.wikipedia.org/wiki/Potentiality_and_actuality>.

_____.2014kk. "Problem of Universals" (February 02). <http://en.wikipedia.org/wiki/Problem_of_universals>.

_____.2014ll. "Metaphysics_(Aristotle)" (February 03). <http://en.wikipedia.org/wiki/Metaphysics_(Aristotle)>.

_____.2014mm. "Nocebo" (February 03). <http://en.wikipedia.org/wiki/Nocebo>.

_____.2014nn. "Vaccine Adverse Event Reporting System" (February 04). <http://en.wikipedia.org/wiki/Vaccine_Adverse_Event_Reporting_System>.

_____.2014oo. "Evil Eye" (February 04). <http://en.wikipedia.org/wiki/Evil_eye>.

_____.2014pp. "Intentionality" (February 05). <http://en.wikipedia.org/wiki/Intentionality>.

_____.2014qq. "Chaos Theory" (February 05). <http://en.wikipedia.org/wiki/Chaos_theory>.

_____.2014rr. "Quantum Zeno Effect" (February 06). <http://en.wikipedia.org/

wiki/Quantum_zeno_effect>.

_____.2014ss. "Quantum Decoherence" (February 06). <http://en.wikipedia.org/ wiki/Quantum_decoherence>.

_____.2014tt. "Wave Function Collapse" (February 06). <http://en.wikipedia.org/ wiki/Wave_function_collapse>.

_____.2014uu. "Chain Reaction" (February 07). <http://en.wikipedia.org/ wiki/Chain_reaction>.

_____.2014vv. "Effectuation" (February 07). <http://en.wikipedia.org/ wiki/ Effectuation>.

_____.2014ww. "Chicken or the Egg" (February 09). <http://en.wikipedia.org/ wiki/Chicken_or_the_egg>.

_____.2014xx. "Cyclic Model" (February 10). <http://en.wikipedia.org/ wiki/Cyclic_model>.

_____.2011nn. "Design Elements and Principles" (September 30). <http://en.wikipedia.org/wiki/Design_elements_and_principles>.

_____.2011oo. "Interpretation (Logic)" (April 13). <http://en.wikipedia.org/ wiki/Interpretation_(Logic)>.

_____.2011pp. "Unsolved Problems in Linguistics" (February 20). <http://en.wikipedia.org/wiki/Unsolved_problems_in_linguistics>.

_____.2008. "Posthumanism" (October 20). <http://en.wikipedia.org/wiki/ Posthumanism>.

_____.2008a. "Transhumanism" (October 20). <http://en.wikipedia.org/wiki/ Transhumanism>.

_____.2008b. "Lowest Common Denominator" (March 26). <http://en.wikipedia.org/ wiki/Least_common_denominator>.

_____.2008c. "Infinity" (November 11). <http://en.wikipedia.org/wiki/Infinity>.

_____.2008d. "Transfinite Number" (November 10). <http://en.wikipedia.org/ wiki/Transfinite_ number>.

_____.2008e. "Quantum Mechanics" (November 26). <http://en.wikipedia.org/wiki/Quantum_mechanics>.

_____.2008f. "Copenhagen Interpretation" (November 26). <http://en.wikipedia.org/wiki/Copenhagen_interpretation >.

_____.2008g. "Many Worlds Interpretation" (November 26). <http://en.wikipedia.org/wiki/Many_Worlds_Interpretation>.

_____.2008h. "Hyperspace (Science Fiction)" (November 23). <http://en.wikipedia.org/wiki/Hyperspace_(science_fiction)>.

_____.2008i. "Time Travel" (November 26). <http://en.wikipedia.org/ wiki/Time_travel#Time_dilation>.

_____.2008j. "Wormhole" (November 25). <http://en.wikipedia.org/wiki/

Wormhole>.

_____.2007. "Linguistics" (March 04). <http://en.wikipedia.org/wiki/Linguistics>.

Wikiversity (WKV). 2008. "Why 10 Dimensions" (November 23). <ttp://en.wikiversity.org/wiki/Why_10_dimensions>.

Wilkins, William E. 1976. "The Concept of a Self-Fulfilling Prophecy." *Sociology of Education*, 49 (2): 175–183. <http://www.jstor.org/discover/10.2307/2112523?uid=3738512&uid=2&uid=4&sid=21103421254063>.

Wittgenstein, Ludwig.1953. *Philosophical Investigations*. G. E. M. Anscombe and R. Rhees, eds. G.E.M. Anscombe, tr. Oxford: Blackwell.

Wolfram, Herwig. 1988. *History of the Goths*. Thomas J. Dunlap, tr. Berkeley, CA: University of California Press.

Wolfram, Stephen. 2002. *A New Kind of Science*. Champaign, IL: Wolfram Media.

Woit, P. 2006. *Not Even Wrong*. London, England: Random House.

Woods, Austin. 2005. *Medium-Range Weather Prediction: The European Approach; The Story of the European Centre for Medium-Range Weather Forecasts*. New York, NY: Springer.

Womack, Mari. 2005. *Symbols and Meaning: A Concise Introduction*. Lanham, MD: AltaMira Press.

World Wide Words (WOR). 2006. "Etheromaniac" (September 09). <http://www.worldwidewords.org/weirdwords/ww-eth1.htm>.

Wright, Robert. 2003. "The War and the Peace" (April 01). *Slate*. <http://www.slate.com/articles/news_and_politics/the_earthling/2003/04/the_war_and_the_peace.html>.

INDEX

•A•

actor/observer difference, 148-149, 255

adverse effect and medicine, 14-15, 264-278, 379-380
  see also Etiology

affordable loss princple, and effectuation, 338, 383

Africa, and the domino theory, 325-326

after-postmodernism
  see After-Postmodernity

after-postmodernity
  and existential dialectics
    (1) freedom/unfreedom and equality/inequality dialectics, 46, 586-590, 593, 600-604, 626-629
    (2) wealth/poverty dialectics, 47, 120-121, 594
    (3) civilization/barbarity dialectics, 53-54, 585, 595
    (4) oppression/self-oppression, 61-62, 591-592
  and civilizational holism
    (1) structure, 634-638
    (2) theories, 639-645
  and post-human civilization vs. post-human post-civilization, 630

and super civilizations, 632-633

and the five theses of post-civilization, 630

and the theoretical debate on civilization, 595, 625-646

and the unified theory of everything, and its solution to the problems of complexity, subjectivity, conflict, and diversity, 25- 26, 64-65, 525

barbarity, and post-civilization, 631

Cophenhagen interpretation vs. Everett's interpretation, 98

from pre-modernity to after-postmodernity in civilization
    (1) the trinity of pre-modernity, 53-54, 60-61, 111, 136, 634-635
    (2) the trinity of modernity, 53-54, 60-61, 111, 137-138, 634-635
    (3) the trinity of post-modernity, 53-54, 60-61, 111, 139, 634-635
    (4) the trinity of after-postmodernity, 53-54, 60-61, 111, 140, 634-635

in regard to different kinds of consciousness

•F•

•G•